'Lost and Found' on Planet Dani

'Lost and Found' on Planet Dani

Andrew Corwin

Troubador Publishing Ltd
Unit E2 Airfield Business Park,
Harrison Road, Market Harborough,
Leicestershire. LE16 7UL
Tel: 0116 2792299
Email: books@troubador.co.uk
Web: www.troubador.co.uk

ISBN 978 1805142 324

British Library Cataloguing in Publication Data.
A catalogue record for this book is available from the British Library.

Front cover image by Giordano Cipriani; Wood carving of Dani people rowing canoe,
Papua, Indonesia – Image 690799992 (gettyimages).

Printed and bound by CPI Group (UK) Ltd, Croydon, CR0 4YY
Typeset in 12pt Jenson Pro by Troubador Publishing Ltd, Leicester, UK

Dedicated to the Dani – unbowed and little
changed over 2000 years

Creator/Contributor: famed Italian travel photographer, Roberto Pazzi; understated 2013 portrait brilliantly capturing the historical essence of the Dani Warrior from the Baliem Valley, West Papua (Indonesia).

The highlands of West Papua do not belong to some distant galaxy, at least as we think of when looking into the starry skies in the dead of night. But this story is no less a 'space odyssey' as was Stanley Kubrick's film epic, prophetically titled, *2001, A Space Odyssey*; invoking the lure of discovery through exploration, no matter the cost; except maybe for the loss of our own humanity.

The Dani people, having inhabited the Baliem Valley for 2000 years, give or take a few hundred, remained isolated from outside influences until well into the 20th century. Exploration of the *'Dutch New Guinea'*, so named at the time, of the island's interior, began in earnest in 1909, with first contact of the Lani, often referred to as the Western Dani in 1920, and 'our' Dani of the central highlands in 1938.[1]

Little has changed in the Baliem Valley of today, except for the town of Wamena and a few villages that are now featured on the map, compared with the cartography of over a century ago.

---

1   *https://en.wikipedia.org/wiki/Dani_people.*

West Pap

INDONESIA

Commissioned by Author, Illustrator: Gustavo Schmitt; map of West Papua of today (2023), employing artful cartography to create a 'fantasy map' rendition. Contributor: Gabbro; Wooden carved statue from indigenous Papuan tribe, Wamena, Papua, Indonesia (modified) – Image ID: PRA0AJ (Alamy).

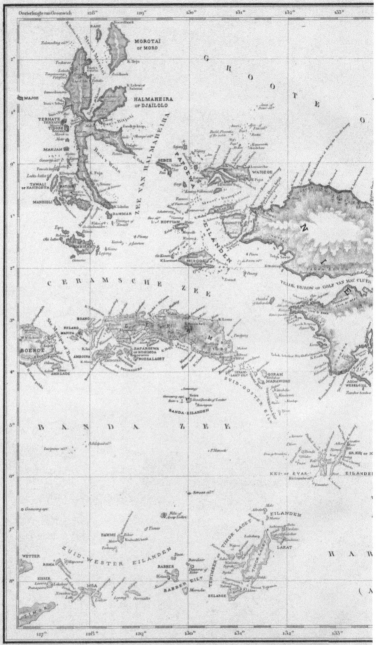

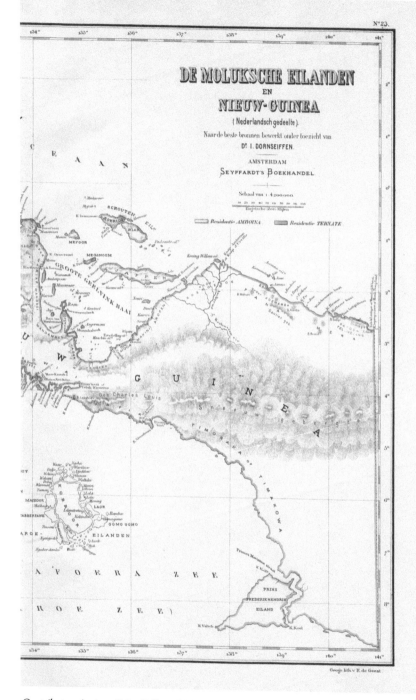

Contributor: Antiqua Print Gallery; DUTCH EAST INDIES: Moluccas Maluku Papua New Guinea. DORNSEIFFEN. 1892 old map highlighting that late into the 19th century, the Baliem Valley (going by different names and spellings) remained unexplored – Image ID: FB7PG.

Prologue

Bakri, clinician, epidemiologist and humanist extraordinaire, and I patrol the 'mean streets' of Wamena, consisting primarily of two parallel rutted dirt roads running through the center of town, connected by several smaller-still intersecting roads and paths. Of course, I am being facetious in suggesting the streets are anything other than welcoming, at least on first impression. At the same time, our sensibilities are assaulted by what should be the ordinary: the sights, sounds, and smells that are anything but. To my dismay alone, knowing Bakri as an unabashed teetotaler, alcohol is strictly prohibited in the town, with only bitter 'kopi' and overly sweetened 'teh' on tap. And yet I drum up images from the 1977, *Star Wars: Episode IV – A New Hope*, movie sequel, notably the bar scene, as I take in the strange and bizarre playing out before us. But with no grace or humility intended, I remind myself that this is not our world. For this is home of the Dani people, in one of the most remote and rugged places on the planet, who live, work, and play, for the most part, as they have for the past 2000 years.

Having finally reached the 'jumping-off point' to our

investigation, destined to prove a metamorphic, life-changing 'wild ride' adventure, we settle into a frustratingly long wait in this capital of Jayawijaya 'highland' Regency, located on the island province, representing the easternmost fringe of the Indonesian archipelago, and going by the name of West Papua.[2] We are not explorers or trekkers, but here because of anecdotal reports of a mystery illness the Jakarta and local press has dubbed 'wabah babi', or 'pig epidemic' in translation.

My job in the navy, at least as I see it, is to listen and learn from Bakri, or Dr. Bakri Ginting for the formally inclined. We have trapsed across the archipelago, although not all 17,000 islands, and taken our brand beyond Indonesia, throughout Southeast Asia. We are like storm chasers, except we hunt down emerging diseases. Our strategy is simple: 'follow the outbreaks', cashing in on the patent idea that most new diseases introduce themselves in epidemic fashion.

Bakri, diminutive in stature and a 'lion' at heart, usually does the leading. I sometimes think he is secretively working for the Indonesian security services, to make sure I do not screw things up, not too much anyways.

We are joined 'at the hip' by virtue of his senior position at LITBANGKES, the Indonesian equivalent of the US National Institutes of Health. And while never formally assigned as my counterpart, we fit like 'hand in glove', leaving out the proverbial 'up to no good' part of the expression. But we are also no 'two peas in a pod', sharing little by way of

---

2   Gus Dur, an honorable, soft-spoken Indonesian cleric whose words
     carried loudly over the archipelago, the first democratically elected
     president in a post Suharto Indonesia, artfully defied Muslim and
     nationalistic sensibilities in renaming the island province of Irian
     Jaya to Papua, on January 1, 2000; meeting and engaging with
     Papuan separatists in Jayapura while deflecting criticisms with
     his characteristic humor; https://West Papuatabloid.org/gus-durs-
     reason-for-changing-irian-jaya-to-papua.html.

temperament and good grace. And yet despite my heathen ways, he looks beyond my rough edges, seeing something that even I do not recognize of myself.

My 'family name', Bonaparte, inspires chuckles, more so because I fit the illusion. Jacques, my given name, less so. I am no giant but feel so next to Bakri, cognizant that I am dwarfed in all things that really matter. His intuitive intellect is bad enough, but his moral compass is so damned infallible, always aligned with 'true north', pointing us in the right direction. Owing to my perceptive sensibilities, I am often left shy and humbled standing by his side.

Relying as always on the tenacity of Bakri in 'moving heaven and earth' to get this far. He is a proud Batak who hails from Jakarta but whose heritage is centered in the Danu Toba region of northern Sumatra. As Christians in predominately Muslim western Indonesia, the Batak can uniquely identify their genealogy and lineage within the Batak Tribe by a linear numbering system. They are close-knit and occupy critical positions in private and public sectors. The Batak share an intense sense of community, an expression of solidarity amplified by the 'Huria Kristen Batak Protestan', or Batak Christian Protestant church. Less than four percent in a country of some 236 million, their numbers belie a substantial societal influence. Often described as the nation's intelligentsia, or benevolent mafia by some, in taking care of their own: depending on who is asking.

Bakri has gotten me out of more messes during my years in Indonesia than I care to admit, given my propensity for lurching from one crisis to the next; I am humbled to be in his towering shadow. And then there is Narsiem, the third wheel to our motorized rickshaw, or 'bajak', in making for such an analogy; Indonesian by birth, Indian by ethnicity. An odd mixing for sure, but 'we three' make for a formidable match;

just three ordinary superheroes taking on the forces of 'no-good', disease-wise.

We finally arrived in Wamena on an Indonesian C-140 military cargo plane from the provincial capital of Jayapura, sitting on boxes of food rations and arms after interminable delays owing to a simmering Papuan separatist movement made explosive with the kidnapping of English and Dutch botany students. I cannot help wondering on whose authority allowed for such 'botanical' expedition against a backdrop of political and ethnic tensions in the first place; appreciating the irony of it all, given that we too are preparing to journey into this restive region. To be fair, until this kidnapping, the insurgency had been seen as pitting a Papuan home-grown freedom movement, relying on homemade weapons – mostly spears and farming axes, hoes, and knives, with a few guns of World War II vintage – in their fight against a well-equipped and even better trained Indonesian military.

This is our fifth day out in Wamena, and after another fruitless attempt to commandeer the only functioning helicopter, operated by a group going by the name of Missionary Air Fellowship – MAF – one of the few foreign-based – non-Muslin – religious charities allowed by the Indonesian government. Their purported mission is to ferry supplies and people throughout this ruggedly inhospitable region, one of the most remote and inaccessible on planet. All the while, spreading their gospel armed with hymns and scripture. To challenge the beliefs and traditions of the Dani Baliem Valley could be inferred as an egregious act of 'entitlement', more fitting a colonial era. The charitable nature in taking up a this noble humanitarian 'calling' belies the fact that this is still a missionary enterprise, MEF, as the name implies.

The pilots are truly heroes, albeit with short lifespans if they are not 'quick learners': flying over this otherwise-impenetrable expanse; launching off and landing on cliffs and riverbeds in what is a highland jungle like no other. They do their own maintenance and repairs on a fleet of small aircraft consisting of two helicopters and assortment of fixed-wing aircraft. They work for 'peanuts', and live in a small compound with their families, relying only on their own ingenuity and fervor to do some good and get through the day: hopefully alive. Unfortunately, faith has proven no protective amulet, with scores having perished over the years.

The MAF is only, 'just' tolerated, by a government that does not take too kindly to missionary intrusions; as there are few local pilots with what it takes: zeal and flying acumen 'straight up', with a 'shot' of daredevil. There are some who possess the 'zeal' without so much the skills; they are literally a dying breed. And then there are those who 'secret' their disposition to suicidal tendencies, rarely sticking around in this life, or any other. And so the MAF get to keep proselytizing, as long they keep to the air.

Our timing is impeccably bad. As in the previous four days, we wake and track along the smaller of the two main streets, with the airstrip used by MAF and the military to our right and the compound that houses MAF families to the left. Once again, the International Committee of the Red Cross, or ICRC, responsible for negotiating the release of the student would-be botanists, win out, having dibs on the one serviceable helicopter in the MAF arsenal of flying machines. "Can we not take the single engine, prop-driven plane sitting in the hanger," I inquire politely.

The reply is always the same: "Waiting on parts. Any day now." Trying not to be flippant, Bakri and me could also be accused of falling into one such category.

I am a tad jealous since this group of negotiators and a smattering of press have taken over the only accommodations with any amenities, and I mean, any: hot running water, bed sheets (but no turn-down service), and of course, a room with a view. Located on the outskirts of town, a bungalow resort that has seen better days. But it still serves as a shiny beacon for the weary traveler, unless of course you go by the name of Jacques or Bakri.

We end up taking a room in a precariously leaning structure that advertises itself as a guesthouse and services visiting civil servants and traders, looking for nothing more than a cheap stay with a roof overhead. I prefer the hard floor in a sleeping bag to the soiled and dampened mattress that Bakri has chosen to brave in our two-cot room.

The few intrepid tourists who would normally make the journey to this distant outpost of the 'empire' are notably absent, owing to the hostage-taking and insurgency. The government is keen to limit and control any news of the crisis; so air transport to Wamena is now restricted to one military flight every three days. The only way in, and out. I would add that special authorization must be first secured from the military and security apparatus headquartered in Jakarta, and again in Jayapura: the two, TNI and BAN, not being mutually exclusive.

The process of obtaining permissions can be appreciably onerous, especially so since the US Naval Medical Research Command (NMRC) – Indonesia, falls under the umbrella of the Indonesian Ministry of Health (MoH), by virtue of a 'country-to-country' agreement that has long expired. But for 'sake of expediency', this relationship has been allowed to continue; neither party benefiting from the severing of ties. This alliance makes for an 'odd coupling' since one might reasonably expect our country operations to be formally linked with and regulated by the Indonesian military; through what would normally be sanctioned under a 'mil-to-mil' relationship: between militaries.

The storied history of NMRC-Indonesia, which includes pioneering in the evaluation of anti-malarial drugs, oral rehydration solution (ORS) for the treatment of cholera and other diarrheal diseases, and recognition of emerging and re-emerging diseases like hepatitis E virus and chikungunya virus, is the stuff of legend. The work of the navy's 'forward' infectious disease laboratory in Indonesia heralds back to 1970; with providing necessary diagnostic capacity to take on the threat posed at the time by rickettsiosis; a rickettsia, infection, associated with vector-borne 'murine' and 'scrub' typhus.

And so it is that the MoH, through LITBANGKES, is the responsible governmental entity overseeing our day-to-day operations; not going so far as to infer the 'bane' of our existence. All Command operations fall under review and approval of LITBANGKES, and must further be okayed by Badan Intelijen Negara, or BIN for short, as the state's overseer of all things falling into that nebulous domain of national intelligence and state security. Additionally, vetting for our investigation to proceed had to include the Tentara Nasional Indonesia – Indonesian National Armed Forces – or TNI, and Komando Daerah Militer – Regional Military Command, or KODAM, West Papua.

As part of a larger process of 'reformasi', post-Suharto, decentralization is intended to 'spread the wealth' as it were, whereas vested authority and decision-making is shifted away from Jakarta; affording greater local autonomy to the provinces. Sounds great in theory, but in practice, getting things done becomes a challenge, adding layers to the approval process for even the simplest of endeavors. But for all the administrative and logistical hurdles, there are few comparable places on the planet from which to detect and track the next disease tsunami: from anti-malarial drug resistance to pandemic threats for which there are no shortage of, certainly not her, in Indonesia.

And so it is: from first getting local permission in traveling to Wamena; to bagging a spot on the military flight from Jayapura. All this against the backdrop of heightened sensitivities concerning this island province; that goes by the name: 'Free West Papua Movement' (OPM), at the center of the current hostage-taking crisis. And while the MoH coordinated with the Indonesian military, our cause in just getting this far was greatly aided by a direct appeal from the US Ambassador. But on the ground, where is really counts, it is left to a persistent Bakri to jump the hurdles and overcome local obstinance designed to deny us 'our destiny'. Ha ha!

Bakri and I are left to contemplate at such an early hour what to do with the rest of our day after dozing on a wooden bench under a lean-to at the airstrip, watching 'our' helicopter lift off with our ICRC friends onboard. I should add that, by mid-morning, the whole of the highlands, including Wamena is enveloped by thick fog, enough so that you can taste it, lick it off your lips. As if 'taking to the air' in a 'teeny tiny' flying machine over this vast mountainous region is not dangerous enough – its secrets hidden by a never-ending canopy of lush green. But to do so in near-zero visibility is just crazy. So flying is restricted to those precious few hours between sunrise, and fog. This means we have only one shot at laying claim to the one functioning helicopter. But this is no 'early bird gets the worm'.

We are nothing more than a nuisance to those holding sway: to be 'paid no mind'. The ICRC claims that were a distraction to the important work at hand, and so, dismissive. At least they said as much directly to Bakri's face. I was able to talk him down from taking a 'high dive' into a pool of despondency.

The prize in beating out the ICRC to the airfield every morning is to rob ourselves of an extra hour's sleep: nothing more! I should add that even covering the 700 US dollars an hour in rental fees has not earned us seats on the helicopter; 'nothing like burning through money with nothing to show for it'. That being a classic navy euphemism. In the end, we were never destined for this whirlybird, not flying out anyways.

As we pass through the rickety gate from the airfield, intended more to keep goats and chickens rather than people from straying onto the runway, we turn left and just begin to walk. Another day, and we are still not airborne.

Our quiet contemplation is rudely interrupted by a not-too-distant chanting that becomes alarmingly louder and louder. Our vision extends about 300 meters to a rising cloud of dust. Within seconds, the first outline of an excited mob becomes visible, waving machetes and farming implements, coming our way. I can think only of a choreographed stampede. The street in both directions has cleared of all routine lending to normalcy. I cannot move my legs, now pinioned to the ground, as I stare at this spectacle like none other I have witnessed, that is until Bakri grabs my hand and yanks me toward the MAF walled compound. Me pounding on steel at the gated entrance, and Bakri banging on the buzzer, we scream over what sounds like an approaching 'choo-choo' train: "Let us in, please let us in."

From the beginning

The start of another 'cherry' of a navy day! This an appropriate way to prepare for the worst possible; adding a little color and sweetness to an old navy taunt: 'Have a great navy day'! Driving in the early morning quiet in Jakarta means dodging and weaving the not-so-mean streets up of 'Kuningan turning into Menteng', and finally the Jalan (street) Percetagan Negara: home to both MoH agencies responsible for public health research and practice, and NMRC-Indonesia.

Arriving at work in my civilian attire, the 'dress of the day' damp from the mind-boggling early morning humidity foretelling of an approaching rainy season that carries with it the promise of relief, I am already frazzled enough to already call it a day. And yet I have dodged the notorious traffic bullet, otherwise referred to as '*lalu lintas buruk*', that can render Jakarta senseless, driving all to their knees; arriving at the ungodly hour when the sun, if you could see it through the purplish haze, would be just rising over the horizon.

Truth of the matter is that I love my work. The best job in the navy, bar none. This being especially so in that I do not have to dress for the part. The politics of having a US navy research laboatory tucked away in west Jakarta forces us to be circumspect, leaving our uniforms to mold at home, to placate local, predominately Muslim, sensibilities. Yet try as we might, we carry the added burden of being 'boulay', the Indonesian word for foreigner, and fit in like all other boulay: sticking out like a sore thumb.

Indo-Café comes in packets – and is far too sweet. But the frothy cappuccino blend gives me a sugar high that lasts me long after my first cup of the day. While not a coffee aficionado, I rate this up there among the best of the '3-in-1' mixes. Settling down to business, I am working on the analysis of my what is currently a 'hot' topic: hepatitis E virus. There are many hepatitis viruses, but HEV, for short, this type has gained my attention because Indonesian Borneo has become the principal foci of epidemic transmission in Southeast Asia. This making for an incredible opportunity to study the disease where it is naturally occurring in the uniquely jungle riverine setting of 'Kalimantan Barat' (West Kalimantan). Much like the 'Baskin and Robbins' flavor of the month, I think of hepatitis and forever changing navy research priorities. For sure, as with ice cream, some new viral hepatitis virus will become in vogue: next month, or next year. I can map out much of my research career to-date, hopping from one hepatitis virus to the next, A, B, C, D, E, and G, across the globe, from: Japan, Egypt, Somalia, Vietnam; and of course, Indonesia.

Managing an 'emerging disease' program is fun. I am left to run my fiefdom because nobody is the wiser; the term on which I have spent too many beer-clouded thoughts trying to figure out how to approach the study of emerging diseases – and have concluded that my mission is to (usually by accident) stumble upon them. Not very complicated – and for sure, my reasoning is in appreciation that I am no rocket scientist, just a navy Commander trying to figure his place in the scheme of things. Not made easy by the cast of characters that comprise our research unit. The navy sends its very best medical researchers here to study and conquer malaria – and so I am surrounded by 'genius': parasitologists, entomologists, epidemiologists, and I.D. clinicians; all focused on the only disease that matters, at least at NMRC-Indonesia. But while I might be outclassed, I am never intimidated.

Settling into my day with my frothy brew of cappuccino in hand, I scan news accounts from the *Jakarta Star*. No *New York Times*, but every major city in Southeast Asia seems to have one; a 'daily' English language newspaper with mostly borrowed stories from both the Indonesian and international press. I get to claim this early morning ritual as work, as I search out local accounts of outbreaks that may or may not suggest the emergence of a new disease entity. Lacking in imagination, I have taken to the belief that the search for new diseases is made easier by 'following the outbreaks'. An approach I liken to the policing of criminal enterprises, going about finding the bad guys; thinking of the catch phrase, 'just follow the money', as portrayed in *The Untouchables* movie, about the taking down of the infamous Al Capone.

Beti is my administrative assistant, and essentially manages my day, if not my life. She is a devout Muslim who appreciates my sense of humor. The two are 'not' mutually exclusive, but I am still appreciative that she is so enlightened as to accept my quirkiness. Beti comes into my office, never knocking, as if feeling she has 'rights' to privacy: mine. "Come, our meeting is beginning." Referring to our 'weekly' gathering of 'emerging eisease' staff. Other than Beti, my small but most capable team consists of Dari, Apok, and Oopi. As I lift from my chair, my knee causes my coffee to spill on a newspaper account of something going by the name of 'wabah babi'.

"You have been in the country, 'how long'?" Beti could not resist. "So, what is it, this 'wabah babi'?" Dari, always thoughtful explains the phrase 'wabah' as outbreak, and 'babi' meaning pig. "Yes, I understand that 'wabah babi' means outbreak, but I am confused as to why a pig outbreak would find its way into the *Jakarta Star*." My team had a gander at the coffee-smudged print, then headed out to explore further, in the Indonesian press.

My first thought was that pig outbreak, 'wabah babi', had something to do with the swine industry; especially in the lakes region of north Sumatra; the consequential impact of which could significantly impact the regional economy. Neither was it lost on me that these massive pig breeding farms were an incongruence, between religious beliefs and economics, in this predominantly Muslim country.

Later that day, Dari came back with something specifically referring to the term, 'wabah babi'; a two-sentence blurb from 'Antara', the National News Agency, without naming a source or veracity of the claim, except to say there were many human deaths and identifying the Grand Baliem Valley of West Papua by name. "We need to set up a meeting with Bakri and take this to P2M for their take. They may have already set about investigating this. The NMRC-Indonesia shares the Jalan (street) Percetakan Negara complex housing LITBANGKES and P2M, the latter serving the same function as the US Centers for Disease Control and Prevention (CDC). Inter-agency competition 'dogs' practical cooperation between the two. To this end, NMRC-Indonesia serves a useful function in straddling this divide, a bridge of sorts, in at least getting the two to sit across from one another at the same table.

"The role of NMRC-Indonesia is most certainly enhanced by the attention paid in building national capabilities, or lack thereof. Both are sorely underfunded, understaffed, and underequipped, making near impossible the task of securing the nation's public health. An archipelago of some

17,000 islands covering 5120 kilometers across, deserves so much better. And yes, I love Indonesia and its people, but do not underestimate the enormity of the disease challenges confronting the country.

"And so we, my fellow sailors and I, misguidedly think of ourselves, our Command, as indispensable. We bring expertise, technology and most importantly funding to the table. While this should endear us to our Indonesian hosts, I suspect envy is the more likely sentiment, breeding a resentment that will eventual be the Commands' downfall, of that, I am sure. Bakri confided 'one fine day', expressing a similar version of the same world view.

> "NMRC-Indonesia is hanging by a few threads. There are those in the ministry who feel that you, not you personally, are robing us of what belongs to us: our right to self-determination, and the means to do so. You, again, this is not about 'you', tout your accomplishments in publications, and train and pay your Indonesian staff far above that what the MoH can support. You, again, not you, rob us of the necessary funds to build our own capabilities. You know the state of our national reference laboratory, never mind the regional labs. NMRC-Indonesia is an excuse used by our government, our ministry, to starve us of the necessary monies to do our job, just by being here. Why invest in LITBANGKES and P2M when we have NMRC-Indonesia?"

Wow, I thought! Better not to say anything. It is not often that Bakri lets loose, but when he does, he does not disappoint. It was hard 'not to take' his tirade too personal, but I understood where he was coming from, and took solace that he would share such feelings with me. It made me feel worthy.

It is worth noting that LITBANGKES and P2M do not normally engage with one another, and are indeed competitive if not 'downright' combative for ministerial recognition and applause, as reflected in their budget appropriations. Fortunately, Bakri is able to navigate the politics and bureaucratic pettiness in getting things done; more like unbridled flattery in the art of coercion. That, and the fact that he worked at P2M before coming over to the enemy at LITBANGKES. So on this morning we amble like 'gunslingers' across the parking lot to the adjoining P2M complex, and discover, well, very little. When confronted, Dr. Sidouso acknowledges he has heard something, but does not take too seriously – at least for now, with more pressing demands taking up his time and resources. Using his Batak magic and an extra pinch of charm, Bakri is still able to get the 'okay' for us to make further inquiries.

We are well practiced in asking for permission to pursue actions leading to the investigation of suspected outbreak events, by acknowledging and deferring to Sidouso's genius in doing so.

As with most outbreaks in Indonesia, a subscription to the local printed press is usually more on target than any information to be had from conventional disease surveillance for the country, which is notoriously lacking by any credible measure in recognition of an unusual cluster of human cases, framed by time and place. While the newspapers get it wrong more than they get it right, and more often months after the fact, they do provide Bakri and me with the only source of alert to the possibility of an outbreak.

Permission

My beautiful 'sky blue' Suzuki Vitara 4x4 is my escape vehicle out of the city, whether from a bad day at the office, or the suffocating air pollution, *'penemaran'*, that hangs over Jakarta on most days; like a 'waterboarding' torture on the 'really' bad days. Barreling down Jalan Kuningan during a late morning lull in the traffic to the main MoH offices, I ask my trusted companion Bakri, "How should we approach this?" Dari in the back seat behind Bakri suggests we should first enjoy the steaming large-pan mushroom pizza we picked up at Pizza Hut, and then ask Dr. Eka Dewi, 'Deputy to the Minister' and good friend, just how she would advise us to proceed, or not. As Director General of LITBANGKES during my early years at the Command, Eka Dewi and I became good friends, a warm relationship that survived her meteoric rise in the ministry.

Funny about that! I owe my equally meteoric climb in the 'scheme of things', nestled comfortably on the small blade of grass I occupy at NMRC-Indonesia, to the likes of Eka Dewi; more so than my navy brethren.

After almost three weeks of learning almost nothing more, even after repeated inquiries to the health office and hospital in Wamena, I was ready to give up on what was becoming nothing more than a fanciful pursuit, probably to nowhere. Repeated attempts through our Command contacts, both in Jakarta and Jayapura, and Embassy, to secure travel authority to West Papua, and specifically the Jayawijaya Regency, have been rebuffed, which, in the Javanese way, were simply ignored. I was exhausted by the pleading in my own voice. The high visibility being given to the hostage situation, which had by now been featured on the likes of CNN and the BBC, had made our partners at LITBANGKES and P2M, and pretty much everyone else, more than a little nervous about gaining us permission to follow up a single press release that could not be corroborated.

"You need to lose some weight," extolled Eka Dewi. I grinned, looking down at my sticky fingers and the tomato sauce and mushrooms clinging to my shirt. I often joined my LITBANGKES colleagues during their Sunday morning walks along Jalan Sudirman, when closed to traffic, which she started. Bakri smiled at me, and I knew it was my turn.

"We need your wise counsel, sage advice, and guidance," I began. "We think something is going on in Irian that may be nothing, or something. Our fear is that the risk of doing nothing may come back to haunt us, if the reported 'wabah babi' turns out to be something of epidemic, or even pandemic, potential, that that could have been stopped, or at least contained, had we acted."

Thoughtful as ever, Eka Dewi looked at Dari, and did the unexpected: she winked, or at least I think that is what she did.

As we filed out of her office in the anteroom, she scolded me in her mocking fashion, "You are too serious, find an Indonesian wife."

Later that day, or evening, after cooking up a pasta and

shell dish washed down with some very frosty Bintang Beer, I jumped to the piercing ring of my mobile.

Hesitantly picking up, not recognizing the number, I immediately recognize the voice. "Can you arrange our ticketing and travel first thing tomorrow morning." More directive than question. "We need to be on the evening flight to Sulawesi, and then onward to Jayapura. Just the two of us! By the way, bring warm clothes; the Papuan highlands can get cold, and the dampness will seep into your bones."

Just getting there

Uneventful, unless you count breaking my routine of sleeping for a near-midnight flight starting out from Jakarta on a Merpati 737 flight, after nearly a three hours' delay before lift-off. The 'service' spread was not so bad, if you are hungering for stale roti (bread) with a thick marmalade spread that tasted as looked. After a nibble, I took a pass. Better the dark of night to hide the choppy Indian Ocean turning into the raging Pacific, in our twenty plus year-old aircraft. Though plenty airworthy, it looked every bit its age, and then some. Except for a change of plane in Makassar (Sulawesi) and the Island of Biak, which once served as the stop-over leg in long-haul transpacific flights when planes were limited in their capacity to stretch their fuel over such vast oceanic distances, I never slept. The plane shuddered and shook, but fortunately, did not 'rock or roll'. Bakri and I had spread ourselves out on the near-empty plane, yet huddled together in catching the breathtaking views as we finally made our approach into Sentani, just outside of Jayapura, the provincial capital for West Papua.

Jayapura has its attractions! The 'seat' of government for the West Papua province, really no more than a picturesque port town port fronting the Yos Sudarso – Humboldt Bay, opening up to the Pacific. But an unsettling gateway nonetheless to one of the most remote places on the planet.

The drive from the airport into Jayapura never ceases to impress, especially for the first-time visitor, winding through lush green hills overlooking the ocean-sized blue waters of 'lake' Sentani. The descent into this seemingly peaceful town quickly gives up any pretense of tranquility; beyond which the few roadside huts give way to a harbor town of mostly one-and two-story cement structures, many boarded up and adorned with graphic graffiti, with a few outlandishly glassed styled buildings attempting to convey an illusion of modernity and failing miserably to do so. Not surprisingly, the architecture of note attempts to underscore the province's indigenous Papuan roots: traditionally styled and the domain of government eccentricities; trying to accommodate local sensibilities; and, of course, a draw for the trickle of visitors managing to get this far.

The town, hemmed in on three sides by hills, loses its luster upon closer inspection. Rapid growth has left the green slopes scarred, a hive of building activity to accommodate the spurt in growth of province. This has always been the way in Indonesia. A rocky coastline that might make an idyllic backdrop for some luxury resort is awash in trash washing up along the shores. And yet, undeniably, there is a freshness to the town, claiming to be a city, that might be confused for novelty, of both place and people. Settled in our 'windowless' rooms, actually advertised as deluxe suites to the back of a three-story building that calls itself a hotel, we make good on our escape to explore our new surroundings.

Having spent the day at the Provincial Military Headquarters armed with 'Surat Jalan' – in hand, issued in Jakarta by BAIS TNI, and our imploring and genuinely confused expressions on our faces, where we are advised to check in the following morning on the chance of hitching a lift on one of the military's C-130s traveling to the restive region. Our destination: 'Planet Dani'. But now, a nap is in order, before heading out on the town for an evening of glitz and glamour.

Bakri read my consternation at not being able to stay at the 'mostly malaria reserved' NMRC-Indonesia satellite research laboratory, with living facilities that stank of cleanliness: bunk beds with freshly washed sheets; and a bathroom reeking of disinfectant. Wearing his damnable familiar smile, he consoled me with a pat, and reminded me: "Just enjoy the ride." He stole my own expression.

Contributors: Nono Sukri and Lenny Ekawati;
US Naval Medical Research Unit No. 2 Satellite (malaria)
Laboratory, Jayapura, Irian Jaya – West Papua.

In my case, cravings can easily get confused for addiction. My four years in Cairo and Somalia, another sea story, were spent yearning in earnest for fast food, no matter the 'make or model'. I tried once to satisfy my hamburger 'urges' with an Egyptian equivalent of the 'Big Mac'.

> *Undercooked and tasting like 'old' meat that had not business in a bun, my treat included oversalted fries, and the dreaded Giardia: a parasite that feasts on the lower bowels. Having Giardia is a most memorable experience, notably accompanied by severe stomach cramping and bloating and the foulest of mucus-laden stools. If that were not enough, the stink from the steady stream of noxious 'passing' gas is enough to halt a charging bull dead in its tracks.*

Bakri started it, by complaining about our rooms and food, and got me thinking, wishing, how much I could use a beer; and not any beer, since I drink mine with ice. At home in Jakarta, Bintang 'settles' me no matter how 'shitty' the day. Bakri knows this. So despite warnings about local unrest and the threat of heavy rains, we navigate the streets trying our best to avoid the gangs of Papuan men and boys aimlessly hovering in small groups along the way to a Javanese-run restaurant and bar, adjacent to a not-so-colorful – except for the stink – local market.

Empty, except for the Sulawesi chef and waiter 'in one', turning a blind eye to my ill-fated attempts to gain his attention, to order some beer. "*Bersuma mau dua beer, dingin dingin.*" 'We want two beers – bir: "ice cold", I implore, and get properly ignored. Bakri then plays the diplomat, and points to the 'Bintang' girl on the advertisement on the wall behind an improvised bar, a plank laid out on two cement blocks. Our host than goes outside and returns with two of the many police patrolling the streets, keeping vigil, ready to snuff out the first firecracker, which left lit, would set off an explosive display of fireworks into the night sky.

"*Tidak bisa minum*" – 'Cannot drink', the senior officer exclaims, pointing to the poster!

In my less-than-perfect *Bahasa*, I ask: "*Ada apa.*" – 'What's the matter?' He politely explains, as one would to a group of drunks, that there is no alcohol permitted to be sold during the curfew. I cannot help thinking out loud: "How do we not know about this", and, of course, "How can we get beer?"

An hour later, I am finishing off the last of my three bottles as my new police friends depart for the streets. My beer cravings satiated, I am now just beginning to understand: the insurgency seems of late to have taken on a new persona with the kidnaping of hostages. Bakri pays the bill, not trusting my judgment as the 'money man', and we leave for our hotel, sharing a dark foreboding of things to come.

Our attempts to gain some better intel from the provincial health office, anything that might provide Bakri and with me clues to the reported 'pig' outbreak and purported deaths, prove futile. "They do not like that we are coming here, afraid we might actually find there is something that should have been investigated, or at least followed-up on." The office reeking of burnt cloves used in local cigarettes makes me nauseous, but we stick around for a morning, just to say that we did.

We manage to break up the boredom of our interminable stay in Jayapura in search of elusive Papuan primitive art; that which has not already been plundered. Including by me. Bakri is a recent convert to this passion of mine. I like to think of my collecting as contributing to the cultural preservation of a past depicted through art, the more bizarre, the better. The thrill of opening a 'treasure chest', that which is the cultural preserve of traditions and beliefs near extinct, is like no other. Indonesia does not fail to deliver for those in search of such discoveries.

In West Papua, all but the hardest woods can be counted on to disintegrate after a few short years; the damp tropical climate of infused heat and humidity giving way to wood-devouring insects. Only the 'Marbau' wood, aptly described by locals as 'iron wood', can stan the test of time. Little by way of carvings and painted reliefs survive beyond a few 'generations'; the most valued having an ancestorial connotation, handed down by patriarchal succession.

But the brilliant artistry that is Papuan primitive art is not locally on display, or easily found out. The passion of those with my ilk is fed by the search: akin to the 'journey', rather than the pot of gold at the end of the rainbow. I traipsed about Jayapura and Sentani eking out those icons that 'speak to me', metaphorically, attesting to their intrinsic value. This proved no easy task since what is not 'made-to-order' is finite; years of 'cultural thievery' having taken their toll. What little remains is mostly hidden away in the dankness of local mud and thatched family dwellings. That is unless armed with a substantial purse while exploring the high-end galleries of Jakarta and Bali, and the likes of Sydney, New York, and Paris, for that matter. And while I am averse to the notion of my own culpability, I do my darndest not to overthink it or try to explain myself. Whisperings of a reputed German entrepreneur making annual pilgrimages to the province for the sole purpose of crating indigenous crafts back to his own country in large shipping containers are galvanizing local sentiment against this expropriation, or at least raising awareness, and ultimately the price.

I felt lacking in objectivity to judge on this matter since I had worked hard over the years and squandered my navy salary to gather up primitive artistic collections from around the archipelago and squeeze it all into my spacious Jakarta apartment. This leading up to my greatest discovery in the many years I have devoted to hunting down the elusive art treasures of Indonesia. From the bizarre to the 'curios'.

Bakri waved me into the sweltering front room of a two-story shophouse that appeared both neighborhood grocery, without electric or perishables, and a souvenir shop, in a small village nestled alongside the shore of Lake Sentani. It was oppressively hot, so I merely gave a cursory look at the assortment of crudely made spears, arrows, and axes, jumbled against the back wall. Without preamble the bedraggled man sitting at the entrance offered: "I am a collector of curios. Can I help you?" In perfect English, no less. It was then that I glanced at Bakri staring intently at something partially hidden among the heap in the darkened far corner. Always prepared, Bakri now shone his penlight at a well-endowed totem figure.

I supposed the 'big penis' was emblematic of virility as it hung from the beautifully sculptured 'iron wood' edifice carved from a single tree, standing a least three meters in height. The huge but anatomically 'right-sized' penis seemed to grace most of the Papuan carvings I had seen, as if to underscore a very Papuan cultural theme. Outside the shop into the light of day, the smooth lines and fine facial and winged features were like nothing I had seen before. I was quite literally dumbstruck. I could only imagine of a lizard spreading it wings, ready to take flight. As the conversation now reverted to *Bahasa* Indonesian, Bakri managed to translate that 'the penis', his name for the totem, not mine, was over four generations old, and had served to hold up, as center post, a Papuan structure used for ceremonial purposes. I figured even failing in our '*wabah babi*' quest yet to start, I would be coming away with something special, a 'big penis'.

From the author's private collection.

UKIRAN-UKIRAN KAYU, IRIAN JAYA; THE ART OF WOODCARVING; Regional Government of Irian Jaya, Jayapura, in cooperation with the United Nations Development Programme, Jakarta; (editor) Jac. Hoogerbrugge, Netherlands, 1977.

This simple, unassuming man, answering to the name of Jesper, later invited us to his home nearby, set in a well-tended terraced tropical garden, introducing us to his family. His features and coloring gave away his mixed heritage, including perhaps some Dutch ancestry. He shared with us his history over overly sweetened tea: two generations removed from his grandfather's Sulawesi roots. When I brought up the always delicate subject of price, he would only say: "Whatever you think is fair." Jesper then fetched an old worn and tattered book, circa 1977, containing a black-and-white 'still' photograph dating back to 1956, eerily featuring an almost replica totem that dwarfed our 'big penis'. "This is for you."

We 'beat a hasty retreat' to our hired pickup as the first plump droplets of rain reverberated against the tin roof, signaling the start of a late afternoon downpour. Once in the cab, I turned to the scraping sound in the back as a large rectangular wooden box was being pushed into the covered truck bed by his son. A drenched Jesper now stood at the window, seemingly oblivious to the rain washing over him, shouting to be heard: "This is a gift for you. You will need a skilled carpenter to fit the pieces together, and brilliance to figure out how the puzzle-like pieces fit together." And as if to explain this gifting: "This is a prized 'Kepala Perahu', or more accurately 'Heluan Perahu' – translated as a boat or canoe prow, from Geelvink Bay; belonging to Numfor Biak Regency off the northwest coast of the province. It represents an artistry that honors our traditions as a seafaring nation archipelago. You will also find that to be true here in Papua."

From the author's private collection.

UKIRAN-UKIRAN KAYU, IRIAN JAYA; THE
ART OF WOODCARVING; Regional Government
of Irian Jaya, Jayapura, in cooperation with the United
Nations Development Programme, Jakarta; (editor)
Jac. Hoogerbrugge, Netherlands, 1977.

I was awakened by Bakri earlier that morning, our final morning in Jayapura, hours before first light. We had arranged a pickup to drive us to the military airfield, in hopes of 'hitching a ride' And now, we sat braced in our webbed seating as the aircraft bucked and shook all the way to our destination, Wamena. And we were lucky, since no civilian aircraft were being allowed into the restive region where insurgency had turned into kidnapping, and, for the Indonesian government, unwanted attention on the global stage.

We are finally ready to begin

We could manage to add only a few details to what we already knew or suspected, as we waited for an available helicopter to begin us on our journey. A Papuan nurse-midwife working with a MAF-associated charity in the village of Ninia had first reported an outbreak phenomenon characterized by flu-like symptoms at early onset, after which taking an abrupt lethal turn after two or three days. Her notebook, more a diary, and neatly recorded patient counts confirmed what we had heard anecdotally back in Wamena. People were drowning as their lungs filled with fluids, not unlike you would see in elderly patients with influenza with bacterial complicating pneumonia.

The actual number of case counts accounted for well over two-thirds of the local population. From rumor and local gossip and early radio calls, we understood that young and old, male and female, nobody was spared. The problem was that the MAF nurse who had worked in Ninia for the past three years had not made her weekly radio rounds since February, two months prior. Bakri and I understood that she may have gone to her home on an extended leave, attending to family matters; and while it was not the norm to abandon a posting without permission or at least notification, it was neither uncommon.

Probably fewer than thirty percent of these remote health stations in the Regency are even staffed, owing to the critical shortage of trained and willing Papuans to take up the cause: 'a calling' that is as arduous as any I could imagine. It is difficult enough to attract and graduate enough auxiliary nursing and midwifery candidates to the single training program located in Jayapura.

Before setting out from Wamena, we had learned that no supplies had been transported by the small MAF fleet to Ninia or the other serviceable communities in the Baliem Valley, not since the hostage-taking. So there was little by way of first-hand information, never mind critical antibiotics routinely used to treat bacterial pneumonia.

"How could this be happening or that nobody seems to know anything, or even bothering to investigate? How can this be?" My comments came as we left what was really nothing more than a health outpost; a grubby six-room building, staffed by an overworked and easily provoked local cadre of three attendants.

"That is why we are here." Bakri's matter-of-fact response to my non-question, more a statement, made me smile and again marvel at his commitment to doing some good for a people and place seemingly forgotten and abandoned by all providences. Such was my Batak friend's earnest, if not 'pure of heart' intentions: to help all Indonesians, these his 'brothers and sisters'.

You know when you have overstayed a stop along the way when the shine of 'newness' fades away, giving way to the mundane and ordinary. We were now just passing the time, anxious to move on, get to where we needed to be. On our last full day in Wamena, we stood in a potato field on the town's outskirts, taking photos with our ever-present shadow, a soldier, who tagged along wherever we went: "This is how I see my life in the future, building a small house here in this open area, and doing something to better the lives of these 'not forgotten', but 'never-even-acknowledged peoples'. All of this will be within my 'line of vision', as I take late afternoon tea on my porch." Tracing with outstretched arm and an imaginary brush, painting the surrounding mountains green with dark puffy clouds as if etched in charcoal floating past scraggly rock summits.

"Mine is Bali, and I hope to make it a better place." Bakri was not impressed with my flippant remark, or about to let my 'jab' spoil his daydream.

"See where that road is going," he said, pointing. "Out of town." But knowing it to 'peter out' shortly after passing across the Baliem river, and to nowhere. I shared: "I hope that is not a euphemism for where we are heading."

Contributor: Dr. Cyrus Simanjuntak; the author (right side), alias Jacques Bonaparte; Dr Cyrus Simanjuntak, alias Bakri Ginting (left side); and soldier (middle) from the Maluku islands chain assigned to the team; exploring near Wamena, 2002.

Our 'investigation' had stalled. Now six long days since arriving in Wamena. My frustration finally turned me to action, or into a crazed fool, which is how I suspected I was coming across. Bakri cautioned me, as he always does, to be gentle, but I could hear my own voice 'crack' as I stood in the doorway of the MAF superintendent's home and pleaded for assistance in getting us out of here. I felt spittle ejecting from my mouth as I talked about our fears that the Dani could 'still be' dying up in the higher reaches of the Baliem Valley, whilst we were sitting every morning for hours on end: waiting our turn. Once the fog settled in, nothing was visible, certainly from the air; making any flight a perilous bet, especially so if trying to land on a mountain top.

Bakri looked really tired the morning of my tirade at the MAF compound. And even though I thought him invincible, I knew my friend was beginning to feel the strain of delay, or just letting it show; that feeling of helplessness when you have neither control nor ability to influence in the face of a purported human catastrophe, almost three months prior.

As an epidemiologist responding to a suspected outbreak, you sometimes act on the hype that your job is about saving lives. But as is the case with most outbreaks in remote areas impacting 'neglected' populations, you are essentially left to collect information in trying to figure the 'who, what, where, and how', long after any chance to 'effect' meaningful actions: save lives, find the source/cause, and control the spread.

At 0400 dark on this early morning, Bakri looked particularly tired. For the seventh day running, we gathered our navy-issued duffle bags and store-bought sleeping bags, and empty cold boxes, and trudged with guarded expectations to the airfield.

Be careful with what you ask! Bakri shook me repeatedly as I dozed on the wooden bench that was feeling all-to-familiar: leaving me stiff and sore. A youngish looking 'aviator', the wraparound sunglasses a dead give-away; whose shoulder epilates clearly distinguished him as a seasoned pilot. He was standing over me as the morning light pierced a mist; for a split-second, giving him an angel-like glow. "You ready?" Definitely an American, with a discernable west Texas drawl, sporting a sunburned face behind 'peach fuzz' that might have passed for whiskers, if not for a complexion as smooth as a 'baby's behind'. We were finally leaving, but not by helicopter! We had been forced to change our itinerary over the last few days, adjusting our plans since we could no longer just drop from the sky. We walked the thirty meters to the sole functioning Cessna in the MAF fleet, a 206, just returned to 'airworthiness' following an engine overhaul, or so we were told. Just maybe, 'my scene' at the superintendent's home had worked some magic. Our gear secured in the small compartment to the back, we boarded and took our seats.

"I did not think you could fly a fixed-winged aircraft at Ninia?" I asked the pilot half-quizzically.

"Let's see," was his earnest response, smiling at his own witty retort.

I reminded myself to be thankful for little things, like this assuredly airworthy aircraft. My confidence in both plane and pilot illogically corresponded to the huge deposit I had made using most of my available cash. At first, I thought of the obvious contradiction of having to pay for transportation since MAF was almost entirely supported by public contributions to support their flight operations, missionary outreach, and humanitarian 'good deeds' to remote jungle highland communities. Everything from the distribution of bibles to ferrying passengers alike, mostly government staff providing basic health and educational services, got a free ride. And while most sympathetic to our plight, our investigation did not 'check any of the boxes' on their mission spreadsheet as to what was humanitarian, and what was not. And so the large payment, in advance no less!

All said, I was in awe of the MAF, their dedication, and their cowboy-like grit in flying over some of the most rugged and remote landscapes on the planet, again, in a four-seater, single-propeller-driven Cessna. The upshot is that the whole of Jayawijaya, and 'not' metaphorically, is an unmarked graveyard of 'too numerous to count' plane wreckages strewn across this vast jungle highland region. Most of which are never found, except for those few accidentally stumbled upon. Such is my appreciation and admiration for the pilots of MAF. Maybe not so much their mission.

Blessedly, our C-130 flying into Wamena had no windows. But now we were airborne in our 'toy' Cessna, my expectations were about to be realized. In fact, I had no idea; possibly some lush 'Garden of Eden' in the company of cannibals. But now looking out at an expansive sea of green, no matter mountains or valleys, or alleyways, I was left to wonder how we could ever manage in finding our way, never mind the figure out the mysteries of 'wabah babi'.

My ignorance had been truly blissful, and made this wonderful adventure just so, until the collision of fantasy and reality. I was not quite prepared for this. I think the moment our 'so small' a plane began shuttering, buffeted by updrafts, low drafts, and every type of side draft conceivable, was when I really understood we were not in for a picnic. Speaking of which, I kept channeling my fears in thinking of, what we were going to eat for lunch, and more importantly, who was going to feed us. And yes, our supply of ramen noodles was enough to last us at least a few weeks.

Just six months prior, I was flying in a three-not-four-seater plane, and no Cessna, which carries cachet, a 'brand name' known quality that is calming to nerves. Sort of like getting your hamburger and fries from a real McDonald's as opposed to the many 'wannabees' you find around Southeast Asia. Reciting a pledge to myself to never ever to put myself in a small plane of questionable pedigree again, over yet another jungle no less.

Then, I was flying from Pontianak in West Kalimantan (or Indonesian Borneo) to the jungle town of Sintang, with the pilot following the Kapuas River for bearings, until heavy rains obliterated any kind of ground visibility. I remember asking him: "Is there a problem, are you used to this kind of flying?" He was silent, 'sweating buckets', and regularly glancing at the fuel gauge, until finally a glorious ray of sunshine signaled a break in the weather. After which we were able to find the river and follow it until our wheels touched down on 'terra firma'.

I might add that the jungles and jungle villages and towns of West Kalimantan had become my home-away-from-Jakarta for months at a time over the last few years, as it did my Indonesian team that included Dari, Apok, and Oopi, and yes, even Beti, as we tracked and documented the first epidemic of newly recognized hepatitis E virus (HEV) in Southeast Asia; another story for another day, should I be so lucky to get through this one.

Bakri and I were mesmerized by the views from our windows. But my grip on the seat armrest tightened as we made for yet another approach to the landing strip, all the while buffeted by the crosswinds. The pilot, calm and in control, kept me from completely losing my mind. This third attempt almost flying into the side of the rocky cliff face. But somehow pulling up just in the 'nick of time'; my cue to shut tight my eyes and offer a silent prayer, desperately hoping the 'god almighty' was listening.

The jarring 'bump' came without warning. My immediate relief was pure and unadulterated as our wheels caught, then gripped, the narrow grassy slope of not more than a few hundred meters. The steep incline, as if by natural design, slowed the whining plane to a stop, along with the 'pilot' furiously stomping on the foot pedal that I took for breaks. This was like no landing I had ever experienced. Immediately upon reaching the end of the airstrip, if you could call it that, we were swarmed by local children carrying even younger children and infants in their arms and on their backs. Rocks were immediately placed behind the wheels to keep the plane from sliding backward and off the ledge.

'People watching a small plane ready to take off from the airfield of Anguruk.' Through the lens of the intrepid adventurer and explorer, Prof. Emeritus (Stanford) Jean-Claude Latombe, who explored the Papuan highlands, and graciously shared his memories with the author.[3]

Our reception was tumultuous, with everybody clicking and clacking and making exaggerated gestures while Bakri and I, still in shock and bewilderment, unclicked our safety harnesses and clambered unsteadily out of the plane. In my case, with

3   https://ai.stanford.edu/~latombe/mountain/photo/irian-jaya-94/ irian-jaya-94.htm.

the utmost haste since I was not sure if the plane was going to stay put or start rolling backward. Ropes were tied to wheel struts and anchored around nearby boulders. The pilot seems both at ease and in his element, handing off unmarked boxes and joining the elders for some tea and a prayer: not at all in any great rush to leave. I am feeling much less so.

After a festive morning, our bellies stuffed with wild boar cooked up from the ground in an earthen oven, I enjoy the practiced spectacle unfolding as the pilot revs up the engine. The crowd gathered to the back of the plane: removing the rope ties and rocks serving as breaks out from behind the wheels; pushing the plane in a half circle 'so as to' face the downward slope; and then pushing up against the wings as the wheels gather 'rolling' momentum, as if 'jump-starting' an old jalopy. And then the '*Pièce de résistance*': the plane catapulted off the lip of the cliff, dipping momentarily, and then, as if catching the air, taking flight.

It really bothered me that I did not even know the pilot's name. Why had I not asked? We may have spoken only a few words between us since first meeting up earlier that morning. Indeed, I knew nothing about this man whose quiet manner disguised a resolve and devotion that made him risk his life every day. He was no thrill seeker! I told Bakri that evening that this is the kind of hero we should be celebrating. There were already too many 'false gods'; movie stars to rock stars, and the billionaires whose 'Forbes' ranking made them instant celebrities, worthy of our adulation.

The investigation

Wet and cold, Ninia was little more than a settlement – a speck on the only map we could locate of Jayawijaya; distinguished from all the other specks by the 'circled' red cross, marking the spot befitting a 'health outpost'.

Ceremonial totem-like pillars crafted from local 'iron wood', with intricate carvings of fierce warriors complete with spears and shields, and, of course, depictions of sexual acts that so characterize local ceremonial art throughout Indonesian Papua, held up the overhang over an oversized veranda. The five rooms of the health center were best described as utilitarian. As best as we could discern, there was a sleeping room for assigned staff, a small office/storeroom, and smaller still, an examination room that was curtained from an area obviously used for obstetric examinations and deliveries; by far the largest, serving as an inpatient ward with six beds, all unoccupied at the time.

The only equipment in the center were two oxygen tanks flaking with age and rust, but beautifully adorned with graffiti depicting pigs. I took notice and mentioned to Bakri how this 'industrial art' could fetch a high price in upscale Kemang, in south Jakarta, home of numerous galleries, expats, and wealthy

Indonesians. "You have become spoiled by the treasures of Indonesia," he jokingly exclaimed; referring to my obsession with the bizarre and whacky that is Indonesian primitive art. Indeed, my condominium was filled with treasures, picked from my time in the field.

On a previous trip to the coast of West Papua, of course with my partner Bakri, I managed to transport a five-meter, hand carved 'dugout' canoe, which I bartered for like the fictional 'Mad Hatter' enabler from the 'Alice in Wonderland' story. I was cunningly suave and polite, yet insistent and unrelenting. Made from a single hollowed tree, which was so narrow the paddlers had to stand. It is my 'pride and joy', if not obvious enough from my 'gushing' on and on about this example of Papuan artistry.

UKIRAN-UKIRAN KAYU, IRIAN JAYA; THE ART OF WOODCARVING; Regional Government of Irian Jaya, Jayapura, in cooperation with the United Nations Development Programme, Jakarta; (editor) Jac. Hoogerbrugge, Netherlands, 1977.

I was able to board a battered old wooden sailing vessel, a traditional *Pinisi*, with my prize. And not without a 'little' help of friend and famed NMRC-Indonesia malaria field researcher Dr. Hassan, who, like any good magician, could be counted on to 'pull a rabbit from a hat'.

My vessel was a motorized Pinisi, or Lambo; Pinisi Freighters in the port of Taopere in Makassar (Ujung Pandang) Photo taken in 6x6 BW format in 1994 by Marc Obrowski (Wikipedia).[4]

We shared a small rectangular 'box' that passed for deluxe steerage accommodations. The cramped space was outfitted with two hammocks that swayed to the rhythm of ocean swells; sweltering by day and cooled by a balmy nightly breeze through open portals. Finally, after an interminable seafaring journey plying the seas in a westerly direction, with a single stop-over in Makassar, the schooner passed into Sunda Kelapa Harbor, the historic Jakarta port dating back to the 13th century.

It was way too big and unwieldly for my condo; I transformed my find into a long table, or rather commissioned a local craftsman in the south Jakarta neighborhood of Kemang

4   *https://en.wikipedia.org/wiki/Pinisi.*

known for its artisans applying their trade with a chisel in hand, turning out impeccable reproductions. My go-to craftsman and his daughter set about the design and crafting of a cradle for my dugout, now repurposed and having found a home.

From the author's private collection.

I need no help in greeting the new day having lain awake since 'zero-dark-thirty', the wee hours of the night, trying to force sleep, but to no avail. Bakri on the other hand seems well rested and chipper for such an early hour. He surprises me with coffee and eggs, along with leftovers from our rice and boiled tuber meal from the previous evening. He has built a small fire in the black iron stove with the dampened kindling wood stacked behind the health center. Yes, Bakri is more the doer on this our first morning in the field, while I am more the zombie.

Everything that first early morning was wet, residue from fog that engulfed us. "Feels like we are on a movie set," I thought out loud, an auspicious start to the day. So thick was the shroud blanketing the plateau that we could not see the circular 'earth and grass' huts of village as we peered down from our pedestal, cluster no more than a 'stone's throw away'. But we could almost taste an overwhelming stench carried by smoke from the household fires as families were also just beginning their day. That very stench would become my daily 'wake-up' call, reminder of just where I was, as if I needed any help in remembering.

"Crap, I have ants in my pants," I whispered to Bakri, maybe a little too loudly. We sat cross-legged on the grassy matting, damp and prickly, teeming with ticks, mites, and perennial infestations. We spoke in hushed tones, back and forth, the village elders conferring among themselves, their entourage looking on. The very first thing I learned as a navy disease detective was the importance of introductions. Outbreaks investigations by design are invasive, whether collecting sensitive personal information, specimens from human or non-human subjects in the form of blood, urine, stool, or sputum, or the mere act of entering someone's home, no matter if even just a thatched hut. Enlisting the support and cooperation of those 'in charge' was a critical 'first step' in winning over the community.

In our case, the stakes were higher. Firstly, we were not Papuans. And secondly, we represented the Government of Indonesia – at least Bakri did. This last point making things dicey since we were literally in the middle of nowhere, amidst a fledgling successionist uprising and clashing allegiances. But it felt here in Ninia that the only loyalty that matters was to one another, and to the traditions that cemented those bonds.

After a grueling session explaining ourselves, our purpose, our plan to the council of elders, we finally made our way in a snake-like procession down a stone-hewn path to the clustering of thatched huts. As we descended, the fog that hung over the health center gave way to a cold drenching rain.

I was struck by the children: all with runny noses and extended bloated stomachs characteristic of kwashiorkor malnutrition – stemming from a lack of protein in the diet; smiling and giggling with one another, pointing to Bakri and me. The adults, however, wore stoic faces giving away nothing but a tinge of suspicion. From hut to hut, the same: dirt floors and walls of lashed tree limbs, together with beaten earth. Most are grouped in familial styled 'compounds', often multi-generational, while others skirted the periphery of the village. I would go so far as to recognize each cluster as a 'clan' or sorts; except that the whole village is probably just 'one big extended family'.

There was a structure built of corrugated metal, a school I was told, and the only structure that might fit the description of public edifice, other than the health center.

Pigs certainly make their presence felt by the sounds of grunts and squealing, perforated by 'loud farts'; roaming freely, in and out of the family dwellings. As much as any family member, they are prized; a source of wealth and prestige that both divides and brings together the community, in the tradition of 'Pig Feast'.[5,6,7]

Contributor: Reinhard Dirscheri/Alamy Stock Photo; Pig Festival in Dani Village, Baliem Valley, West Papua, Indonesia – Image ID: CBCKDH (Alamy).

5   https://papuaheritage.org/index.php/en/theme/pigs-and-
     pig-ceremonies-new-guinea#:~:text=Joewò%2C%20pig%20
     celebration%2C%20is%20of,great%20social%20importance%20
     for%20Papuans.
6   https://onlinelibrary.wiley.com/doi/10.1002/j.1834-4461.1972.
     tb00312.x.
7   https://en.wikipedia.org/wiki/Dani_people#:~:text=The%20
     Dani%20use%20an%20earth%20oven%20method%20of,of%20
     sweet%20potato%20or%20banana%20inside%20banana%20
     leaves.

Our approach in obtaining information and specimens was to first read a 'statement' explaining the purpose of our work, the interview and blood collection activities, and most importantly, making sure that participation was 'voluntary'. Yet there was no way of ensuring that our local helpers, who translated from a prepared Bahasa Indonesian version of the 'consent form', communicated the message as intended; neither Bakri nor I spoke but a sprinkling of words and phrases of the local Dani dialect, or any for that matter.

For most, just receiving this kind of attention from two foreigners was gratefully appreciated, although we made clear that we were not conducting 'home' clinics. Nevertheless, the 100 percent participation rate left me less than confident that the notion of 'voluntary' was fully understood. Our insistence in making sure the 'informed voluntary consent' document was fully read out, from beginning to end, elicited lots of giggles; and not just from the interviewee, but also the interviewer, and the swarm of faces looking on. Indeed, we were sorely tempted to abandon this critical element in the investigative process. I was not kidding myself. We were only going through the motions to satisfy a very Western notion of implied ethical standards.

After a morning of household interviews, covering thirty families, and I mean whole families, generational, the linguistic and cultural challenges to our standardized list of questions left us exhausted. Our two translators: the teacher in the village anointed so by some government official in Wamena, making up in enthusiasm for the lack of any formal training; and a self-appointed elder. They had their own ideas regarding which questions to ask and how to elicit any kind of response. Wa and Dodo, named respectively, nevertheless gave their all, and commanded the attention and cooperation of all those we encountered.

Squatting in the mud in front of the household, we relied on one 'responsible' adult to speak on behalf of all family members. This approach saved time but did little to assure us as to the accuracy of the information being passed. Bakri devised a calendar recall method using a local wedding four months prior, in framing questions regarding illness, including associated influenza specific signs and symptoms, by the outbreak period. The only answers that I had confidence in were family deaths attributed to the illness described. Less clear was if these deaths were reported to the health center, or not, making validation difficult as to how representative was the data taken from the record books.

I was struck by the stunting of the population, unable to estimate the ages of the children based on my initial observations: the very young often turned out to be not so young. Conversely, the very old not so old.

Collecting venous bloods using plastic syringes allows for 'filled' test tubes to be removed and replaced, providing for multiple samples, proved easy, much more so than we expected. The Dani did not 'blanch': not so much as a peep. Bakri showing off his wonderful way in making all feel at ease through his laughter and gentle touch. This was the general response, until we attempted with limited success 'finger sticks' on young children; a useful and seemingly innocuous method of obtaining bloods, particularly for malaria screening purposes: yielding just a 0.1–0.2 ml blot on filter paper. The truth of the matter, 'finger sticks', while seemingly less invasive than collecting bloods with a syringe, and shedding far less blood, hurt like all hell. But the cartoon bandages applied after the sticks became a real prize.

Over the next two days, we worked to translate the data extracted and not so accurately scribbled into our database, using logbooks since we began our expedition with no expectation of electricity for electronic data entry. That reminded me to report to Jakarta, and more specifically Captain Rick Lavender, my Commanding Officer, using the satellite phone, otherwise referred to as the SAT! This can pose problems by virtue of location, where we work: usually in the middle of nowhere. I have spent hours waving the 'ten-kilo' SAT over my head, trying desperately to get a signal in making a connection. For sure, good comic relief to anyone looking on. Nothing bringing more of a smile to the faces of onlookers than some deranged 'boulay'. Except to our Dani hosts, I probably resembled more an alien from the celestial night skies.

Captain Lavender is freakishly demanding, but no less giving. His tolerance of mediocrity, or just getting by, is 'a big fat zero'! None of us have gone unscathed when he goes off on someone or something. This especially so of newly introduced information technology. Most emblematic is Rick's tendency to fight 'tooth and nail' for 'his' people, 'taking it' to the senior leadership if need be. And for that, there are those of us who would follow Rick in jumping off the proverbial cliff.

A military organization, at least one that retains its independence from the whims of politicians and tyrants, sometimes indistinguishable, is unlike any other, valuing 'leadership' above all else. Epitomized by an undeniable and undefinable quality that cannot be store bought; that being to 'lead by example', from the front rather from the rear. Anyone in any navy will tell you that there is no greater show of 'leadership' than to inspire those in need of inspiration, and that of taking responsibility for the inevitable screw-ups. That is not to say that some senior officers and enlisted, those that make it to the top of the heap, do 'not' aspire to such expectations.

At NMRC-Indonesia, supporting the navy's infectious disease research mission in Southeast Asia is a daunting undertaking, all the while maintaining the highest scientific and ethical standards: mandated and ever-so-closely scrutinized. This being especially so as a foreign military entity, American no less, 'smack dab' in the heart of the Indonesian capital.

Unfortunately, I am only able to manage a few words as I struggle to gain elevation in the hope of maintaining satellite connectivity. Regardless of utility, I am forced by decree from my Command to carry my bulky and weighty phone contraption everywhere and anywhere.

What became apparent during our initial assessment in matching interview findings with health center records was the importance of antibiotic and antipyretic treatment in preventing deaths. It was that simple! More importantly, by retrospective review of health center records, the number of illnesses during the previous four months far exceeded those from the same period for the five years prior. This simple analysis was 'proof positive' that we were indeed 'on to something'; investigating an epidemic phenomenon with high case fatalities: deaths associated with epidemic illness. Less clear was why this outbreak was first reported as 'wabah babi'. Was there any evidence of sick pigs, more than the usual, leading up to the outbreak, in trying to identify a possible causal relationship; perhaps a mixing, as in putting in a blender, of 'swine' and 'human' influenza A viruses in creating a novel *Frankenstein* virus, that just might have proved lethal? But the enigma of 'wabah babi', regardless if interpreted as 'swine flu' or 'swine plague', remained just: a mystery! But clear to us, Bakri and me, was that we had stumbled upon an epidemic, largely unreported, which killed too many people to have gone unnoticed and unreported, which is tragically what happened.

The journey

I have never been a trekker! Yes, I have foraged, gotten lost, and rappelled cliff walls and waterfalls in the jungles of Panama; part of my navy 'medicine in the tropics' training at Fort Sherman. Playing the intrepid 'Indiana Jones', I have had my sneakers sucked off my feet (and lost for all eternity) as I sank knee-deep in mud along the banks of the Kapuas River, which snakes its way through western Indonesian Borneo, all the while pushing and pulling our motorbikes as we slogged through the muck along a disused logging road in the middle of the night, during torrential monsoon rains, no less. At the time, in search of unraveling the epidemic nature of a newly recognized hepatitis E virus.

And no, I have never climbed a mountain, and I am most certainly not a candidate for 'Everest' fame. That said, I am a runner, a swimmer, and carry the imprinted allusion that I am a warrior (as the navy likes to portray its sailors); if not by what comes naturally, then certainly by sheer grit and determination.

In the days before fitness trends invaded hotel accommodations, at least in the class of hotels my navy travel allowance would allow for, I outdistanced and outran packs of feral dogs: from Hanoi, Ho Chi Minh City, Phnom Penh, Bangkok and Vientiane to the east, Cairo and Mogadishu and Kismayo somewhere in the middle, and Houston, New Orleans, La Paz and Guatemala City to the west. In Guatemala, there was the added imperative of speed while running in the crime-ridden neighborhoods of Zona 11 in the dark morning hours infamous for the headless corpses that newly littered the streets almost daily.

The point being that I thought of myself as 'navy fit'.

So as I looked from my perch looking into the valley below, a green, seemingly pastoral, setting created the illusion of what would be an idyllic 'walk in the park'. How could I have been so wrong?

Bakri and I set out on a cold and drizzle-laden early morning in our quest for answers, with our escort of four locals – Ramu, Laksi, Lek and Jar – who would serve as our porters and guides, at least to the next clifftop village. Any anxieties about the journey were eased knowing our group sported a single, reworked long-gun that looked to be a remnant from the Dutch colonial times; that along with the traditional Irianese stick-to-fitted-stone, hewn surprisingly sharp and leather bound into crude but effective hatchets: used for chopping everything from trees to tribal combatants. After what seemed forever (the better part of a morning), we became bogged down in a highland jungle marsh after a scary descent where every step threatened to dislodge the rock strewn 'clay' terrain, turning the hillside into an earthy avalanche. As exhaustion began to sap my initial exuberance, I could not help noticing that Bakri seemed to grow stronger as we continued onward. And of course, our new friends were unfazed.

During the crossing of a long, narrow tree-rooted ledge off a slick vertical rock wall, Ramu held one hand, and Jar the other, letting myself be transported as if in a trance. Bakri, well aware of my 'fear of heights', shouted out: "You are 'Spider-Man."[8]

To suggest that I was not petrified would be a failure in acknowledging my intense phobia. That extended to any height over a few meters. The saving grace was that I was beyond exhausted, which allowed me to disconnect from my surrounding, no longer thinking of my imminent death.

After two days of laborious hiking and a cold, wet, sleepless night in my damp sleeping bag, a bulky and musty smelling albatross that weighed a ton – but hey, I was not doing the carrying – I was no longer even thinking of the poisonous snakes I anticipated lurking under every rock, hanging from every tree, or hidden from behind every bush; and yes, another of my extreme phobias! This adventure was turning into a journey of 'rediscovery': that of confronting my frailties and demons. But putting things into their proper perspective, the adage, 'get over it' seemed most apt.

By the end of our fourth day, as I blundered through the thick vegetation, 'still being led by the hand' by Ramu, we suddenly came upon a bluff of at least 300 meters in height, which had been all but hidden from view on the ground by the thick jungle canopy, until almost bumping into it. Looking up, Bakri and I were awestruck by the sight of what was more 'stone age' than anything we could have dreamt up.

---

8   *https://i.pinimg.com/originals/fe/88/7e/ fe887e911d13940ffba33b9c13f7678e.jpg.*

First encounter

The inhabitants of the small community that made this clifftop home stared down on our small group of travelers. I heard a dull roar in the space between my ears, drowning out all other 'white noise', even my own thoughts. I was 'shattered'! Nothing could have prepared me for this encounter. I felt physically unable to take another step, despite Bakri's prodding to move on.

It was inexplicable to me that Bakri never complained, uttered a negative word, and always took in every experience, the good bad and the ugly, with a kind of glorious wonder that I could only envy. Maybe this was about being a Christian Batak from western-most most Indonesia in a predominately Muslim country, where tolerance in a religious and cultural sense is always being tested. I would later learn that Bakri had a heart condition, which would have raised a 'red flag' to his taking part on the escapade we had embarked upon, if only I had known! Looking back, this made Bakri even more the 'superhero', towering above the likes of even superman, the original 'man of steel'.

Despite his encouragement, I felt rooted to the ground. Never ever had I felt so drained – and not because I had been eating only instant ramen noodles and boiled eggs benefiting from a garnish of wild but edible plants for which I have no name – adding a splash of color and minty flavoring to our meagre 'eats' the last few days of our march.

I remember murmuring to Laksi that I really could not go on, could not climb the cliff before us. But I did, with Bakri's barking encouragement.

Ramu yanked me up by my reaching arm up and over the lip of steep of the large boulder I was clinging to, 'for dear life.' I sat exhausted, sapped of energy and will; pounding heart threatening to blow my chest apart, wide open. I gingerly prodded my shoulder, massaging with my fingers, feeling as if ripped from its socket. It was only after a momentary pause that I glanced down the gently sloping plateau to the picturesque village that unfolded before my eyes. With the backdrop of the mountains shrouded in the passing clouds, it could have been a luxurious resort billing itself as the fabled 'Shangri-la', certainly of West Papua.

Contributor: Burt de Ruter; Ariel view of a Dani village in the Baliem Valley. West Papua, Indonesia – Image ID: 2DHWG3W (Alamy).

Circular sticked huts with thick overhanging thatched domed 'hats' dotted the rocky slope as I looked down; otherwise known as *honai*, the most common traditional home in West Papua, but especially so for the Dani.[9] "So this is Soba," looking upon the village below us – a statement, more matter-of-fact, to confirm aloud that we were truly here, to Bakri, and myself no less.

There were two notable structures that stood out: a small rectangular room of no more than three square meters lengthwise, with poorly fitted warped planks leaving gapping slits to the ground below; and mesh wired cages that housed rabbits. Ramu, in his very limited Indonesian vocabulary, eventually conveyed that the wooden structure served as a rudimentary clinic on the rare visits of the missionary nurse traveling from Nina, likely the same person that encouraged the breeding of rabbits as a means of upping the protein intake of the community, particularly so of the young children.

It was therefore of no surprise after exchanging pleasantries with the assumed village elders that we realized we were being honored with a boiled rabbit. I began salivating at the thought of gorging on this treat, that is until our unskinned and undercooked meal was presented to us. I was relieved following some urgent persuasion and instruction by Ramu, after which the rabbit was removed. Our meal returned, transformed into a charred vestige of its former self. There was an attempt to adorn our rabbit with earth-baked tubers and root vegetables that included sweet potatoes and cassava; the garnish becoming meal enough for me.

I should point out that the earthy to sweet range of flavors from the 'roots and tubers' mined from the ground are arguably one of nature's most nutritious gifts. Lucky that, for us. While

9   *https://westpapuadiary.com/papuan-traditional-house/.*

rabbit would certainly be a welcome protein addition to the menu, a 'fickle' affection for these creatures saved them from becoming food staples, as least in Soba.

Bakri did better than I with the rabbit. Later that night, as Bakri slept soundly by the sound of his rhythmic breathing, I would regret my earlier show of 'rabbit' bravado, heaving up the gamey meat and the remainder of my stomach contents.

Language was becoming a real barrier as Bakri and I tried to communicate to communicate, short of 'standing on our heads'. We tried to decipher their experiences during the outbreak with Laksi and Ramu translating the intelligible into meaningful; putting together a record of illnesses and related deaths from the time of the outbreak, at least those compatible with 'flu-like' symptoms. This meant understanding the frequency of similar outbreak episodes from a historical perspective. To arrive at impact measures as reflected in rates, Bakri organized our visits so we could establish a demographic profile, which consisted of going from hut to hut and recording age estimates and sex of each member of the family unit.

I began to feel the cold stares, no longer smiling faces, as morning turned to afternoon. Indeed, we were all unnerved; Bakri repeating, "This is okay," over and over, as if his words, his mantra, served as a good-luck talisman. Evident was the growing suspicion on why we were collecting this information. And frankly, what good were we, having nothing much to offer other our investigative curiosity.

We carried with us satchels with packets of coloring books and crayons, pens and notebooks, and primary school 'language' and 'color by number' books. These 'gifts' evoked curiosity, but also confusion as to their utility. Their world had little use if not for some utilitarian function. I demonstrated the magic that is Crayola, the brand of waxed crayons; illustrating the aesthetic worth of art, drawing crude 'stick figures' that I hoped would be recognized as people, Dani, like themselves. Bakri turned clown-magician-teacher, all in one, using white chalk to write the ABCs on one of two blackboards he so carefully carried in a burlap sack slung under his arm since leaving Ninia.

"Climb higher and wave the phone over your head," Bakri instructed, as I tried to get any kind of signal from our satellite phone, or SAT, for short. The navy likes to keep track of its officers, especially those not keeping to a strict itinerary, traipsing about in one of the world's most stunningly remote locations: over 7000 square kilometers of mostly impregnable mountainous jungle terrain. I envisioned the fallout arising from an American naval officer gone missing. An increasingly sensationalized hostage-taking crisis gaining visibility thanks to an overly zealous international media presence would surely add to the furor should our odyssey happen to take a 'wrong turn'.

I ran up and down and sideways, stood on boulders and the precipice of a cliff, and still could not make any connection. Appreciably, Bakri too was apprehensive since he was, after all, responsible for me. I should have practiced my navigation skills as I pointed the small rubber-encased metal antennae attached to my SAT when I had a chance in Jayapura and Wamena. So I was overjoyed when not only did I get a signal but managed to finally make contact with my Command in Jakarta. I could barely 'catch' a word with the heavy static accompanying the gargled transmission. My real interest other than adhering to standard protocol in the field, letting someone know you were alive, was to confirm of our MAF pick up that had been tentatively planned for the following day.

So much for my 'delusions of grandeur', or that news of our expedition was being impatiently anticipated! Realization (and relief) set in that the two of us were for all intents 'were out of sight, out of mind'. This might have dampened our enthusiasm if we were just mortals. To the contrary, it served to energize our resolve, feeling every bit the 'African explorer' of the 'dark continent', or at least the Baliem Valley. Except for that, the 'greats', Livingstone, Stanley, Burton, Speke, and Banks, all failed in their quest to discover the source of the Nile.

My mind tends to wander, taking detours at the slightest of hypnotic suggestion:

This mission reminded me of the time when I was assigned to a similar navy medical research command in Egypt, working out of Somalia. In the waning days of the Mohamed Siad Barre reign, when much of the country had fallen into the hands of bandits and warring factions, I was 'dropped' into one of the last government-held towns in the south of the country, Kismayo, with its sandy streets and spectacular ocean views and a most definite Arabesque feel as reflected in the architecture and numerous mosques. The purpose of our work was in establishing prevalence of HIV and hepatitis C virus among local women roundup by the military police, mostly for the offense of 'hanging out on the street'. I did feel a little badly, thinking just maybe our study population had been detained for the purpose of 'bleeding', solely for the benefit of our research interests.

I recalled the small Cessna Embassy plane flying repeatedly over a cratered runway adjacent to the charred remains of what I guess was the terminal building. After making a few passes, the 'pilot' found a usable section of tarmac, meaning not cratered by recent 'shelling', that would allow for an abbreviated landing. Upon touching down, the 'pilot', who doubled as the military attaché at the Embassy, waved us away from the plane, obviously eager to get back in the air. The propeller was still turning, the engine never shutting down, as my Egyptian technician and Somali government counterpart, the only gynecologist in the country who served as the National Director of the Center for Sexually Transmitted Diseases, and myself, exited the cabin door and made haste to a waiting military Jeep. My instructions when I had inquired how I would know when he would return for us left me unnerved, especially so since we had no means of communication at our disposal: "I will fly low over the town a few times to signal you to get your asses back to the airport. And no dilly-dallying."

Feasting on fresh lobsters over the next few days, taking up residence in one of Barre's many villas, all went according to plan, except for a few tense moments at a roadblock on our return to the deserted airport, manned by non-uniformed soldiers toting AK-47s. Fortunately, they belonged to a militia supporting the soon-to-be exiled government.

What so strikes me about the similarities between our current situation and my Kismayo adventure was that the navy would let me loose under such circumstances, with little other than a 'picnic lunch' and naïve sense of invulnerability. Then as in now, 'not a whit of good sense', I felt the 'adrenaline rush' that should have read like a 'warning label', like the idiom: 'don't try this at home'.

Epiphany

I regained my resolve to see through this journey to its conclusion with our impending lift-off scheduled for the next day. My mind was churning out a diary of thoughts as I interpreted the steady flow of impulses from my every encounter. I managed to ditch my preconceived notions that had been like weights; most definitely dragging me down under. The Dani have survived and thrived in one of the most remote regions of the planet. Only first encountered in their native Baliem Valley, sometimes referred to as the Grand Valley, in 1938, this tribe attracted 'stone-age' stereotyping. The 'primitive' connotation belying a mastery in the art of 'mummification'; for the purpose in preserving the dead so their spirits could live on. Even more telling is how outsiders often distinguish the Dani from the other two related tribes that populate the Grand Baliem Valley, the Lani and Yali, by the size and shape of their 'kotekas' – penis gourds – worn by the men to exaggerate their sexual prowess: or maybe for the more obvious utilitarian purpose of keeping their genitals intact. Regardless, the casual observer may not recognize the complexity of a culture driven by the past, enabling them to survive and even thrive in this most inhospitable environment; but only so if you are 'boulay'.

Their welcoming manner is not about finding favor, but rather, a genuine warmth and openness reflected by their excited but shy smiles and exuberant embraces. Even at my earnest but failed best to ingratiate myself, 'all the while' clueless of Dani etiquette, I was made to feel 'at one' on their planet, in their world.

It is worth noting that the Dani we encountered in Wamena, with their body adornments and traditional trappings, were not part of any display put on for anyone's benefit, certainly not ours. They had not been spoiled so much by the 'bright lights' and 'big city' temptations. And yes, I am making a run at humor; the notion that Wamena is anything other than a small market town attempting to project the nation's prerogative over a region 'that does and does not' want to be governed.

The men, with their 'kotekas', sized and shaped to denote their respective tribal grouping; wild boar tusks piercing their noses in a display meant to evoke their warrior lineage and likely appease the ancestors, whose spirits roam at will and can play havoc with fate if not suitably honored; and the women, young and old, carrying infants in slings hanging over bared breasts, generally found in small groups, weaving and gossiping while selling the 'fruits of their labor', the vegetables and legumes grown in their community gardens. Notably absent from this mosaic are children, except for the very young at their mother's side. To my inquiry: "Better they learn something useful in the village," a young girl, maybe the daughter of one of the Javanese transplants sent to administer the regency, volunteered. That same evening, I thought of her words, and just maybe, a harbinger of things to come.

The occasional visitor can still be entertained in the nearby villages with a 'bakar batu', otherwise referred to as a traditional 'pig feast'. It is easy enough to chance upon this scrumptious display of earthy cookery rooted in some ancient Polynesian migration to this place; more an excuse to celebrate the passages in life, including death.

There are always those few with something to sell, earning a few rupiah making masks, spears, axes, and my favorite, primitive, and not-so primitive art; fetching the mostly Sulawesian and Moluccan shop owners a small profit from the likes of me. I came to learn of a German who came through a few years back when the insurgency was more an inconvenience and restricted to the remote reaches of the region far enough away to be 'out of sight out of mind', buying up enough to fill a shipping container back in Jayapura. But I am not one to pass judgement given my own proclivity; only to say I am more selective, with an 'eye' for the sublime.

I make this distinction because of how our understanding and appreciation of the Dani was only realized when we came to their villages and homes, and engaged them as one would a friend, for which they reciprocated. I was at times overwhelmed by my own feelings of belonging, as someone would always be clasping my hand in the villages we visited along our trek as if protecting me, afraid some mean-spirited ancestor would fate me to 'bad luck'.

Bakri fared so much better at engaging with our hosts, maybe because of his kindhearted nature, always looking for the good in people. The simplicity of the Dani and their embracing welcomes was more than humbling. Children, no matter how small or how old are treated with an endearing reverence and allowed the freedom to be 'children'. Strikingly, it is often the older children caring for those younger than themselves; handed such a loving responsibility at such an early age.

Pigs, as I would discover, were treated as family, and an ever-present squealing reminder of how the Dani shared their existence with these precious possessions. With stone and stick implements that serve as tools integral to their survival, they subsist using traditional agrarian cultivation of terraced gardens; ideally suited to the topography and soils of their highlands' home. "Nothing 'stone age' in that," I offered, one evening over a meal of 'ramen'. It became apparent that maybe the Dani's 'good nature', smiling accept when expressing concern for 'our' well-being, eager in sharing what little food they had with us, might be mistaken for something akin to 'primitive'; a misnomer if ever there was one. Even as we traversed the jungle valleys and mountains that separated the cliff-dwelling communities, our self-appointed guides would forage and share grubs and roots as we rested intermittently, Bakri and me, exhausted.

I forgive myself for my anger, bordering on incongruity, in making sense of what was clearly a ferocious disease 'culling' of the Dani population, leaving some villages with few survivors. While children dominated in terms of actual cases, it was the nominally healthy adults whom 'bore the brunt' of disease burden as reflected in the high (specific) attack rates, as reported from family retrospective interviews and documented from health center records cases.[10]

Based on only empirical, observational-driven evidence, the culprit appears to be: a *flu babi*; maybe a reassorted 'swine' and 'human' influenza A virus; or simply a 'human' influenza

---

10 *Attack rates reflect: the number of affected persons in a specific population during an outbreak period, e.g. young adults aged 20 to 39 years of age/the number of persons in that specific population X 1000 persons (sometimes per 100,000 in the event of an outbreak involving just a few cases, but no less of an outbreak phenomenon). Such rates allow epidemiologists to determine the actual impact of an outbreak in a specific population, from which comparisons with other specific populations relative to the outbreak event.*

A virus imposed on a 'most' vulnerable population; by way of soldiers sent to the province to take on a growing rebellion, with deadly consequences on a 'naïve' indigenous population owing to their isolation: both 'blessing and curse'.

Most striking was that such a calamity could have gone unnoticed, even in this remote jungle highland regency? How is it that this epidemic phenomenon was only picked up on the radar because of a newspaper account that was more to do about a 'swine' plague or flu? And to the present, how is it that only Bakri and I, an estimated three to four months 'after the fact', are wandering about looking for clues in documenting this frightful occurrence? And maybe more introspectively, how is it that we have now so little to offer other than our intrusiveness?

The making of a 'mess of things'

Another night, waking every few hours if just to reassure myself that all is right in the world. I steal advantage of such interruptions to momentarily gaze at the brilliantly lit stars against a blackened sky, whenever the clouds see fit to part. "How miniscule is life, our place in the cosmos," I cannot help but 'mouth', looking up.

My hammock served its purpose, keeping me off the ground, but left me bunched up in the middle; the netting sagging under my weight no matter how tightly stretched at the ends. This night, I only spill 'one time' as I struggle to untangle my contorted self in my twisted cocoon, awakening from deep slumber only when absorbing the shock of my fall. And yet, being no big fan of the crawly things that slithered and marched along the jungle floor, I was quite 'okay' with my sleeping arrangement.

I awake in a groggy state. But the whistling Bakri seems rested enough and eager to get started on this new day. I heard his breathing at night, steady and rhythmic. 'Damn him'!

The canopy above us already buzzing with coos and caws of our winged friends. Today will be our last day in between destinations. Tonight, we should be feasting in Soba, or so I am told, the last village on our itinerary before returning to the teeming 'metropolis' that is Wamena. But not until dosing myself with a morning packet of 'Indo-Café' Cappuccino and the accompanying sugar high.

We would lay claim to both a start of the investigation and a fraction of Jayawijaya, using slim findings from 'slim pickings' to validate or at least corroborate reports that had been passed to the health authority in Wamena from the mission health centers scattered throughout the Regency. Yes, if anyone had even bothered to gleam over the 'chicken scratch' from the penciled-in forms stored in the broom-sized records room at Jayawijaya general hospital during our first few days in town, this epidemic would have been recognized and acted upon months earlier in all likelihood.

Surveillance as a key public health function is all about generating data in a standardized manner for reporting purposes. Unfortunately, surveillance adapted for 'early outbreak warning' is beyond the means of the local heath care system, that simply put, is not equipped to respond to epidemic phenomenon when it comes to Dani deaths, outside of Wamena, that is. Health care workers in the town are far too burdened – and untrained – to take up outbreak detection and response responsibilities. So most outbreaks are never even recognized, except, 'as in our case', by some local journalist in a local newspaper account, albeit way too late to mount an effective intervention. Fast forward fifteen years: electronically relayed data with programmed instant interpretation and accompanying alerts and whistles now drives 'usually' timely responses. At least in theory.

Bakri showed his fun side in blowing up multicolored balloons of all shapes and sizes, and fashioning them into artful animals, to the delight of the entire village. He had carried his 'tricks' in one of the many pockets sewn into his safari-style vest, his safari-style shirt, his safari-style pants, and his safari-style backpack and equipment duffle bag. And of course, his safari-style fanny pack. Enough said! But yes, he looked outfitted for a safari trek.

We were beyond prepared for our expedition, with folding fish rods, hooks and lines, and an assortment of medicines that included antibiotics for diarrhea and anti-malarial drugs: enough to set up our own pharmacy. And yet we somehow forgot our sunscreen. My pink skin boiled to a lobster red. When not hidden by the triple canopy rain forests, we were bombarded by the intense ultraviolet-laden rays, especially at the higher mountainous elevations, ranging from 4000 to 7000 feet above sea level. At least Bakri had the good sense to come 'hat' prepared. And so it was I came to look 'not bronzed', but as if I had just popped out of an oven: crispy.

We sped up our household interviews, historically linking any illness or deaths to the epidemic period. Since our departure was planned for the next day, we could not delay in getting on with a 'very' loose and convenient sampling of family units in painting an epidemic portrait for this hilltop community. As in the previous villages we visited, Ramu would hijack and hastily train up 'locals' in conducting interviews, all for the price of cinnamon and peppermint sticks, which Bakri kept hidden from me throughout the journey, stashing his precious cargo in yet another set of pockets.

Bakri and I were pretty much frozen out of any communications, except for some universal hand expressions, in the absence of any skills in deciphering even fragments of 'that' spoken by the Dani, descending from the 'Trans-New Guinea' family of languages. 'More often than not', our attempts at communicating even the simplest of greetings were met by frustratingly blank stares. And while we sometimes encountered a smattering of Bahasa Indonesian, it was usually sufficiently diluted by the Dani language to confound our attempts at communicating as such. And while we did not resort to 'standing on our heads' in conveying our intentions, I certainly became adept to making up my own 'sign language' for whatever the occasion with wild hand gestures and stick drawing in the dirt. From the reaction of my intended audience, I was probably thought possessed by some mischievous ancestorial spirit, or some extraterrestrial traveler to 'give a wide berth to': kept at distance.

To convey the challenge faced in making sense of the Dani language, it is important to distinguish the three principal linguistic dialects spoken by the indigenous peoples of the Baliem Valley: Lower, Middle, and Upper Grand Valley. That, and the simple reason that we spoke 'none of the above': not a word.

That each dialect consists of sub-dialects, in some instances spoken and understood by a single village, owing to and contributing toward the geographical separation and isolation of communities, from one another; maybe best described as a 'linguistic evolution'.

My very novice impression was a Dani language, regardless of dialect, held fast by a linguistic tradition that did not value so much emphasis on vocal expression, whereas communication of ideas and thoughts was better expressed by actions and deeds. By way of example, there are only two words in the Dani 'linguistic family tree' used to describe color: 'mil' for cool/dark colors; and 'mola' for warm/light colors. And yet, I was totally befuddled every time I tried to utter even a simple greeting. Not just because of the distinctive vocabularies of each dialect, but the cultural norms and settings which dictated the 'right' greeting. In the Middle Grand Valley Dialect: 'wa' is used for a general greeting; 'lauk' to a woman or by a woman; 'lauknyak' by a group of women or to a group of women; 'nayak' or 'hal loak nak' by a man to a man; and 'nayaklak' by a man to a group of men. Cultural considerations aside, there are also different greetings for the time of day: for morning; evening; and of course, there is night. So failing in even the basics of ethnographic familiarity during our preparations for this undertaking made comprehension a struggle, adding to our exclusion.

As we made our way to the only sizable, leveled ground, as the natural light began to fade with the end of the day, we were confronted by a group of villagers who collectively corralled and 'pushed and pulled' us to a small hut nearby. Excitedly, they barked commands to Ramu, who conveyed the urgency of attending to an old woman, who, between high fevers and soaking sweats, lay prostrate on the dirt floor of her family 'honaï', rasping for each breath.

I had a bad, bad feeling about giving off any appearance that we could offer up anything to help this clearly dying woman. My discomfort was further compounded by the large following we had attracted as I would guess the entire community, every man, woman, and child, now clustered around the hut where Bakri and I hovered on our knees in carrying out the most basic of examinations. Wouldn't you know it, Bakri came up with a stethoscope from one of his many pockets and registered what we already knew about her weakened state: I could barely feel a pulse. The dying embers of what was once a small fire in the corner of the rounded hut bled smoke throughout the darkened room of no more than a few meters end to end and a low-ceilinged thatched roof not allowing us to stand erect, with only a sliver of fading daylight peeking through a smaller-still entryway. My thoughts and our whispered back-and-forth chatter are continuously interrupted by the squeals of pigs that also claim possession of the space.

Did I mention the stench that greeted us upon first entering the 'honai'? While not prone to gagging, my reflex was just that. Bile rising in my throat, 'it was all I could do' to keep from retching up the contents of my near-empty stomach. If I could conjure up a picture sufficiently descriptive of the 'vile' smell that overwhelmed us, it would be hanging in the *Louvre.*

"Malaria," Bakri exclaimed softly, although I was lost in how he drew such a conclusion. We were in the highlands after all.[11] Her 'hot and cold' spells as Ramu translated into Indonesian as 'panas dan dingin' suggested drenching sweats following by teeth-chattering chills, certainly reminiscent of malaria, but by no means the only responsible malady. Regardless, her state of exhaustion, while not coma-like, left her unresponsive. We both recognized there was nothing in our 'bag of tricks' enabling us to put off the inevitable. Bakri felt he had to, even symbolically, offer her up something, anything. He reached into yet another pocket in the leg of his cargo pants and took a chloroquine tablet and placed it under her tongue. He mumbled something I could not hear, our cue to back out into the fading light that still belonged to the day. Ramu guided us to a small lean-to shelter after conferring with the village elders, in symbolic ritual, as in all the villages we had visited. There was just enough room for Bakri and me to bed down for the night, after feasting on surprisingly delicious grub worms roasted on a spit that tasted like bacon, mixed with our remaining stock of rice. We sampled grub worms back in Wamena, at the wet market, with not just a

---

11   *https://www.thelancet.com/journals/lansea/article/PIIS2772-3682(22)00067-1/fulltext.*

little hesitancy. Bakri was particularly reluctant to savor the delights of the local street cuisine. But there is nothing like a few weeks in the 'bush' on a diet of mostly ramen noodles and rice, with a staple of sweet potato and sometimes banana mixed in for good measure, to make culinary adventurers of us all, the likes of which would make the 'new breed' of culinary explorers nod approvingly.

Feeling an almost-euphoric exhilaration of knowing we would grab a ride on the MAF helicopter coming for us in the early morning, as prearranged when we were still in Wamena trying to Commandeer the only airworthy MAF Cessna to Ninia (marking the start of our jungle adventure), exhaustion transitioned into the wonderful abandon of deep sleep, having eluded me from the start, since we departed on the late-night flight way back when across the archipelago. Bakri, on the other hand, fared much better, waking every morning with a hearty yawn and an exclamation of how refreshed he felt. We blindly trusted, with desperate exuberance, the Javanese MAF logistics manager that their one helicopter would be repaired by the time we were ready for our return flight.

I had no concept of time as I abruptly awoke from my deep slumber, except for feeling and tasting the blackness that engulfed me. I lay still a moment in gathering my wits, taking care not to move a muscle. And then it struck me: an unholy, almost satanic wailing that pierced the silence that envelops and comforts you as if a cocoon in the dark of the darkest night.

How unlike me to be too descriptive, too flowery, too verbose, in complicating what should be simple reflection of my thoughts. But I lay awake through the night, not stirring, not even giving into the demanding urge to get up and pee. The chorus of cries that seemed more animal than human shook my being, as if serving notice to us. I tensed my body and prepared for my reckoning as I heard feet stomping the earth.

Reaching into my soul, I knew what had happened, and truly expected to be trussed and herded away to our retribution.

As the 'cool' shade of darkness gave way to the 'not so cool' shade of early morning, having endured a night of no end, I finally turned my head toward Bakri. He was staring but not seeing, looking to the heavens, flat on his back. Only his blinking eyes gave evidence to life. "Are you okay?" I asked. He turned his head, blinked again, and slowly exhaled, as one would do in realizing you 'dodged a bullet', a euphemism for surviving a cataclysmic event. I half-expected Bakri to touch his face, move his arms and legs, just to make sure everything still worked – was still there. Again, trying to provoke some kind of reaction, I exclaimed, "I am okay, are you okay?"

Finally, Bakri nodded his head, and sat up – almost bumping his head on our slanting roof. "Yes, but I am not sure how this will turn out." It was more than apparent that neither of us expected to last the night, without having to utter a word between us.

We greeted each morning since the start of our journey since setting off from Ninia with refreshing unintelligible chatter between Ramu, Jar and our two other porters as they sat around a small fire boiling water (coffee for me and tea for Bakri) and poking at sweet potatoes laid out over the embers wrapped in banana leaves – but not this morning. We crawled out from our rough shelter into an eerie calm. The ground was still damp with dew, and we could almost see our breath in the cold morning fog that engulfed and obscured everything around us.

Bakri stifled my urge to call out for Ramu. Instead, he began walking into the heavy mist, following the worn path that led to the rocky outcrop. Yesterday afternoon, we caught a spectacular view from this very same overhang that benefited from a backdrop of sculptured white clouds brush-painted against a dazzling bluer-than-blue sky canvas. We were rewarded with a snapshot of the 'picture-perfect' valley below, in the direction opposite from where we made our entrance into the village. And while barely visible except for glints of sunlight that refracted off waters mostly hidden by a dense green jungle foliage, we were able to make out a narrow river, at least from this distance, accentuated by twists and turns as it traversed the valley floor.

I felt drawn, more like panicked, into making for the river, and off this clifftop perch. "Let's go down to the river," I called out, having to catch my breath mid-sentence while trying to sound in control, which I was not. All the while trailing, Bakri at a distance in keeping with my healthy fear of heights, from any height: or maybe better put, my fear of falling. "We cannot, our ride will be arriving soon," he said as he lifted his head upward and scanned the low-lying clouds, as if expecting our promised helicopter to suddenly appear.

Claustrophobia is an intense feeling of fear and anxiety associated with 'enclosed spaces' that can suddenly overwhelm clear and rationale thinking, and yet I was most definitely feeling claustrophobic on this open ground. Maybe it was standing blind on this exposed ledge enveloped by darkened clouds that unnerved me. Or maybe just the spirit of the old woman exacting her revenge. No matter, I felt my heart beating wildly in my chest, and began looking for some way off the ledge and escaping into the canyon; any way that did not involve plummeting feet or headfirst. Bakri must have sensed my desperation and drew close to me; he would never leave my side. At which point I completely lost it! I grabbed onto him as I took a step on what I thought might be a path that would lead us down and away from here.

We tumbled, slipped, and clung to the steep slope. I managed to cut myself badly grabbing at anything to stop myself from 'sliding', letting lose an avalanche of lose earth; tangled in brush with inch-long thorns made me 'scream out'. Bakri spilled beside me, cartwheeling head over heels. We managed to stop short of an even steeper drop-off, all the while clinging to one another. "*Ada apa*," Bakri shouted, essentially conveying his sentiments as to 'what the fuck' just happened. I felt the fool for my panic that put us perilously 'just' hanging on. And for sure, I realized that our actions would only confirm to the villagers that we had sought to escape our fate, proving ourselves guilty.

To my utter amazement, hands reached out and gently reached for us: many hands. I felt dizzy, and yes, ashamed. We were both hoisted onto the backs of Laksi and Ramu, with our two other traveling companions in tow. With almost supernatural strength and balance, returning us up the near-vertical slope and to the village. The whole community had turned out, and with a gentleness I had never know before, came together to hug, and hold, Bakri and me.

One, a young woman with a wide-eyed toddler sitting astride her shoulders, holding firm his legs wrapped around her neck, refused to leave my side for most of our stay. She wore the child like an extra appendage. Our '*wabah babi*' was probably the furthest thing from her thoughts. But our visit would in all likelihood leave something 'lasting'. How could I not be humbled by this showering of genuine affection. An affirmation that just maybe, we had done something 'good', just by coming here.

Photo contributor: Dr. Cyrus Simanjuntak; investigating 'wabah babi' outbreak, waiting on helicopter the morning of author's departure from Dani village.

I felt shame! The shrieks lasting throughout the night were driven by loss, so profound as to bring the community together in a shared expression of despair. It had nothing to do with Bakri and me. We had gotten it all wrong. Funny how this realization helped to 'humanize' the mournful sadness felt by the villagers, at least to me; although I could only imagine how someone might interpret such 'thoughts' as denigrating, 'colonial' in thinking. Was I? I hoped not.

"Bakri, look what they have done," I stuttered. My very first thought was to panic. In what world did this happen? This act of self-mutilation, leaving a bloodied raw stub with the top half of a single finger amputated. The old women of the village, I would learn, preserved this gruesome tradition as their way of grieving for friend or family. Others had taken a less debilitating show of grief by rubbing ash on their faces.

But as the villagers crowded around us, I had never felt more loved or touched. They had lost someone special: loved! Now their tears and tugging sadness were born from an innocence, fearing they somehow offended us.

The rotor of the small helicopter nearly dug into the flattened mound of earth, as the skilled pilot leveled out from a near dive just in the nick of time, gently coaxing the skids into 'kissing' the ground.

My feelings bordered on righteous indignation, once again, on how this epidemic could have wiped out more than a third of Soba, within just a few days. But more to the point, how we failed so miserably in providing for early detection and response to this calamity. Not just here, but in countless communities across the Baliem Valley.

The pilot, an Indonesia-American, I gathered from his accent and the ease in which he transitioned from Bahasa to English and back again, like a small 'songbird' flitting in and out of branches. To my relief, he conveyed a professional demeanor that left little doubt to his piloting skills. "Hi, *amigo*, my name is John!" Uhm, maybe the MAF was now sourcing pilots from West Texas.

We managed to cram all our supplies in a cubbyhole at the back of the airship, and boarded together with Ramu, leaving Luk and our other two 'companions' to return to Ninia on their own. As the four-seater craft with three passengers plus John rose, dipped and lifted into a sky that had turned out brilliantly blue in honor of our departure, I could not help but breathe a sigh of relief.

We had confirmed that '*wabah babi*' was no disease aberration; not a figment of someone's wild imagination. Our preliminary findings laid bare the ferocity of this epidemic that killed so many, in so short a time. I was still smarting from the thorns that had embedded in my hands and feet, most of which Bakri removed before applying a soothing antiseptic cream, having miraculously pulled out from one of his many pockets. Always the magician. The roar of the rotors, the vibrations of which lulled me to a 'good place', especially so following the intensity felt of the last twenty-four hours. Sleep came quickly.

Cast adrift

Startled awake after what seemed just a few moments of slumber, I saw the tops of trees reaching up to meet us. My view was from the right-side window, meaning we were falling on our side: the right side. And just like that, my world took a turn for the worst. And then nothing.

I felt mightily sore when I regained consciousness, all over. I had no idea for how long I was 'out for the count', only knowing that I was still in the helicopter, pinned against the interior side door that took the brunt of our fall, as I soon discovered. Gingerly, I carried out a body check, as you would an automobile. Something was dripping down the side of my face. I first tried wiggling fingers and toes, feeling immediate relief that everything still wiggled as it should. Sitting up front and still strapped to my seat, I found the door to my escape would not budge, no matter how hard I pounded and pushed. It soon dawned on me that the helicopter was lying on its side: my side. I went from awake, confused, frightened, to lightheaded, in less than a nanosecond. And then nothing.

The silence around me was interrupted by the excited chatter of birds, except for the ringing in my ears. I remember thinking, 'birds really do chirp'. It took me a few minutes more before I dared open my eyes.

When I finally managed to look around, I found myself alone. Was I abandoned? Where were Bakri, Ramu and our pilot? The door on the pilot's side facing upward was wide open. As I began to struggle from my position, I began to feel woozy, and found myself dry heaving, the aftertaste of raw rabbit making me, 'all the more' nauseous. Finally, dizziness gave way to darkness as I blacked out; all the while thinking of my precarious circumstances in a helicopter that might likely explode, leaving me a burnt crisp.

I heard him before seeing Bakri hovering over me, yelling my name. I lay very still and understood that I was no longer curled in a fetal ball against jagged metal but laid out on a wet ground. As I tried to sit up, Bakri pushed me back down. "There is an ugly cut on your head. You look more the swashbuckling pirate you pretend to be. A 'big' improvement!" Did I detect a bit of rank humor?

"Shit, that hurts," I exclaimed, jolting my head back and trying to push Ramu away. But he would not be deterred, dousing the wound with 'rubbing alcohol' from a plastic squirt bottle while Bakri debrided the gash, irrigating it thoroughly. "What happened?" I asked.

"Our fall was cushioned by the thick foliage, which surely saved our lives," Bakri replied. I noticed that his arm did not seem right, hanging unnaturally by his side. Ramu was also badly cut up, although the dried blood on his leg was a good sign that he was no longer bleeding out.

I had so many questions, but seriously could not organize nor vocalize my thoughts, confused as they were. Finally, I asked, "Where is John, 'pilot' John?" I corrected myself. I immediately sensed something was wrong, taking in the somber expression on Bakri's face. "Please, what happened?"

Bakri explained that John managed to climb out of the mangled aircraft and pulled us all through the pried door on the pilot's side. The jagged edges of wreckage had left all of us with deep lacerations, most likely from getting hastily dragged through the door.

He took the portable radio transmitter and our SAT phone and is looking to position himself in one of the towering treetops in the hope of gaining some connectivity. At least that was my understanding of Bakri's explanation for John's absence. But his tone belied something else, maybe even sinister by the way he sneered.

We did not know if he had time to send out a Mayday call as our copter plunged to the earth, succumbing to the laws of gravity. "When? How long ago has he been away?" Clearly, my questions reflected my disorientation, certainly with respect to time. I was not even sure how many times I had lost consciousness, never mind how much time had passed since we fell to earth. I cannot recall if Bakri responded to my question.

Regaining consciousness is not the same as the senses, but fast enough to register the ache felt over my body. Not only did I hurt all over, but I discovered a severe burn on my inner thigh. "How did that happen?" I could only wonder. My scalp felt on fire. I dared not touch the deep gash that ran across the top of my head, extending my eyebrow; a bloody pink froth continued to trickle out and ooze down the right side of my face, pooling just inside the rim of my earlobe. Bakri went overboard, smearing, again, the topical antibiotic directly into the wound. After which, he wrapped my head 'mummy'-style with a three-foot gauze bandage. "Always prepared," I mumbled half-jokingly.

"We can check the bleeding later. You will not be so funny if I must take needle and thread and stitch you up," he intoned, as if to 'lighten' the mood.

I closed my eyes again as I lost all sense of balance. I would have fallen on my back, except that I was already so, spared the muddy ground by a wet plastic tarp. Although I had nothing left to retch up, I felt so much the better for trying. The next thing I knew was I was again in the 'land of the living', shrouded by the complete blackness that could only mean night. I could make out a few stars overhead through the dense jungle canopy towering overhead. I called out softly to Bakri, who appeared to be sleeping soundly beside me. At some point, I left him to his dreams as I did the same, dozing off and on the rest of night.

When I awoke again, a small fire brought relief from the early morning dampness that chilled my bones. I was concussed and needed to stay awake; but I kept drifting off into 'la-la land'. "Are you okay?" I asked, poking Bakri gently on his side. With no reply or movement, I slowly sat up and took stock of my friend. He was running a high fever, and his pale coloring made me forget the insane pounding going on inside my head. Okay, now it was my turn to be mother hen.

"Ramu," I sputtered, trying to get across that I needed his help. I rolled my hands over and over each other – trying to figure a way to get Ramu to turn Bakri over onto his side. I then felt around his dislocated shoulder, where the head of his 'humerus' bone, aptly referred to a 'funny' bone, had dislodged from his shoulder joint. I then guided Ramu's hands and placed them on Bakri's arm, and squeezed my own hands open and shut, in demonstrating to his role in the procedure I was about to perform. I needn't have bothered. Ramu knew instinctively what to do. Counting backwards, "*Tiga dua satu,*" (3 2 1) so each of us could prepare ourselves, including Bakri, I pulled rather than jerked Bakri's arm downward so as not to tear bone from tendons, as Ramu maintained a tight grip to keep him from pulling away. The moment I yanked, Bakri 'shrieked like a banshee', and tried to wriggle free as I maneuvered the bone back into the socket. "Kind of like orbital docking a space shuttle to a starship." I exhaled; of course, thinking of the 'USS Enterprise' from the 'Star Trek' series. Now covered by a fine sheen of sweat, Bakri groaned, and then smiled. I looked over at Ramu who appeared unperturbed, as I would expect of any 'second in command'. He would have done 'Spok' proud.

"Where is John?" After some back and forth, I understood that our 'pilot' hero had kept his cool and somehow stalled the fall of the helicopter, and then pulled himself up and out the door, helping both Bakri and Ramu do the same. Apparently, while I was unconscious and bleeding profusely from a head wound, they seized the imperative to exit the copter, dragging my inert body in tow; as quickly as possible given the very real possibility of our 'ride' erupting into a fireball as leaking fuel mixed with oil pooled under my limp torso, making for a 'most' combustible brew. Still unsure if he was able to make any contact before or after our violent landing, or if the helicopter was fitted with some kind of emergency beacon to signal our location, I hoped for the best, and yet managed my expectations with no illusion of a quick rescue.

More concerning was his disappearance the previous day. Bakri was equally worried. He remembered John walking, maybe limping, beyond the small clearing made by the helicopter; now resembling a beached whale lying on its side. "Maybe he saw something from the air, a settlement maybe, and was seeking out help," I offered by way of explanation. Upon further inspection, it appeared that the radio had been ripped from its casing. More concerning was that our SAT phone was nowhere to found. We could only surmise that he was attempting to communicate our position and circumstances from a better vantage point: maybe higher elevation.

My knee-jerk reaction was to search for John. I gingerly

moved from a sitting to standing position, feeling myself slipping back into a dizzy state of consciousness. I fell back on my haunches and laid myself down. I was again sweating profusely despite the early morning coolness, made more so by a wet dew that settled over night, soaking through everything, including the clothes I was wearing.

Ramu was again shaking me from yet another of my slumbers, holding a tin cup of porridge that tasted distinctly earthy. This time, I felt mildly refreshed. He had erected a makeshift tarp overhead to protect us from the steady drizzle that was now falling. Gingerly, I stood up holding my tin, and began walking around the wreckage, as if in doing so I would gain perspective and somehow make everything right. Trying to assert some kind of control over our situation, I tried to figure out the direction John had taken, to track him, and find him. The ground was slick, and I took a wrong step – unceremoniously falling on my already sore ass.

Do we leave the copter and search for him? Maybe not a great idea! What little I knew, none from actual experience, was to stick with downed aircraft, especially if the location had somehow been transmitted. A search-and-rescue mission might be already underway. Indeed, we had surpassed the twenty-four-hour mark since falling out of the sky. So why were we still here?

Adding to our woes was food, or the lack of. My intense craving was only made worse by the porridge we just split between the three of us; by no means enough to satisfy anyone's hunger. With almost no space onboard the helicopter to stow our gear except for what we could reasonably place on our laps and between our bunched legs, and a stingy weight allowance, we were forced to abandon what little in the way of supplies we carried, including my beloved coffee; bequeathing it to the peoples of Soba whom we had so endeared ourselves with, of course. Thankfully, Ramu had the good sense to use the tarp to collect rainwater, so thirst was not much of an immediate problem so long as there was no let-up in the steady rain that had been falling since mid-morning. At least one of us was doing more than just thinking. Adding to our discomfort was that the rainwater was pooling on the ground, no matter huddling under the tarp used to cover the helicopter's rotary blade.

Trying 'levity' at keeping myself warm, "I do not think our pilot will mind, and certainly the helicopter will not be needing this anymore," talking loudly, more a distraction to myself than to Bakri and Ramu.

Bakri, always the hero, the champion of others, insisted we needed to go search for John. As an American of Indonesian descent with less than a month working with the MAF, he was way out of his league wandering about the jungle. He was our priority.

I should note that jungle survival is an 'art', mostly learned, skills honed by practice and improvisation: making do with less. While I could claim my training had prepared me for just such a scenario, I felt completely unprepared and exposed, both to our predicament and my 'supposed' expertise.

"Nobody is going to see us, even if they have our approximate location, not through this dense jungle foliage. Let's burn a clearing!" Ramu had said little until now, but he was clearly now voicing his own thoughts.

Bakri nodded. "Makes good sense."

It felt good to decide on a course of action. We agree in clearing the earth around the wreckage site of all vegetation, expanding out in a five-meter circle, until we had created a 'firebreak'. Our strategy is to initiate a 'burn' inside the break, around the site of the wreckage, all the while not falling victim to what might be construed in hindsight as an act of insanity; so as not to set ourselves on fire or succumb to smoke inhalation; owing to some fickle 'quirk of fate' or gust of wind. After a grueling day of slashing, we began our 'burn' just as the daylight began to fade. The intention was to make our location more visible by illuminating the resulting flames against the canvas of a night sky, at least to a passing aircraft.

We needed a big fire! Using carefully placed cuttings and shavings strategically placed in concentric fashion extending outward, we lit our handmade torches went about setting the forest ablaze. Or so we tried. The dampened earth seemed intent on frustrating our attempts. We needed regroup and think this through.

We abandoned our improvised torches and worked through most of the night to create a pit of red-hot embers, which we transported with Bakri's folding shovel that unfolded to reveal a dozen functions, like a Swiss army knife, to ignite strategically placed bales of forest debris forming a 'ring of fire'. If the forest around us did not burn down, at least we could design a pattern of pinpricks circling our encampment. Again, the goal was the same, to create an aerial signature that a passing plane could home in on.

Trying to rationalize this possibly crazy act, carried out maybe more in defiance of our ability to do much else, I figured John might get his bearings and use the fire as a beacon, if he was still alive and able, and did not get consumed by fire and smoke. For that matter, I had no idea if the 'burn' we cut would protect the three of us from a self-inflicted fiery end.

What to do

Following all our preparation, the bonfires gave off a lot of smoke and not much else. With little permanent vegetation anchored to the jungle floor, and the vegetation bundled together in piles kept damp by the steady drizzle through the night and early morning, it became apparent we were not going to light up the jungle around us, no matter our inventiveness.

Exhausted and feeling more than a little beaten down by our increasingly desperate circumstances, I began to feel (maybe for the first time) anxious that we might not be found anytime soon. Not wanting to add fuel to our despondency, I stayed quiet. But not Bakri: "I read that a good proportion of ten to fifteen plane crashes in Papua per year are never found or stay hidden for years." We were thinking alike, or rather, I was thinking what Bakri was voicing.

"You would think we should have at least heard if not spotted some search aircraft overhead by now," I sullenly replied, feeling like I had to say something. Ramu came to where Bakri and I were sitting, and brought his finger to his lips, for what I took to be the universal sign for 'keep quiet and listen'. And so we did!

Straining, we heard a subtle thrashing coming from the

dense brush beyond the clearing. This was soon accompanied by hooting noises that could have easily been confused for bird calls. Animal or human, friend or foe, we were both eager and little bit hesitant to discover the source, as the sound drew nearer, and louder. John poked his head through the thicket near the tail end of the wreckage. Cursing and swatting away real and imaginary flying insects, 'pilot' John emerged: less of a savior and more of the survivor of an air crash. What was left of his clothes, now rags, clung to his body. Strikingly, body art painted in blood red now adorned his face and chest, as if he had done himself up like a 'native warrior': an 'Indian Brave' to be precise. My impression was that he had wandered these last few days aimlessly, looking for whatever. But I was sure he would help us understand his actions given the opportunity.

I should mention that for the last three days we were constantly being buzzed by our flying friends insistent on making their presence felt with kamikaze runs strategically aimed to inflict the most discomfort. In the early morning and early evening hours, my ears were red as I attempted to squash these vicious biting machines. Squashing these flying nuisances requires stealth, speed, cunning and, above all, patience; they are 'smart buggers'. The vector ecology of these pests strongly suggested *Anopheles* mosquitoes, associated with transmission of malaria.

Worth noting that highland malaria in Papua Indonesia had recently been documented by my close friend, companion, and neighbor, navy entomologist extraordinaire, Commander Norman Bates. Bundled away in the same condominium for the past decade, we are much-loved 'outcasts', vexing the Command with our 'wild ways' as the two single officers. And yes, I too find his name disturbing: rehashing memories and bringing on nightmares, recollecting my favorite 'Alfred Hitchcock' thriller: *Psycho*. What I know about malaria, not so much, I learned from Norman. The positive news was that the 'incubation period', that interval between infection and onset of illness, generally ranges from one week to a month, meaning: I would likely be rescued or already dead before any expression of signs and symptoms; there being no shortage of ways to die out here. Aside for the medicinal brew Ramu ground up from foraged plants and crushed beetle-like crawlies into a tea-like concoction, a cure all, I left my malaria fate to gods.

I was surprised by Bakri's initial reaction to John's sudden appearance into the little clearing that had become our refuge from the many imagined and all-too-real threats lurking about the inhospitable jungle that surrounded us, threatening to devour us: "Where have you been?" He huffed and puffed, almost accusatory. Ramu, always reserved, acted even more so. He nodded his head from side to side but said nothing. And yet the expression on his face made clear he was none too eager to embrace this new member of our clan. This confused me, and I felt immediately apologetic for the less-than-warm welcome offered up by Ramu and Bakri. Bakri I think 'sensed' my discomfort, and pulled me aside, and half-whispered: "I will explain what happened later."

Spinning straw into gold[12]

Having just arrived in Wamena, it became readily apparent to Colonel Dowdy, the Defense Attaché at the American Embassy in Jakarta, and Captain Rick Lavender, Commanding Officer, NMRC-Indonesia, that Brigadier General Widodo, a 'one-star' and senior officer responsible for directing efforts to secure the release of the hostages, was not playing into their narrative. He made it abundantly clear that diverting 'his' air assets, consisting of three Cessnas and one Bell heavy-lift helicopter, all newly painted in steel military gray, was not on the cards.

"We simply do not have the wherewithal to commit any of our assets at this time, given the overriding demands posed by our hostage dilemma. Can you 'not' understand that." More a statement than a question.

Indeed, the first encounter with General Widodo was terse and unproductive.

"Why does the American navy have a medical command in Indonesia, and more to the point, an American naval officer wandering about the midst of an insurgency, and counterinsurgency, no less."

---

12   *https://en.wikipedia.org/wiki/Rumpelstiltskin.*

"Fair enough," Captain Lavender countered, and explained the Command's history both in the region and Indonesia, its affiliation with the MoH based on a formal memorandum of understanding between both countries; invited by the Indonesian government in 1970 to set up shop initially to combat a rickettsial disease threat. "That mission has morphed into a permanent research presence at the behest your past and current president, one in the same."

Surprisingly, as a foreign military entity, NMRC-Indonesia is partnered with the Ministry of Health, although all operational activities must be vetted and approved by the national and local security apparatus. Even so, Rick was surprised, maybe a tad bit impressed, that Commander Jacques had wrangled permissions to participate in this LITBANGKES/P2M-led outbreak expedition, now gone terribly wrong. He understood that Jacques had spearheaded this ill-fated adventure. "But hey, that is the nature of the beast," was his way of thinking.

Thinking, 'I really need to perfect my spiel not only to the Indonesians, but in responding to the flurry of queries sure to follow' – namely from the navy's Pacific Command headquarters out of Pearl Harbor, Hawaii. Heck, probably less than three percent of the navy was even aware of the infectious disease research mission being carried out by the likes of his Command, as part of a larger network of Department of Defense (DoD) 'Infectious Disease Laboratories' scattered across the globe: working out of U DoD laboratories in Bangkok, Cairo, Peru, Kenya, and of course Indonesia.

In a bout of frustration during an exchange with the General, Captain Lavender abandoned any and all pretense of diplomatic etiquette in favor of 'cutting loose': "This is what we do," as if trying to justify himself, and by extension, his Command. He paused at hearing the shrillness in his own voice carry; sounding way too defensive.

"Taking research to the next step, in and out of the laboratory, demands access to the very disease pathogens under the microscope, as they occur in nature. That is why we wok in regions 'heavy' with malaria and investigate outbreaks in tracking down emerging disease threats. How else do you test new diagnostics and treatments – how we protect soldiers: yours, and ours, deploying to areas ripe with disease?"

"This is why we work where we do!"

Rick well understood the common denominator of the countries hosting many of these forward medical research capabilities: 'strong men', authoritative in governance and not necessarily endeared to the populations they rule, certainly as in the case of Indonesia.

Colonel Dowdy, who was not all that 'dowdy', with a telling reserved sense of humor and a ready smile, was certainly appreciative. Although not so much about the actual research being conducted. These medical research activities provide invaluable intelligence that translated into disease threat assessments for would-be military deployments to anywhere, at any time. Evidence from the literature lays bare the history of warfare in realizing the firepower of infectious diseases, whether spread by vectors like mosquitoes and ticks, or exposure to contaminated water or foods, or through aerosolized airborne transmission. Notwithstanding, the universal observation is that infectious diseases have killed far more combatants than the conventional weapons of the day. Contributing in no small measure to the outcome of many armed conflicts.

Nothing like a ship unable to leave port because its sailors are laid out with debilitating diarrhea, cramps, and fever; the stench is always a giveaway, if not the overflow of human excreta clogging the waste disposal systems. In Vietnam, America and its allies, platoons to brigades, were often manned at less-than-optimal strength, thanks notably to the toll inflicted by disease pathogens more at home in the tropics.

General Widodo was smart, ambitious, a highly regarded soldier, and very well connected, being married to Soto's daughter: Soto being the benevolent dictator credited in holding together this vast archipelago and bringing some vibrancy to what was a struggling agrarian-based economy; now turning the corner to one of massive industrialization, all in the name of 'made in Indonesia'. Colonel Dowdy showed his tact and good sense by massaging his message and expressing appreciation for General Widodo's predicament, and his appreciation for whatever support he could lend to the search efforts.

Captain Lavender, with less impressive Indonesian language credentials, also managed to remind the General of NMRC-Indonesia's close partnership with the Indonesian military in conducting studies to evaluate new anti-malarial therapies to benefit immunologically naïve soldiers living in malaria-free areas, principally in the western-most regions of Java and Sumatra. "Those very soldiers who deploy to highly malarias areas, as in West Papua, having no prior exposure to the malaria, fall victim to the parasite, filling hospital beds and mortuaries – that means they are no good to you."

General Widodo, being nobody's fool, responded calmly: "Thank you for this 'kind' lesson, Captain! And here I thought I was Commanding a '*Terracotta*' army. We take advantage of one another, yes! But to be sure, you do this for your military," with emphasis on the: 'your military'.

Both Colonel Dowdy and Captain Lavender were well aware of the added scrutiny regarding NMRC-Indonesia's recent operations: the navy, in its infinite wisdom, assigning a navy Commander, and husband of the Central Intelligence Agency Station Chief in Jakarta, no secret, certainly not to the Indonesians, as the Command's Executive Officer. This kind of negative attention was further exasperated by someone's decision before Captain Lavender assumed Command to build a landing strip using the navy's Seabees – the construction arm of the US navy – at one of NMRC-Indonesia's jungle malaria study sites along the northwest coast of West Papua. To say that this action was intended to support the logistical demands in managing a semi-permanent field research activity without benefit of roads, alongside a very shallow but treacherous coastline, making boat landings all but impossible except in rubber motorized dinghies, would not be a stretch of the truth. But neither would be the perception of a hidden agenda in the face of an ongoing separatist insurgency. To say that the general's apparent antagonism was unwarranted would be honestly, disingenuous.

General Widodo assigned a Lieutenant Colonel from his staff to oversee whatever needed to be done in the search effort, with the caveat:

> "Within the constraints of limited resources, please know we will do our best. But the reality is such that we continue to find aircraft wreckages dating back to the 'Second World War'. Papua is rich in beauty, natural resources, and yet-to-be-discovered crash sites. So do not be too optimistic."

With that, perfunctory introductions were made with the Indonesian lead, Lieutenant Colonel Sukri, in a rescue operation that was looking more like a 'recovery' with each passing day.

Getting found, but still lost

"He did not even check on you!" Bakri exclaimed. After pulling himself out of the helicopter, our 'pilot' John, as I would learn, did nothing but 'rant and rave' at Bakri and Ramu for overloading the aircraft, before storming off into the dense brush with the transmitter radio after having yanked it out of its mounting; all the while Bakri and Ramu struggled to extricate me and my dead weight from the cockpit. Bakri's expression was one of unforgiving disgust on how someone could abandon his passengers. If an analogy was to be made, taking into account Bakri's keen sense of responsibility and honor that defined his very being, this was no different than a ship's captain opting to be the 'first' in abandoning ship and crew: nothing short of sacrilegious to those so inclined.

John slept soundly after collapsing on our improvised shelter shortly after his miraculous return. He mumbled, took a few steps, stumbled, and then crumpled into a fetal ball almost immediately upon breaking into what had become 'our' sanctuary.

I tried to make sense out of what Bakri had described of John's very erratic behavior. Granted, we had known him for less than two hours, but I could not believe that the MAF would have taken on anyone who was anything but stable to the point of being boringly dependable. I laughed to myself and thought out loud that pilot John may have been in a state of shock, having just confronted his own fate and that of his passengers in a near-fatal air crash. His actions were nevertheless inexplicable: running away from the wrecked helicopter, even if not of his own making, but most certainly on his watch, without rendering any assistance to Ramu, Bakri or me. Maybe his behavior could be explained by his own perceived culpability or poorly honed coping skills. "People snap, so let's just try and get on with the job of surviving this," I voiced, maybe a bit too forcefully.

John, seemed to have regained his authoritative coolness, if only to preserve his own sense of control. Bakri and I decided not to bring up his crazed behavior after the crash. But we were interested in what he had found during his jungle sojourn.

"Confused, I went about checking out some clearing I view from the air, before we made our descent."

Trying not to smirk, I voiced: "Some descent!"

Bakri asked John if he thought there were any settlements in the immediate area. "More than that, were you able to send off any signal or radio call giving out our last coordinates before making our 'descent'?" I have never seen Bakri sneer, but he came close in spitting out the word 'descent'.

John shook his head and mumbled: "There was no time for that."

I asked if the MAF or aviation authorities out of Wamena had any way of tracking our position. "Were we on anyone's radar?" I sounded more perturbed than I intended. But John's continued evasiveness in responding to our insistent questioning was beginning to test my composure and Bakri's overall good nature. With our resolve waning, along with our depleted stash of ramen noodles, our terse interrogation ended. Almost. One last question I thought without much confidence of getting any kind of intelligible reply: "Where is the radio from the helicopter you made off with?"

On the subject of food, Ramu proved an excellent provider, bringing relief from our now-depleted energy and persistent hunger. Grubs are thick, slimy, worm-like creatures that best resemble a gigantic, pus-filled maggot; easy to find in the decaying stumps and branches littering the ground and providing a steady source of protein; that is, if you can keep from 'chucking' them back up. I eventually got over my 'gagging reflex' by conjuring up images of marshmallows browned over a fire. That did the trick, as did the fire.

Maybe it was the intonation of my voice, sounding distinctively shrill even for me in my panicky state. But for whatever the reason, John hit the silent button, and gave up a halfhearted shrug. I think at that moment, Bakri, Ramu, and me, understood that something was terribly amiss with our John, and that we needed to tread cautiously.

It was Ramu who first spoke in a hushed whisper to Bakri, and Bakri who then did the same with me. I remember the lesson played as a child, a game really, learning how messages can get distorted and confused; when one person passes on a communication to the next, and down the line to the last person, who must then repeat the original message. In this case, it was just the three of us, and John. Lacking conviction and avoiding responsibility, I did as any American would do, subscribing to a vote: "Who wishes to stay, or leave and search for a way out?"

Hunger and thirst were sapping me of all energy. I was completely disoriented and probably still concussed from my injury. My mind playing tricks on my brain, conjured up images of our savaged corpses lying within shouting distance of the shiny metal hulk that was our 'ride', only now camouflaged by jungle rot as our would-be rescuers shook their collective heads as to why we broke camp and strayed from the crash site. A big 'no no' if survival training is your thing!

Politics always gets in the way

Captain Lavender's head was spinning, after his midnight back-and-forth grilling with a one-star admiral out of 'Pearl' – for Pearl Harbor, Hawaii: otherwise referred to as the PACOM Surgeon. In this case, Admiral Wong was representing the four-star Pacific Fleet Commander. In the navy, routine operations get extra scrutiny as to how the t's are crossed, and i's dotted as everyone runs to 'cover their asses' when something goes wrong. The muffled transmission from the SAT connection left Rick questioning just how much help would come by way of the navy, or indeed the Department of Defense. Tentative inquiries by the Embassy in Jakarta about the possibility of air search and recovery assistance were met with incredulity by the Foreign Ministry: as if the mere act of entertaining such an offer would be tantamount to relinquishing sovereignty over Irian Jaya, or West Papua. As if the circumstances were not already stressed by the continued international coverage of the hostage situation; and the byproduct of creating demands (which the Western World is so accustomed in issuing) for redressing historical wrongs; generally a continuum of policies put in place by the very same countries, Portugal and the Netherlands, that inspired just such a colonial mentality and de facto claim by the Indonesian government, in the name of national integrity.

"Good morning to you too," Colonel Dowdy exclaimed as Rick approached the small table looking as 'shitty' as he was feeling, with a 'long stare' lacking in focus. Breakfast was not part of Rick's routine, instead relying on a 'fix' of coffee to make it through the morning.

"Looks really appetizing," was Rick's only reply, looking down at the two runny eggs that splashed bright orange on the Colonel's white plate, with burnt toast on the side.

"I received a call from the 'DCM' last night" – Deputy Chief of Mission for those not familiar with Embassy lingo – "but did not want to wake you," motioning for Rick to sit down. It seems that General Widodo, through his 'chain of command', has issued a complaint on how we are disrupting his operations. Robert has suggested we take it easy in making too many, if any, demands."

Rick is a lot of things, but not loud. His outburst even under the circumstances seemed to give voice to the stress and anxiety he felt, catching all in the crowded hotel dining room off guard. "That fucking asshole." Although it was in no way clear if he was referring to Robert, well known for his 'spineless' demeanor and eagerness to please the Ambassador and anyone he felt could further his career prospects, or the General. Fortunately, the clientele staying at the Sunset Guest Lodge were mostly Indonesian traders from Sulawesi, and while startled by Rick's outburst, were without the necessary mastery to make sense of the nuances and slang of the distinctively Americanized version of the English language. Maybe not so fortunate was the presence of two reporters from the Indonesian weekly magazine, 'Minggu', sitting at the far end of the room.

Not lost on either Rick or the Colonel was the fine line they had to walk, in pushing, without pushing too hard.

Lieutenant Colonel Sukri entered the dining area shortly after the 'loud' drama, oblivious to Rick's spent frustration. "Just wanted to let you know we have two Cessnas in the air and hope to bring in a third from Jayapura in the next day."

Search for a way out

We had the laminated map used by John that unfolded, spread over his knee during our brief flight. It was stained with grease and sweat with lots of unintelligible markings crudely circled with red marker, but I was able to make out a scraggly blue broken line that 'zigzagged' through a valley sided by mountainous slopes; I supposed the same river we had seen from our high-altitude perch before falling out of the sky. John remained silent as I tried to get him to look at the map. "Crap, John, we need your help," I implored. To which he glanced down, slumped his shoulders, and turned away.

"Bakri, my problem is I have no idea where we are on this map." Not really a map, but aeronautical chart, showing off topographic features and elevations. But that made me no more the wiser. There was a compass imprinted on the laminated fold-out, showing an east-to-west heading of 'our' supposed river. This was more speculation on my part, based on the scraggly broken blue line, our river, I supposed, moving from higher ground to lower; if that was what the numbered coordinates reflected on the topographical depiction of the area covered.

Impressing even myself, I figured that with the sun rising in the east and setting to the west, we would head in the same direction of the sun's movement, tracking its progress from early morning to end of day, and maybe, just maybe, avoiding any too steep a rise in elevation, get somewhere, anywhere, in the right direction. *Yes, I thought, we are hopelessly lost.*

Having spent the better part of the morning slashing through vines, thickets of thorny bush, and every other obstruction that could possibly hamper our forward movement, we stopped and took stock of our situation. We had been climbing uphill for the last few hours, trying to give ourselves as good a viewing vantage as possible. Bakri and Ramu wanted to climb into the trees and scan the horizon in the hope of focusing our march on something, anything, to ensure we were walking in a straight line, or close to it, so as not to 'chase our tails' and end up back at the crash site. This made good sense, or so it seemed. It was the first time I observed Bakri giving up his prized binoculars that hung from his neck like a religious medallion, instructing Ramu on their use. Ramu, of course, would be the one to scale the tallest tree we could find. Unfortunately, he was unable to make much of the topography, hidden by a thick expanse of forest that seemed to stretch on forever. Later, back from his space exploration, he drew three stick figures in the soft earth with his pointed walking stick, a fair caricature given how we now resembled the skeletal X-ray 'negatives' of our former selves. With at least a destination in mind, we headed off in that general direction.

I should note that we could have taken advantage, at least in walking a straight line, of the helicopter's compass, if that was even an option. But the crash had rendered our direction-finder useless, with a cracked glass shell casing and a needle that had lost its way.

We woke to another day, more like three since leaving to what now felt like the homey comforts of the clearing. We tried to spot our position relative to the 'supposed' river at least twice daily. But with our energy sapped and views obstructed by ever-taller trees, we were left trusting our intuition, and then following Ramu in heading in opposite direction: 'how is that for logic.'

Downward would have taken us to the river, which we could have followed until coming across some help. But it was clear Ramu was leading us to a higher elevation, as evidenced by the colder mornings, generally enveloped in a wet fog. We still managed to find good eats – thanks, Ramu – demonstrating his scavenging prowess; feasting on edible and not-so-edible root delights dug out from the ground. We also sampled some delicious, stripped tree bark boiled with an assortment of grubs and ants, crushed into a steaming broth of protein. Actually, I think we were all adapting well to what felt sometimes more like an adventuresome trekking experience, although ever so conscious that we could die out here, and remain lost for all eternity. After all, we were in the wilds of West Papua. Kind of like being in 'injun' country – a term referring to the North American Indians, harking back to the 'old' Cowboy and Indian 'westerns' I watched as a child – although the dubbed in Spanish, which may have warped the translation. Except that we were in Dani territory, and this was all too real.

Without any suggestion of delirium, I could not help thinking of all the lost aircraft, American, Australian, and Japanese, that littered neighboring PNG and to a lesser extent Indonesian Papua, dating back some sixty years, from the battle for the Pacific. How many skeletons of both aircraft and crew lay still hidden in this insane jungle? How many airmen had indeed survived crashes, only to succumb to their injuries or desperation, all the while knowing their remains would likely never be found.[13]

As we trudged onward, we almost, and I stress 'almost', became numb to our aches and pains, and sense of aimless wandering. It became apparent to me how the human mind could adapt itself to such conditions, and in a funny way, find such solitude and even what might be described as a freedom from all the concerns and anxieties of the day. This was no picnic but finding some solace in our predicament proved almost liberating. It is like you do not even realize how much you need a vacation until you are lying on the beach with the waves licking your toes. Okay, maybe I am a bit delirious!

John remained stoically quiet as we forged ahead in single file: to avoid the wasted energy of having to cut through the dense brush, and the fact that we only had one machete. We took turns at 'point', being in the lead and swinging the machete. At one point, standing behind Ramu, I got in the way of his swing and forcefully connected with his backhand, ending up with a contusion to the side of my face. I joked later with Bakri that Ramu had all the makings of a professional tennis player. So much for my poor excuse for humor in trying to make light of our situation gauging from Bakri's reaction, and the blank stare from Ramu.

In the fifth day since leaving the crash site, my most-dreaded fear materialized as I felt something drop from above

---

13　*The US Department of Defense continues to search for human remains and downed aircraft, working through the Joint Task Force – Full Accounting (JTF-FA) Command based out of Hawaii. JTF-FA was established for the sole purpose of conducting search and recovery operations, principally of lost aircraft and crews in the far-flung reaches of the Pacific and Asia over the course of half a century of wars and conflicts that have characterized d US engagement in the Asia Pacific theatre. PHOTOS and NUMBER OF AIRCRAFT LOST OVER PNG AND PAPUA.*

onto my hat, over my shoulder, and slide to the ground: all in an instant. It was at least a meter in length and thin as a guardrail; I knew instantly that this was a snake encounter. Somewhere between it sliding from my shoulder to the ground, I leapt at least two meters. While I do tend to exaggerate, this was no exaggeration. My screams instantly brought Ramu to my side, wielding his machete. But my snake had disappeared, with Bakri all the while bent over in hysterics, laughing so uncontrollably that he was beginning to turn a brilliant blue. I could not help to fall victim to Bakri's contagious laughter, in my case brought on by a pumping adrenaline, appreciating that I probably frightened the snake to near death and sent it scurrying for cover in the underbrush carpeted by rotting leaves.

We were no longer climbing trees in trying to determine our progress and direction. After ascending an increasingly steep cliff all afternoon, grabbing at it, finding footholds, using the snarly roots imbedded into the rock face like scaffolding on a building construction site, we emerged onto grassy plain; most certainly, a more hospitable terrain from whence we came. To the east of us, by way of position plotting the course of the now setting sun, the ground gently sloped until it dropped away, rewarding us with a panoramic view of the entire valley and into the next.

The low-lying jungle floor left behind had been savaged by armies of red ants that had more than once threatened to overwhelm all in their path, not least us. As such, we had to take great care in preparing our precarious sleeping arrangements, forcing us to clear an area beforehand of all detritus debris: rotting leaves, branches, roots, plants, and more; never mind the slithering and crawling creatures, real or imagined. We would go so far as to scorch the ground beneath us, ever mindful that we were more likely to set the jungle and ourselves on fire first. We went so far as to encircle ourselves with a ring of fire, sort of, that needed to be tended throughout the night: meaning rotating a 'watch', which only served to leave us sleep deprived in the morning. Sleep was challenge enough, at least for me, despite my exhaustion. So fair to say, I became a listless follower, with Ramu leading the way.

As we prepared to make our version of a 'camp' for the night, luxuriating in the cool fresh air, it was clear that our water situation was becoming critical. At lower elevations, we quenched our thirst mostly by sucking the moisture from assorted roots and stems that Ramu intuitively knew how to extract with precision cuts, and from the occasional slow-moving streams we chanced upon; the latter requiring purification by boiling, akin to a baptism. We might have erred in not following these small waterways to larger tributaries into larger-still river systems. The one stream we did follow for the better part of a day petered out into a rocky crevice, the bottom of which was dank and dark, leading to nowhere: at least nowhere we wanted to venture.

Found

We were struggling, some more than others. John said little, taking up the rear with what came across as quiet, almost robotic resolve. Of course, Ramu continued to wield his machete, blindly thrashing all real and imagined obstacles from our path. Bakri was resolute in his assurance that we would walk out of this predicament, with the zeal of a 19th century missionary explorer setting out in search of the source for the river Nile: personifying 'Dr. Livingstone, I presume?' And then there was me; escaping the drudgery in disjointed daydreams, complete with faded and pixel-strength images, as I trudged forever onward trying to keep my place in our small procession.

I could not help losing myself in remembrance: marching that resembled goosesteps, one foot before the other, in step with my college friends, after a night of sucking down that toxic rum-laden brew infamously known as the 'hurricane': from the French Quarter to the trolley to dorm, during my university days in New Orleans. Without feeling the least bit nostalgic, I began conjuring up lucid memories from my younger days. Anything to escape this reality, threatening to rob me of my sanity. Yes, without question, I was flagging more than the rest, except maybe for John, who seemed already lost in his own world.

Thankfully, we were again climbing. Again looking forward to swatting away the mosquitoes and humidity. Really, we were going up and down, up and down, without expectations. But our physical state was now beginning to drag on our forward momentum like a 'ball and chain'.

As we approached yet another clearing, something had changed: more man-made than owing to the elevation. The trees, now noticeably smaller and spaced, bore cutting marks. Many were mere stumps of their former selves. This kind of scarring was telltale throughout Indonesia as the jungles and forests were 'butchered' for their timber. This was clearly a small-scale enterprise, likely serving to supply firewood and building material to a nearby homestead.

Without any warning, and with little fanfare, a small group of men emerged from a rocky formation and nonchalantly proceeded to walk right past us. I was struck with the absurdity of our encounter, with our saviors giving only a passing nod in acknowledging our presence, before moving past us. Bakri and Ramu immediately turned and chased after the group. Bakri later returned and pronounced, "Wait here," followed by a "Thank God." Nothing more.

But there was something that stirred my emotions as he broke into sobs, his shoulders shaking and his chest heaving: almost like a pump. Bakri as with any good Batak from northern Sumatra is a Protestant Christian (although many Batak have now taken to the Islam faith); only second to that of his standing, 'numbering', within the Batak pecking order. For Bakri, his place within the kinship system, a genealogical mapping of lineage, defined his place on this earth, giving order to his existence. Having accompanied Bakri to the Huria Kirsten Batak Protestan (Batak Christian Protestant Church), serving as the traditional Evangelical Lutheran Church of the Batak Toba, heathen that I am, I understood the depth of his religious faith and source of his firmly held beliefs, moral and otherwise. Located in Menteng, the priciest of neighborhoods in Jakarta, in the middle of the Central Business District, close to the US Ambassador's residence, and family compound of the President, the church stands just across the street from the home of my dear friend, Dr. Narsiem.

I am always awed by the status accorded the Batak in Indonesian society, a secular Christian ethnic tribe, apart from the Indonesian Chinese community, in a sea of Muslims.[14] And yes, I always understood the depth of his faith and firmly held convictions, but never had I heard him thank God. But that may have more to do with Bakri's humility, knowing my affinity for pagan worship. Just kidding!

The Batak are recognized as part of the intelligentsia of Indonesian society. They are well educated and trusted, securing prominence in the highest echelons of government and business. No easy feat in a country that boasts the largest Muslim population of any nation. And yet the Batak are no less a tribe as are the Dani. The close bonds that characterize the Batak serve us well in Wamena. When we need cash, Indonesian Rupia, to cover our operational costs on the ground (me carrying only my NMRC-Indonesia issued credit card – useless in making local purchases and procuring services), it is the chance encounter between Bakri and the Director of the local Bank Negara Indonesia (BNI), a Batak, that enables us to access funds. Bearing witness of two strangers exchanging 'numbers', signifying their respective place in the Batak

*hierarchy and linear-vertical, genealogical relationship,
warmly embracing each other, a powerful reminder as
what it means to belong to a tribe.*

After what felt like, well, like forever, Ramu and our 'finders'
reappeared, carrying banana stalks, tubers and sticks of wood,
nestled into earthen pouches made from intertwining twigs,
much like that of a bird's nest, and slung over muscular
shoulders.

Walking further along while struggling to keep up, we
caught the first whiff of smoke, just before emerging on a
grassy plateau dotted with no more than a dozen earthen huts.
We were immediately greeted by wide-eyed stares. But unlike
our previous encounters since the start of our journey into
the highlands, there was no gaggle of excited onlookers; only
a stone-faced following whose silence felt almost threatening.

Facing the music back in Jakarta

Usually relaxed, with a knack for letting proverbial 'shit storms' not get the better of him, Rick pivoted from his meeting with Ambassador Kile and exited the chancellery building in the Embassy compound. He felt himself leaning against the imposing 'hanging tree' in the Embassy compound, located on a grassy, almost park-like square connecting all the Embassy buildings, for support. *Maybe only fitting,* he thought, since the 'hanging tree' was supposedly used to dispose of prisoners during the Japanese occupation during the 'second' *World War.* This artifact of the Embassy's shadowy past still spooks the local security staff patrolling the grounds at night.

A double cheeseburger right off the grill at the Embassy's canteen, dripping of greasy animal fat and smothered in a sea of – 'Hunt's' tomato sauce and Hellmann's mayonnaise – 'the real deal', was exactly what Rick craved. Indulging in the face of the calamity was part of his persona, and now was certainly not the time to deny himself. This is worth the mention since Indonesian ketchups, all brands, border on the sickeningly sweet, and have no place gracing a sloppy cheeseburger.

He pondered at how things could have gone so wrong. Could he have made better decisions? Should he have been more cautious in allowing his sailor to go on such an investigation against a backdrop of prevailing civil unrest, in one of the most remote corners of the planet? *Damned it all*, Rick thought. "There are, of course, risks inherent to the work we do – so I will not make excuses. That would come across as just such: lame excuses!"

The only good news was that the Indonesian military had indeed launched a promised beefed-up air search with the aid of satellite imagery compliments of NASA. The not-so-good news was, however, bountiful: hostage crisis; separatist violence; and no trace of even the wreckage, or last-minute communications offering up longitude and latitude coordinates. But 'hope springs eternal' – against all odds – although not so much from Rick's way of thinking. Afterall, the mangled remains of an Indonesian cargo plane were recently discovered, including its three occupants, only thirty-five years 'too late', after disappearing on a routine supply flight ferrying rice to troops stationed in the restive province.

While not actually halting recovery operations, Ambassador Kile reflected that the search for the intrepid navy doctor and his Batak colleague was probably just days short of being called off, as all air assets were now being deployed in search of the young hostages and their hostage-takers; what with ICRC-led negotiations going nowhere. No matter the pressures, the Indonesian government was not going to cede to secessionist demands for a 'Free Papuan State', nor a plebiscite – putting succession to a vote. That was not going to happen. More likely, the military was preparing for both an air and ground assault in the face of continued Papuan intransigence. Indonesian belligerence and bellicosity was becoming increasingly hostile toward any pretension of negotiations. As for ICRC, they were no longer trusted by either side.

The savory cheeseburger did nothing to take Rick Lavender's mind off what was turning into a real debacle, and how to explain that to his PACOM bosses without serious repercussions both to his Command and his career. "Oh hell, I am ready to retire, have been for a long time now." The lunchtime crowd was beginning to file in, and he was just rising from his chair when a hand on his shoulder made him cock his head to identify this intrusion of both his space and thoughts. Colonel Dowdy signaled for Rick to join him while he checked his mail at the Embassy post office. "Just returned?" Rick tried to initiate a conversation, knowing full well the Defense Attaché had just flown in from Papua, coming straight to the Embassy from the airport.

"Yup, and bone tired. I have assigned Major Mudd to fill in for us as far as having someone on the ground to interface with the Indonesians; none too happy about that with the new baby and all."

"Tough shit." Rick not one to hide his thoughts. Dowdy seemed to sigh. "Yup, my sentiments exactly. You gotta know this has nothing to do with your leadership, your Command. You gotta know that, we all know that."

"Yes, let Mudd deal with LTC Sukri. Good luck with that," an exasperated Rick let out.

"The Ambassador is pissed with the *Minggu* piece trying to froth up public sentiment that our operations are covert, and against the sovereign interests of Indonesia," exclaimed Rick. "The article goes so far as to suggest the pig outbreak was fabricated, and somehow intended to allow us to spy on the military's activities in Papua as the hostage crisis is coming to a head, and what this means for the 'Free (East) Papua Movement' (OPM). The implication being that America is clandestinely supporting a breakup of the archipelago, including the dicey East Timor challenge to Indonesian rule.

The authors, the same two we had the pleasure of meeting in Wamena, went so far as to speculate about the real purpose of constructing a landing strip in Papua, by navy Seabees, no less: having nothing to do with malaria treatment trials. They went on to write that the drugs being evaluated, anyhow, are mostly unaffordable as treatment options for Indonesians, certainly in the case of TNI. The 'take home' message being the airstrip, symbolic of US intentions, will be used in flying in supplies, including arms, to the secessionists and their sympathizers."

"Shit, that could rock not only our mil-to-mil relationship, but the 'whole shebang'," invoking a 1920s all-American phrase, "and not just a little off-kilter. Remember, we are now the region's official 'boogeyman': talking geopolitics. This would be perceived as a military intrusion, and no less. All making for some very bad optics."

Rick agreed fully with Dowdy's take on the wider implication of what was becoming a diplomatic disaster.

"I cannot fathom how Captain Jamison – the former Commanding officer of NMRC-Indonesia – could have so recklessly supported such a foolish proposition, especially with sensitivities running high what with 'secessionist' tendencies. Of course, the potential of having such an action misread, misconstrued, was always there, and should have been anticipated."

"Don't forget my predecessor," the Colonel chipped in.

"One last thing," Dowdy whispered as they stood in front of the door to the postal section. "The MAF pilot, the one who flew the helicopter: born in America to naturalized Indonesian parents, was in the military. A Warrant Officer. Learned to fly compliments of the army, until 'separated' last year. The problem I am hearing from my sources at the Pentagon was that he was medically discharged with some serious psychological issues. Seems he purposely crashed a helicopter just as he was completing his flight training. Apparently the MAF, in a rush, had brought him on as a temporary replacement for one of their pilots without the standard vetting of any new hires. Of course, the military is secretive when it comes to sharing such sensitive information, considered privileged. I don't know how 'this plays' into our crash, but you should know. And after all, you are a 'doc.'" The door suddenly opened, and a blast of cold air sent a shiver through Rick.

The Colonel walked Rick to the swinging steal entrance leading out to the parking area for 'official' staff. He would head home directly. He would work in his shorts and sandals, shirt being optional. A beer might also go well with the solitude to be found on veranda overlooking the garden. 'Jolly Rodgers,' his one-eyed cat, would be sure to come rubbing himself up against his leg. He had a lot to think about, his future for starters. His 'fun' meter had long since expired; maybe it was time to move on from the navy. Putting those thoughts aside, he had a conference call to prepare for that evening with the PACOM Surgeon General. He understood that there would be others on the line, guessing the dreaded 'echo chamber' that is the Bureau of Navy Medicine (BUMED) would join in on the fun. "Yes, they do love a party." The glum expression on his face not matching his words. Winny was not sure what to make of the remark. Though it was always wiser not 'read' too much into whatever Rick was thinking, never mind saying.

From being lost, to captive

We followed, and the village led. Our escort, young and old alike, seemed less enthused by our presence, at least compared with previous Dani receptions we encountered. We were pulled and tugged by the crowd that had formed around us as we proceeded to a grouping of four, maybe five, 'kampungs': extended family compounds. As in the other villages we had visited, each *kampung* has a hut or huts reserved for males, separate, and for females, with no such domiciliary restrictions for the very young, who roamed at will. Additional non-segregated structures were used for communal cooking and sheltering of the family's most prized possession: pampered and much-loved pigs.

I had come to understand that men and women, husbands and wives, do not share the same roof, and despite the best efforts of Christian missionaries, their reach had not extended to polygamy and ritualistic animalism that have triumphantly prevailed. Ancestral worship, I learn from Ramu, is still central to the Dani 'belief system'. This is most evident by the reverence accorded those mummified warriors watching over the tribe. Leather-like, wrinkled and pruned, some having aged over 300 years: serving as an expression of that worship. So I am not totally unprepared, but still surprised when we were directed to the entrance of one of the larger 'kampungs', where two old men I guessed passing as village 'Big Men' posed with a 'mummy' sitting crouched, for all time. *It is not likely this 'fella' would be stretching his legs any time soon,* I thought irreverently.

Ancestral worship of this deity-like 'artifact', or 'Atou' involves a complex set of 'beliefs' that extend to and beyond spirit world. Adherence to the 'patriarchal' traditions underpins societal precepts that the Dani recognize as key to their survival: strength in keeping a garden; power to cure disease and prevent outbreaks; and keeping fertile, the soils for planting and the women for childbearing.[15,16,17]

There was a lot of back and forth between the 'Big Men' and a group of younger men who had shadowed our entourage since entering the village. I looked imploringly to Ramu for some kind of understanding. He stood stoically, paying no attention me, nor making any attempt to interpret what was being said. Until this point, I think we all felt saved; one step away from being reunited with pillows, bed sheets, showers, clean clothes and all the trappings of the life we know it, at least for Bakri and myself. But like that of a bad omen, something ominous was happening; the atmosphere chilled perceptively. Faces grew sterner as the banter grew louder. I was no longer feeling quite saved; more like, 'from the frying pan into the fire'.

We were settled in a 'kampung' distant from the rest, almost hidden by a clump of trees and seemingly smaller than the other compounds. What I would come to refer to as our 'kampung' consisted of just a few derelict huts, leaving us with

---

15 *http://factsanddetails.com/indonesia/Minorities_and_Regions/ sub6_3j/entry-4037.html.*

16 *https://westpapuadiary.com/dani-tribe/.*

17 *https://westpapuadiary.com/west-papua-culture-and-culinary-the- dani-tribe-people/.*

the impression that the site had been, maybe not so long ago, abandoned.

With relief tempered by apprehension, I tried to make myself comfortable on the filthy dirt floor of the hut we took up occupancy in. With only a thin streak of light filtering in from the small entrance way, it took a few minutes to adjust to the dimly lit interior and get our bearings. The earthen floor is littered with pig 'shit' and small pellet droppings – knowing how the descriptive term, 'pigsty', came to be. Tufts of fur balls float by in stale air – the smell overpowering. I found myself gagging when one snags in the back of my throat. Suckling baby pig 'scours', a foul-smelling, light-colored diarrhea, now harden with a crusty outer layer over time, adding to my gag reflex.

The sores on my legs and arms, mostly souvenirs from my tumble into the thorny brush some weeks prior, and more recently acquired during our trek through the highland wilderness, are healing nicely, thank you! I keep from looking too closely at the blisters on my swollen feet, that first bled and have since hardened into calluses one might find on an old 'croc' – even though I had never actually petted one.

Everyone else appeared exhausted, but okay. At least nobody was complaining. I think we were all thankful to be alive, and reasonably safe. Although 'reasonable' is a relative term, and measured against where we were just a few hours earlier: lost and acutely afraid, in my own case. Bakri even managed a smile, and, in his own way, a joke about our situation: "We have stayed in worse places and had to pay for the privilege." Indeed, we had!

John continued to say little, which was becoming more and more worrisome. He acknowledged his surroundings, contributing to 'our group' mentality: meaning, he was readily recognizable as one of us. He expressed himself with a nod of the head in signifying his assent. I felt it important to continue to engage him, with smiles, words of encouragement and general greetings, despite his behavior that might be described as unhinged.

Although exhausted, the first night brought me little sleep. A cold rain made even more so by the high humidity made me shiver well into the next morning. Ramu explained that we needed to make our own fire. "This means we need to go out and get some wood," translated Bakri, all the while smiling at his own attempt at subtle humor; and a not-so-subtle reminder that there was no room service in our *kampung*, five-star *'honai'* suite. This was made obvious the previous evening when we were treated to some carrots and tubers that were gritty and barely cooked. We were all hungry, if not slowly starving. Our weakened state becoming more and more debilitating with the passing of time. So we ventured outside of our otherwise-deserted *kampung* in search of anything to start and build a fire with, having exhausted our supply of matches. Otherwise, we would have to eat the grub we had scavenged raw.

We needed protein, but even more so, we needed to fill our stomachs. We all recognized that this would be a challenge, since we had seen no gardens and few pigs and piglets wandering about, not at least that belonged to us. Theft of precious pigs among the Dani was not tolerated; I could only imagine the penalty for such an egregious act of theft. In the American Wild West, justice was meted out by the 'hangman' for stealing a horse, well into the 19th century.

We headed for the clump of stunted trees that separated and hid our 'kampung' from our neighbors, only to be immediately set upon by a group of young children, with their characteristic smiles so wonderfully expressive of their unabashed delight in the novelty of having 'these strange visitors' in their midst; we could have come from another planet given their non-existent frame of reference. We slowly moved toward a clump of trees that had an indigenous fig-like fruit hanging from the branches, otherwise known as *Kaumu Musong*. These trees were in turn fenced by stalks of passion bananas bunched together. Clearly, we had stumbled into a semi-wild fruit garden that literally brought me to my knees, overcome with joy, like some long-ago adventurer feeling terra firma underfoot following a long sea voyage with no sight of land. My real fear of starvation could be put aside for now, maybe for another day. Ramu was excitedly animated, pointing beyond the tree line to a larger grouping of trees that at first glance had some exotic flappy fruit hanging in the hundreds from the larger branches. "*Kelelawar buah*," he yelled, and I had never heard him yell. Since '*buah*' means fruit in *Bahasa* Indonesian, I was thinking, *some kind of fruit or nut.*

When I looked at Bakri with my "what's that mean" expression on my face, he translated: "Fruit bats." Walking toward the grove of tall fig trees, I stepped into an 'ah-ha' moment: sinking into '*bat guano*', or poop, underfoot.

I still did not realize the significance of Ramu's discovery at first, and I guessed neither did Bakri. I was nonetheless feeling as if we had chanced on some 'Garden of Eden' as I began chewing on the figs that had fallen to the ground. I was famished! A little tart, not so sweet, like the southern Mediterranean figs you buy in the supermarket, enough so that the sticky juices that now coated my mouth and slithered down my throat made me feel both lightheaded and energized with this sugary elixir, like a witch's potion.

It was then that I first sensed, then heard, movement from the direction we had come from, and as if in slow motion, watched as Ramu was set upon by three imposing men. Everything then happened in an instant. Looking both deranged and enraged at the same time, they were beating him with walking canes without mercy as Ramu howled with pain. Without thinking, I rushed alongside Bakri, and yes, John, to Ramu's defense. Bakri pushed one of the attackers away, who then turned and walloped him in the stomach with the same stick used in beating Ramu. Bakri shrieked and doubled over, collapsing first to his knees, then to the ground, all the while holding his belly. Our 'saviors turned attackers' then backed away. I had managed to fall on my face, as I lost my footing on the slippery figs that littered the ground around us. It was John who stood menacingly between us and our trio of assailants; swinging the canvas bag always slung over shoulder. It was as if he had suddenly regained his senses and took to 'playing the hero'. And for that, I was thankful.

By then, there was a noisy crowd that had gathered around us, keeping their distance, but corralling us nevertheless. It was then that the two 'Big Men' we encountered on our arrival pushed themselves to the front of the excited villagers. They kneeled on the ground before us, and then turned their attention to the three men who attacked us. I only knew that we were the subject of a back-and-forth exchange. I feared the heated discourse might turn violent; the 'Old Men' where clearly at a disadvantage. There was no yelling, but voices were raised; more than enough 'testosterone' to go around. In the end, the 'Big Men', agitated enough to be making threatening gestures with their hand-tooled axes and spears, apparently posing, while scolding our three provocateurs; or maybe that was my imagination playing out what I hoped was taking place.

I watched Ramu scoop out the pasty over-ripened banana passion fruit with his fingers and apply it to his bleeding lacerations. Despite his beating, he calmly described the medicinal quality of the yellowish paste, in healing everything from headaches to epileptic seizures to open wounds. Bakri's stomach and right side were black and blue, and his short breaths suggested a broken rib, or ribs. From his now-frayed multi-pocketed vest, I pulled out an Ace Bandage and rapped it around his midsection. There was no easy fix for a broken rib, except to limit your movement and numb yourself with the likes of Ibuprofen, which we still had enough of to get him through the next few days.

I put the obvious to Ramu: "What happened?" But it was intuitively clear that our presence had seriously disrupted the ebb and flow of village normalcy. Indeed, we managed to tear apart the social fabric of the community in the first few days having tried to settle in without causing a stir: bringing attention to ourselves. In that regard, we were failing miserably.

Lunch with the General

Following the departure of the ICRC, *thank goodness*, thought General Widodo, 'all bets are off': meaning his soldiers were now free to take whatever action was deemed necessary in rescuing those remaining captives and in eliminating this clear and present threat to the nation's security. The increasingly erratic demands by the Movement's leadership had put the ICRC in an untenable position, leading to a breakdown in negotiations and abandonment of any kind of peaceful resolution to the hostage situation.

Off on another tangent:

Western interests are now actively looking to break up 'his' country, in supporting and giving refuge to any self-proclaimed group seeking to right a colonial wrong and declare their independence. It was happening in East Timor with the Australians now parroting slogans about how wronged the Timorese people had been by an Indonesia only asserting its national prerogative. Yes, sovereignty! This was the same Australia that continues to recognize the Queen of England as 'Head of State', administering Papua New Guinea (PNG) until their independence in September 1975; and which to this day continues to subjugate the country through forced economic dependence for the sake of exploiting the country's mineral wealth. And yes, Australia would love nothing better than to gain 'rights' to the vast oil reserves believed to be buried on the Timorese side of the Timor Gap: that area of sea that separates Australia from East Timor. And then there is Portugal, playing the provocateur in their open support of Timorese aspirations for independence; the same Portuguese who gave East Timor nothing by way of means to govern themselves, leaving little trace of infrastructure, education, and health care over their 300-year colonial rule.

Feeling his anger building as his face visibly reddened, he remarked to his guests: "Separatist movements are allowed, even encouraged, to establish an illusion of governance, self-rule, in countries like Australia, Sweden, Portugal and the Netherlands, which provide not only funding but advocacy in international forums like the United Nations." His disguise of 'resolute calmness' failed to mask his growing sense of outrage as he powered on: "The leadership of the 'Acehnese Independence Movement' direct their campaign of terror from the safety of Sweden, making the Swedes complicit in the slaughter of our soldiers, government officials and our citizens."[18]

His audience of senior military officers applauded the fervor of the General's nationalistic appeal, as they dug into their meal of Javanese delights; compliments of the host for this gathering: the US mining giant, 'PT Freeport Indonesia'. This was no coincidence or one-off, with PT Freeport Indonesia

---

18 *https://en.wikipedia.org/wiki/Papua_conflict.*

based in Timika, Mimika Regency, on the southwest coast of West Papua, mining some of the largest copper and gold deposits in the world. Indeed, Indonesian military operations in the whole of the province are largely bankrolled through their longstanding arrangement with their PT Freeport benefactor.[19]

It would be correct to assume that Widodo saw himself as a champion of Indonesian aspirations to assert its regional preeminence, bridging both Pacific and Indian Oceans. It would be equally safe to assume that his blood pressure, already dangerously high, reached even higher peaks when challenged about Indonesian national interests and integrity.

After seeing off his guests as they boarded the Gulfstream jet at the Freeport hangar, Widodo mustered his small group of close confidants, including Lieutenant Colonel Sukri, and plotted well into the night what could only be described as an airborne 'shock and awe' tactical assault to free the remaining hostages being held near Mapenduma, located about halfway between Timika and Wamena; with Timika to the southwest and Wamena to the northeast. Helicopters would ferry in 'his' commandos for a rescue mission.

Lieutenant Colonel Sukri asked: "Do we continue with our search for the Jakarta team investigating 'wabah babi'? The Embassy pulled their military representative back to Jakarta earlier in the week." Widodo understood the politics and potential repercussions in shutting down, 'no longer' a rescue but recovery operation. "We need those air assets in conducting our reconnaissance flights over Mapenduma! Keep one of the Cessnas on station so we can at least say we have not given up the hunt."

19   https://www.forbes.com/sites/greatspeculations/2014/10/06/
a-closer-look-at-freeports-indonesian-mining-
operations/#51ab37591fbc.

Passing time with nowhere to go

It was almost like an old Charlie Chaplin film, except in color, and personal. I awoke before the ending. I rarely dreamed, making the visual only more spectacular and maybe just a little disturbing. I felt my forehead for a trace of fever and was not disappointed. Of course, I was sick. But here were the 'spirits' up to their old shenanigans, taking advantage, in leading me astray.

> *The navy sent me to Belize to pilot a novel approach to community-based surveillance, working among Mayan communities in the Cayo district in the western part of the country. As is my fate, the entire country of Belize is claimed by Guatemala — and I found myself carrying out my research sandwiched between the British and Belize Defense Forces, and an opposing Guatemalan army, along the contested border region. This at a time when Belize was preparing for 'independence' from Great Britain. It was feared that such a festive occasion could marred by Guatemalan 'opportunism' — taking advantage of a waning British presence.*
>
> *It was against this backdrop that I first fell 'head-*

over-heals' in love, with an El Salvadorian dentist working for the MoH. Her brother was also employed as the only doctor at the Cayo district hospital in San Agnacio town – both made refugees by the civil war raging in their county.

She was suitably exotic, an old woman with a young daughter. I was more than smitten! I had found the 'love of my life', quite by accident – riding in the back of the government truck that carried her to the small clinic in Benque Viejo twice monthly, where I was working from. After many months, I finally found my nerve to engage her in more than friendly 'chit chat'. It was late, back at university, that my young heart discovered the 'ache' that comes with loss – the 'knee-buckling' kind; reason enough to give up on life. I was seriously shattered and still bear the emotional scars that have doomed my relationships since.

That night, I dreamt of a 'different' life: one in which I had not forsaken most vestiges of normalcy; one in which I was not so alone – and not to be confused with 'lonely'. My life: 'could have, should have', been so different.

Still in the dark, I felt reality, and not just my present circumstances. It was then I knew I had to move on, leave the past in the past. I could finally get on with my life.

I awoke cold and sore, thanks to the rock-hard earthen floor. We had been 'licking our wounds', both literarily and figuratively; killing time! With stomachs now full, and 'body and soul' on the mend, maybe for the first time since embarking on our journey – 'falling from the heavens' – it was time to begin exploring this place, and planning and preparing for what comes next. We feasted the night before on the fruit bats, fried up in a batter of coconut milk and sweet potato, and were none the worse for it.

The Nipah Virus (NiV) likely traveled westward, after first making the journey northward from Australia's Northern Territories and the northern tip of Queensland to neighboring PNG. 'Hitching a ride' on the all too likely culprit: the seemingly harmless fruit bat. Human cases are generally attributed to exposure to fruit bats, with some evidence of human-to-human transmission. In the case of the recent Malaysia outbreak that first attracted so much attention to NiV in the region, the virus most probably passed to humans from infected pigs.[20]

What I know about NiV is little, but enough to give me pause. It is easy in my line of work to fall victim to hypochondria; sensing a pathogen lurking about, ready to pounce. Many a warm Jakarta evening blanketed in prickly dampness that sticks to the skin, swatting away the pesky mosquitoes insistently buzzing around my ears, I convinced myself, and with good reason, that I would assuredly fall prey to some vector-borne virus like dengue or chikungunya. The difference here is that NiV infection, generally characterized by acute encephalitis, or swelling of the brain for the non-initiated, is the estimated deaths among those infected by the virus: forty-five to seventy-five percent of cases.[21]

Unable to pause from my meal, slobber running down my chin, I still play the role of 'food critique': "This tastes like barbecue duck – who knew bat could be so good." Throwing all caution to the wind', we feasted. Filling our bellies, and antidote to our protein deficits, proved a 'bat revelation'. I sat on a stump in the compound for a goodly part of the evening, not wishing to soil the experience of our meal in the odorous filth of our 'honai', gazing up at the low-flying shadows streaking

20 https://en.wikipedia.org/wiki/1998–1999_Malaysia_Nipah_virus_outbreak.

21 https://www.who.int/news-room/fact-sheets/detail/nipah-virus.

like missiles across moon lit sky. "Yes, I am alive, and I will stay that way."

It was, of course, Ramu who immediately recognized the 'food value' hanging from the trees just before we were viciously attacked for having trespassed into the community's garden. And it was again Ramu who figured out, after days of experimenting, how to snare our first fruit bat, which was no small feat. Indeed, we were all consumed with coming up with a way of capturing our prey, short of praying for one to drop dead of 'old age' and fall from their upside-down perch. More importantly, we were able to lose ourselves in this mental exercise to mentally escape from our predicament. Eventually, Ramu, an accomplished hunter and gatherer, came up with the idea of stringing a bed netting between two poles in our small compound, soaked in a sticky, almost syrupy broth of boiled banana passion fruit and indigenous figs, with some pounded cassava added for good measure.

Stomachs full and hunger less pressing, our thoughts turned to our informal captivity. The 'Big Men', who were always in each other's company, paid us a visit soon after our memorable thrashing, offering up a scrumptious treat of a baby pig cooked over 'hot' rocks, wrapped in large banana leaves with sweet potatoes and a mashed red fruit known locally as 'bush tawi'. And yes, I find myself thinking of late about food, all types, all the time. Bakri, always virtuous and seeking *and finding* the good in people, was really touched by this apparent display of contrition. "Their way of an apology. They are just shy and are trying to make up for the crazy actions of a few trying to prove their warrior heritage. We should feel the dignity in their shame, that brought them in person to make us this gift." I was not sure if Bakri's words truly conveyed his sentiment, as I struggled in piecing together his sentiment, but the meaning was well understood.

We were nevertheless caught up somewhere in between, our special status as guests and that of prisoners. Free to wander the village and the surrounding area, but now less inclined to do so: no longer sure what figured as a transgression, to be interpreted as an offense. Ramu pretty much 'flew solo' in exploring the village and taking every opportunity to assimilate himself, proving particularly adept in children's games.

I was even greeted in a not-so-hostile way by one of our assailants as I walked past a *kampung* that looked well cared for. I recognized him by his enormous penis gourd: more stick to whack someone over the head with. He was so engrossed in carving some kind of gardening implement, from the looks of it, that he barely gave me a glance, which I took as progress in my own assimilation.

Lots to think about back in Jakarta

Pacing around a house far too big for just himself in the upscale Jakarta neighborhood of Kemang, a heaven for expats and wealthy Indonesians, Captain Rick made no pretenses of his disdain for navy double-speak or the cover-your-ass – CYA – crisis-management culture; which the navy both rewarded and excelled at. *Surely,* he thought, *a recipe for disaster if the navy had to ever take on a 'real' combatant.* His early Saturday morning conference call with the Pacific Command in Hawaii, their night, did little in calming his already pensive and sometimes aggressively impatient nature. "Fuck it!" Half-remembering how his favorite author, the great southern novelist 'James Lee Burke', referred to the expression: 'not spoken as a profanity, but as a sonnet'. Regardless of the sentiment, designed to be spoken more to oneself than to anyone within listening distance, that is how he felt. As most senior officers, he felt conflicted. He loved the navy: the clarity of purpose; and 'being all about the mission', in navy-speak. But mostly, for cutting through all the 'bullshit': saying what needs to be said without any pretense or 'sugar coating'. But at the same time, he knew it was time to quit. "First thing Monday," he gleefully shouted to an audience of one, his 'one-eyed' cat; inherited when he moved into the house from the previous renter. Yes, he would hand in his request for retire at the start of the new week.

On a much more personal level, he felt that, somehow, he could have done more in pushing the 'powers that be' in their search efforts. He had pushed the envelope by his insistence that more could be done, and had been cautioned, by the Ambassador no less, to be more respectful when speaking his mind, especially when it came to his opinion of General Widodo. At the same time, the added attention to NMRC-Indonesia's presence in the country spurred by the events in West Papua let loose a 'generally hostile' media 'scrum' turning into a 'feeding frenzy', as to the 'real' mission of the navy's medical research operations in the archipelago. To the government, NMRC-Indonesia was becoming an irritant, and increasingly turning into a liability in the face of growing public demands for accountability and a ratcheting up anti-colonial rhetoric.

"Yes, first thing Monday!" And yet his thoughts immediately turned to his feeling of helplessness, as if he was now abandoning whatever hope existed in finding his jungle adventurer. There would be no fanfare in trying to make meaningful his loss. Hell, he was not even sure if his intrepid Commander had any living relatives. Jacques never spoke of family, and spent his navy career traipsing around the world, somehow thriving in places that most avoided like the plague. But Jacques was quiet about his exploits, almost shadowy, going out of his way to avoid attracting attention to himself. Indeed, he often joked that he made it this far in the navy by keeping his head low, staying off the radar. Rick could not help smiling as he recalled Jacques' failed attempt to cut his own hair; and the ensuing laughter when Rick, being Rick, suggested all in good humor that Jacques' new look had the distinctive 'patchiness' associated with tertiary syphilis, which brought on a round of laughter at one of his weekly Command staff meetings. And while 'presumed missing' in navy-speak, he understood that Jacques and Bakri would in all likelihood remain so until the wreckage from the crash could be found, if ever.

No longer welcome

"Ramu has taken up with one of the women," exclaimed Bakri.

"Maybe two, or even three," I just had to add. Days turned to weeks, and I had lost track of time. We were free to leave if there was anywhere to go. Ramu had climbed a large tree some days earlier to gain some sense of our surroundings, and what direction we would need to travel in if we were so inclined. But with no map or coordinates, we would likely end up going around in circles. My expertise at orienteering, done best with a map and compass, was now limited to: 'the sun rises in the east and sets in the west'. I knew only that PNG was to the east, and the Pacific Ocean to the west. But that knowledge was of no value to us, except that the Pacific Ocean sounded better than the equally remote highlands of PNG. It was probable that Wamena was 'north by northwest' to our present location, but we clearly were not going to trek back to Wamena on foot. Possibly, we could take our chances in finding a stream or river and following it. But that option was not without risks: we had no way of knowing where the currents led to; or if the waters were safe – thinking of freshwater crocodiles. That did not even touch upon such natural hazards as rapids and waterfalls, and undercurrents that could pull even the strongest swimmer into the depths and a watery grave.

Our amateurish reconnaissance of the village revealed not a trace of outside influences, and our conspicuous attempts to disguise our prying were met by amused stares and cold silence.

Not a single visitor came to our humble dwelling, except for the young children gathering outside the compound, 'whooping and hollering'; that is until novelty of our homestay wore off. It was only when visiting the garden plots that we could engage the villagers freely, outside of their highly stratified societal norms dictated by an etiquette that I struggled to make sense of.

And yet, we were feeding ourselves and growing stronger. We were gifted two squealing piglets by our 'Big Men' benefactors. We all became doting parents to our playful brood, dishing out waste and scraps mixed with grass and roots.

"We need to fatten them up, so we can do the same. I fear our welcome will soon turn into something else, maybe not so friendly." Bakri was becoming increasingly antsy. "We need to prepare ourselves," he implored with a hint of urgency.

And while Ramu continued to be our principal provider, Bakri and I were feeling more confident in our foraging and indigenous-cooking skills. But his disappearances were growing longer and with increasing frequency, as if he were now settling into some kind of matrimonial bliss; abandoning his family, community, and us; for this, his newly found home. He no longer slept in our hut, and was becoming more aloof, less ready to engage in the humorous banter that fueled our good spirits.

John, too, seemed strangely 'settled', and took on an almost Hindu 'holy man' persona complete with braided locks and beard, not to mention his stench; refusing to indulge in our daily bathing ritual. There was a small stream about thirty meters from our *kampung* that was wonderfully refreshing, serving as a communal watering hole for the entire village, except for that of John. But that was all about to change.

An angry General

There is nothing like failure, more often perceived than real, to challenge rational actions. Widodo was smarting, overly sensitive, to what he played out in his head, as his Gulfstream G-V made its final approach into Halim International (Military) Airport on the outskirts of Jakarta. He was cognizant that his invitation by the TNI High Command was nothing short of a summons. His family connections would not shield him in what had been until now a stellar career. News of the failed rescue mission, daring as it was, was not well received. His intel had failed him badly. The small armada, a reference usually given to ships but in this case a fleet of five helicopters outfitted for the special forces under his command, found the village of Geselama that had been 'ground zero' in the hostage-taking saga hastily deserted, or at least temporarily abandoned. But it was the loss of one of his helicopters and five of his commandos that gnawed at his gut; he seethed with an anger that only comes from a very personal sense of failure. Being responsible for men who die in battle was his cross to bear. He wore his men and mission as his badge of honor and duty; he loved them, and they loved him right back. His usual self-confidence and resolve, he thought, would be sorely tested today, more so than in any firefight, as he braced himself for landing. The stakes were high. Not only for his Command but his legacy. *Not so easy living up to the faith of the nation you have been entrusted with,* he thought. All the while, keenly appreciative that the persona he endeavored to cultivate as the true protector of the nation was now at stake.

Wamena simmering

Settled! Nono Maraud had finally eased into his new job at the Bank Nacional Indonesia, or BNI, as Deputy Branch Director, although for the three weeks since his hastily arranged move from Makassar, he had been 'Deputy' under the tutelage of mentor and friend, Gindo,.Until Gindo had suddenly taken ill and flown to Jakarta. The 'plan', at least for now, was to move into the director's residence, albeit temporarily, until he could find something suitable to rent. His wife and two young children would join him after he felt comfortably assured this move was more than just filling a temporary gap left by Gindo's sudden departure. He was, after all, very junior to assume full control of the branch, even in a place like Wamena. His wife would have to sort out schooling for his five-year-old son, which could really become a problem. But such a hardship posting would surely be to his career advantage, or so he hoped.

Nono awoke to the crowing of the wretched rooster every morning before daybreak, killing any hope of a leisurely sleep in. Burying his head in the pillow never worked in silencing his world, but he did so anyway. "Today is Sunday, my day," he shouted aloud, giving notice, chastising his morning nemesis.

The 'pembantu' – maid – was preparing a breakfast of boiled chicken in a sloppy rice, leftover from the night before, as he ambled into the kitchen area.

Icha was twenty-three and took her job seriously. From a poor coastal village in West Java, she had been brought to Wamena by her then-husband, a trader from Makassar who serviced the local military garrison. That is until he failed to return from a day hike to a nearby village in search of masks and other tribal art to sell to the few tourists that made their way to Wamena, seeking out the ultimate adventure. He was rumored to have made more than a few enemies in his dealings with the local merchants, fueling speculation that he met a premeditated and murderous fate.

Icha, six months pregnant at the time and left to fend for herself, found sanctuary in the director's home. A devout Christian, a Batak, he took Icha in and treated her like a daughter; the one and the same who befriended Bakri when we first arrived in Wamena, finding solace in coming across a fellow Batak, here in the middle of nowhere. I told Gindo that he 'lucked out' with Bakri, of all the Batak to run into, over a scrumptious Padang feast that he and Icha cooked up together for us, our first Sunday in town. She planned to stay only a short while until she could manage the finances to move herself and now young daughter back to Java. And despite having only minimal schooling, she took quickly to her new role in running the household.

"Bapak Nono, selamat pagi," welcomed Icha as she toiled over a hot fire in warming water for his bath. To Nono, this meant no electricity, again. "Did you smell the smoke from the market?" she asked absent-mindedly, not really expecting or caring for his response, and quickly added, "There is talk that many in the community are angry about reports from the nearby village of Luci, where soldiers suspecting locals of terrorist sympathies burned many of the houses and took at least a dozen young men into custody." Speaking more rapidly now, Icha went on to say that there was now a nightly curfew in place restricting the military to their bases since two soldiers were attacked with machetes on the main street in front of the BNI building two nights ago. "I heard that both were killed, and that their heads were cut from their bodies. So be careful, and please, eh Bapak Nono, do not go out after dark." Nono took some of the reports he too had heard as exaggerated, but still, was already rethinking his plan to bring his family to Wamena.

A mess of our own making

"What was he thinking?" shouted Bakri. I had never seen him this angry. His issues with John were deep-rooted, emanating from whatever took place during my escape from consciousness after our helicopter plunged to the ground, those many weeks earlier. Bakri had confided his suspicions that our crash was somehow deliberate, although he would never elaborate. I know Bakri, and he is not prone to speculation; nor had I ever heard him besmirch anyone. I urged him to put his feelings aside, at least for the time being.

"Let's just deal with the 'here and now', we can figure out the rest later."

We were set upon by a seriously angry mob: men, women, the old and the young, shouting in our direction. More worrisome was the presence of the 'Big Men', leading, no longer trying to restrain, what was clearly an expression of community outrage. Ramu tried to translate, barely able to keep up with the rancorous conversation: "John, had been found fondling a young girl, a child, in the banana grove, just minutes before."

With stoic expressions, the 'Big Men' made clear we were no longer welcome, and to leave immediately. I flinched as a stone struck me just above my right eye. I wipe the blood from my vision; it was now running freely from a gaping wound. Ramu turned quickly and led Bakri and me away from the mayhem, past our *kampung*, and down the path that led past the creek and into the jungle. "Where is John?" I murmured. Ramu's breathing was heavy and raspy as we hurried along, just short of running.

"We go. John will stay in the village."

We passed the pools of water that served as the communal bathing area and continued to follow the small stream, making our way down the slope; using the gully likely carved into the earth from excess runoff during the rains to guide us. I was having difficulty in keeping focused on what was immediately in front of me, as I repeatedly blinked, trying to clear the stinging blood-mixed sweat that cascaded down my face. One second, I was on my feet and trying to make sense of everything that happened in the last few minutes, and the next flying head over heels after catching my now-tattered sneaker on a slightly elevated tree root that snaked its way across our path.

Hunched against a tangled clump of roots that would be almost impossible to trace back to any one tree, Bakri and I waited for Ramu to return, after he insisted that we needed some provisions left in our hut if we had any chance in making our way out of this mess. We had literally run off into the jungle with just the clothes on our back. I was not only sore, but sure I had wrenched my back and bruised, if not broken, a few ribs during my short flight and crash landing. At least the blood from my wound had begun to congeal. I could not help myself in prodding Bakri: "I think we got lucky since we needed to break free of our host Dani family." Poorly timed and of even poorer good etiquette given the circumstances, my attempt at humor succeeded in transforming his glum expression into a trace of a smile. Indeed, Bakri had been urging for some weeks now that we needed to move on if we stood any chance of being rescued.

He would always add, "We need to rescue ourselves."

I found myself dozing, and thinking how my line of work, investigating little-known diseases in remote and even lesser-understood populations, lacked any cultural clarity from which to derive context; a key ingredient to understanding those practices that potentially influence the spread of disease. Except from our own superficial observations and explanations from Ramu, Bakri and I had not a clue about the societal norms of the people we came to help. I had little interest in familiarizing myself with the cultural peculiarities of the Dani before starting out on our investigation, at least not enough to properly research the anthropological literature beforehand. I had no idea what would happen to John, except a keen sense that we as a group would likely be held accountable for his transgression, even if only by association. After all, our Dani brothers and sisters viewed us, except maybe for Ramu, as a tribe, no less. They had received us warmly into their community, homes, without any expectations in return. And we had failed to live up to that expression of kindness; like a crazed dog, biting the hand that feeds it.

"Ouch." It hurt to breathe! Bakri tightly bound the bandage around my ribcage; the same bandage he wore for weeks following the beating we took in the palm banana patch, not so long ago.

We listened attentively to Ramu, who explained: "What is done, is done." I was struck by his use of this very Western slang, which was essentially an expression of 'get over it'. He would not respond when we asked about John, and what happened to him. At the same time, we did not push this topic of conversation. We were just thankful that he had returned to us, although neither Bakri nor me expressed that concern, except between ourselves; we had our doubts. Ramu managed to bring our few possessions from the hut we occupied, including our now prized Ace Bandage. Cause enough to celebrate our dismal prospects.

We had been a team, Bakri, Ramu, and me, for something close to three months now, although I was becoming increasingly fuzzy with time. I had long ago given up trying to figure out the day of the week – especially so since there was no need in knowing. And all this time, we hardly knew anything about Ramu, his: life; loves; and family. What made him tick. He rarely showed any expression, except the pride and confidence he exuded whenever he sourced our next meal, especially so when are lives depended on it. His yelp of glee in spotting the fruit bats hanging from the banana palms was one of the few times he showed real emotion; my encounter with the snake did bring a smile to his face, although I think he felt 'shy' for me when I nearly jumped out of my skin.

But now, he was clearly agitated now, and seemed to have little patience for our attempts at humor, which was basically how Bakri and I dealt with calamity. "You can come back to your new family when this is over," Bakri remarked in earnest, sensing as did I without a word between us the very personal struggle Ramu was now agonizing over.

After days of marching, slogging a more apt description, we reached a small plateau from where we spied a large river in the distance. By this point, my body ached from toe to sunburned scalp. Indeed, my toenails now resembled gnarled tree roots twisting and turning into a 'kris'-like dagger: an intricately forged knife that holds symbolic if not mythical qualities passed down from generation to generation, meaning father to son; the Javanese equivalent of an ancestral family crest. I could not lay claim to such privileged origins as such that the 'kris' represented, except perhaps to some long-distant relative, maybe a conquistador, or even a Don Quixote, with toenails that curled and took on symbolic shapes if left untended: like the slippers of a court jester.

We were unquestionably burning up far more calories than we could make up for. Bakri and me, not so much Ramu, craved everything in sight. I no longer had any reservations putting in my mouth whatever in my reach: slimy or scaley; even if it wiggled or slithered; and went 'pop' with an explosion of juices, much like biting into a chocolate-covered cherry. Even the fish bone buried deep in my lower gum brought surprising relief, allowing me to focus on the searing pain instead of my hunger, if only just for a moment. I did not really pay much attention at first, since there were thankfully no mirrors, but looking at Bakri's skeletal self was plenty enough reminder of my own frailty. Ramu did his best, exhausted as he was, in wrapping uncooked grub worms excavated from decaying tree limbs in fresh green minty leaves picked from branches overhead. Most definitely an acquired taste unless, but not so much when, you are truly 'dying' of hunger.

Every time we figured we were heading further down into the valley where we first caught a glimpse of the snaking emerald-green waters that would lead us away from this place, we were forced to climb up, over, and around yet another obstacle in our way. "Did you notice there are no straight lines here," I mentioned to Bakri.

"Sure there are, just follow your nose in a straight line". We were talking 'gibberish,' but a least still talking.

My movements became increasingly careless, swinging my arms every which way and wandering from our procession of three. Even my greatest fear did not evoke more than a mild surprise when realized. Fortunately, the snake I literally grabbed onto as I swatted away what I thought was a thick vine in front of my face appeared more startled than I and scurried into the bush as soon as it hit the ground. That was when I lost all semblance of my normally calm demeanor. Ha ha! I began to run away from the group, back down the hill we had been climbing for what seemed a good stretch, until Ramu tackled me to the ground. I lay dazed, and really okay with closing my eyes and letting nature have its way with me.

I saw rather than heard Bakri screaming into my face. And then like a rush of wind the silence that engulfed me was shattered; my hearing returned with a vengeance. He was then hugging me, and I could feel his hot tears on my chest. We ended up hugging each other as if we only had each other to hold on to, that is until Ramu gently separated us and stood us up, taking each of us by the hand. As if we were small children, he held tightly, and we returned the favor, never letting go. I felt safe, as he half-walked us, half-dragged us onward.

Our jungle opened up onto a rocky, moss-carpeted outcropping, making our precarious trek even more so; we were slipping and sliding as if on slick ice. Thinking I could not feel more damaged, I fell hard on my ass, and pulled Bakri and Ramu down with me. An 'out-of-body' experience: I imagined the 'slapstick' comical relief from an appreciative audience had this been a scene from a Charlie Chaplin silent-film classic.[22] We shook off our fall and stood ourselves up, holding on to one another for support. As we gingerly made our way to a distant ledge, still holding on to one another, my senses kicked in: I 'smelled' running water, if that is even possible. As our pace quickened, I was struck by the rushing sound of what could only be fast-moving 'white' water: rapids. And finally, the river came into view.

---

22 *The Rink (1916) Charlie Chaplin Skating; https://en.wikipedia. org/wiki/The_Rink_(film).*

Seeking validation

General Widodo had yet another epiphany. It came to him in the middle of another of many sleepless nights, as he played and replayed, scene for scene, his meeting with the TNI leadership. He was not so much humiliated as made scapegoat for the failed rescue attempt that had gone spectacularly wrong. Of course, he took 'Command' seriously, and strongly believed that he bore ultimate responsibility for whatever failure: and fail he did.

The senior TNI leadership had gone so far as to encourage the media to focus on his own culpability, having little by way of understanding as to the difficulties in mounting any rescue operation, especially one 'smack-dab' in the middle of the rugged jungle highlands.

Chanting 'intel, intel, intel' had become an obsession for Widodo; without which, he 'driving blind' – completely lost. The OPM dealt with any real or perceived betrayal with immediate and brutal Papuan justice. Moreover, accurate intel was nearly impossible to come by given the growing resentment of most Papuans to Jakarta-based rule. Simply, Papuans could not be relied on to spy on their own. The General wanted to be prepared, with his own 'eyes and ears' to the ground; leaving a Kopassus observation team on the ground to report on the whereabouts of the OPM and their hostages.[23]

But what really 'ate his crow', an expression he adopted as his own while in Georgia (USA) attending Commando training at Fort Benning, was that 'his' soldiers were taking the brunt of criticism being levied at the heavy-handed enforcement of Indonesian claims over Papua, which was actually being perpetrated at the hands of poorly disciplined TNI soldiers; hastily plucked from their bases in Java, Sumatra, and Makassar, to keep the growing OPM insurgency in check. The consummate pragmatist, he understood that TNI had been seriously embarrassed under the glare of an international media spotlight, or 'circus' as he preferred to think of it. He was lucky to be allowed 'a second chance', to get back on the same plane he had flown in on and return to his Command. This time, he would leave nothing to chance.

The plan was brilliant in its simplicity. *Stick to the basic rule*, he thought: 'Less is more'. He confided to his close confidant, Colonel Agus. Ironically, the Colonel, who served as an aide-de-camp to General Salim, the second-highest ranking member in the Office of Strategic Policy, an autonomous TNI 'think tank' whose small size and relative anonymity belied its enormous influence on the decision-making of the General Staff, had been sent to Papua after the rescue debacle with orders to keep the TNI leadership appraised of the situation, and more to the point, on what plan General Widodo was concocting. There was no ambiguity as to the Colonel's mission. But still, Widodo saw in Colonel Agus an ally; an old friend from his cadet days at the Indonesian Military Academy, with whom he was able to express his unorthodox views as to how

---

23   *https://en.wikipedia.org/wiki/Kopassus.*

to shape 'special forces' in becoming more relevant to the needs of the military, and the nation.

Widodo was all too aware that many of the TNI leadership attributed his meteoric rise in the ranks to his 'family' connections as son-in-law to the President. And while this kind of patronage is very much ingrained in the advancement process throughout the TNI Officer Corps, his obscenely exceeded the norms of acceptability, as if that were possible, he thought to himself. He knew that it was the perception of privilege and entitlement that his marriage conferred, like a crown of thorns, that generated resentment. For better or worse, he was now part of the ruling family oligarchy. And that alone made him a magnet, more a target, for the ceaseless yet veiled criticism from within the senior ranks; many of whom believed that 'change was in the wind'.

At least that was how he processed his not-so-subtle reprimand. He knew that many of his fellow officers did not expect him to succeed with this mission. *Indeed*, he thought, *they were gleeful in their expectations that I would fail, and in spectacular style; like a fireworks display gone terribly wrong.* Well, this was his chance to prove himself worthy, and silence the critics.

Decision time

Muddy and seemingly impenetrable, the flow of the river was inexplicably interrupted by jutting boulders poking out from the waters. Small whirlpools and ripples forming concentric rings on the surface signaled the presence of treacherous undercurrents that could pull even the strongest of swimmers under.[24]

Contributor: Michele Burgess; suspension bridge across the Baliem River, Baliem Valley, Papua, Indonesia – Image ID: BWD3J5 (Alamy).

---

24   *http://www.peterloud.co.uk/photos/Indonesia/Papua.html.*

What little I knew about river travel was that it could be relaxing and joyful, as was my rafting experience on the Citarik River in Sukabumi – about seventy-five kilometers to the south of Jakarta – near the coast, one 'fine' day with some good friends and cold drinks. I should have sold 'rights' of our excursion to Coke for one of their commercials. Idyllic or carefree, either will do in describing our Sunday outing. Passing quaint villages along the riverbanks: bodysurfing in wetsuits on the 'faster' stretches; and lazily floating on our backs in the 'slower' sections.

I remember the exact 'moment of realization' that we were sharing our passage with human waste from those, the very same, 'quaint' villages; the inhabitants of which use the river for all their bodily needs, not least a convenient place to 'shit'. I recalled commenting to Norman that the excreta – not sure of how many ways to say 'shit' – was bobbing along with the current a whole lot faster than we were.

What I remember most was how satisfyingly exhausted I was following this watery trek, sleeping the entire three hours back to Jakarta after a late lunch at a nearly deserted beachside seafood restaurant following our river adventure. And how I ached all over for the next few days.

So much for my river rafting fitness, I mused, reminiscing; my way to escape the interminable reality of our present situation.

Well, we had no paddles, no raft, and definitely had no life preservers. Moreover, Bakri was not shy in stating his horror of taking to the river. "You know very well I cannot swim." I assured him that he was better off drowning, lest he became a croc meal. Bakri, forever Bakri, could not help himself to a smile at my attempt of 'morbid' humor. Truth be told, I had no idea if there were crocs in this stretch of the river, and just too tired to give a dam. We spent the next few days resting, gorging on fish, mostly small minnows, trapped in pools behind rock dams that Ramu managed to scoop; and scavenging the riverbank for tree limbs and brush material from which to build our raft.

"This will be our spaceship that would take us back to 'mother earth'." Bakri was not impressed with my analogy, at least not this time. He was responsible for pulling vines and stripping bark, from which we fashioned our craft. As we experimented with different designs, a 'feather-quality lightness' pierced the prevailing atmosphere and transformed our spirits from the 'gloom and doom' to something akin to hopefulness.

At night, we roasted our catch of the day, became sloppy drunk on the now-boiled river water, as we sat around a campfire and stared into the hallucinogenic flames; although Bakri, ever so perceptive, attributed our good spirits to the delicious mushrooms Ramu had been collecting in this near-utopia. We were so enthralled with our sense of well-being that on our last night before setting off, we laced flowers and mushrooms into a festoon to adorn our raft.

Despite all the potential dangers, the rapids, crocs, boulders, and of course drowning, we pushed off early the following morning. More apprehensive now, fitted with a single rope made of intertwined vines tied around each of our waists, we pushed our long sticks into the deepening river until we could not touch the bottom. We were now at the whimsical mercy of the river. Our long sticks now only good for pushing against rocks that could easily pulverize our raft and in shallows that threatened our already-slow forward movement.

We exchanged our long sticks, as the current picked up speed, to improvised paddles that 'do' as advertised. Trading in on my survival skills learned from jungle warfare training in Panama, where I served as an instructor for the navy's easy-breezy course in 'tropical medicine' at the famed Gorgas Memorial Laboratory. Stoking up fond memories as impressionable junior officer who searched out just such adventures, we cut our worn and torn pant legs and fitted them tightly over the V of short, shaped branches.

I was feeling very proud of myself.

Audacious

The perimeter to the airfield had been finally secured. And so was the aftermath of an almost-successful attempt by hundreds of local Papuans, wielding crude hatchets and spears, bent on destroying the parked helicopters being prepped for take-off; only to be dispersed by soldiers firing rubber bullets into the chaos. It was not lost on General Widodo that the secrecy surrounding this mission aptly named '*Operation Cenderawasih*' – after the elusive '*bird of paradise*' – prized by 'skin hunters' for their colorful coats and plumage and hunted almost to extinction.[25] And so forced the decision to move up the rescue operation by several hours. Likely, the OPM had already been alerted that something was up, or about to go down, putting the carefully choreographed tactical mission in jeopardy before even getting underway.

'Speed dial to fast forward': Widodo's normal outwardly 'calm' demeanor was splintering like a windshield struck at high speed by an errant pebble. He paced nervously back and forth in the crude, hastily constructed shed just adjacent to the airstrip that served as the flight control center for the earlier

---

25   *https://en.wikipedia.org/wiki/Bird-of-paradise.*

hostage negotiations and now rescue operations. His two, not one, aides-de-camp knew enough to keep their distance, outside. Colonel Augus was lost in his own thoughts standing silently in the corner of the room: waiting, anticipating, steeling himself for the worst-case scenario should the mission go bad. The American phrase 'going belly up' came to mind, although on second thought, Widodo's favorite American slang of 'going to shit' seemed more appropriate in preparing himself for the worst. Without the benefit of Widodo's family ties, the Colonel appreciated his own vulnerability when it came to being held accountable, should this mission fail.

Crackle on a radio transmission sounds just so: like crackle. Even the senior enlisted manning the communications board jumped as the 'crackle' sliced through the tension hanging heavy in the confined space. Pencil in hand, he decoded the numeric gibberish, matching number combinations with the alphabetic chart in front of him. His earphones lay unplugged and draped over his neck, so Widodo and Augus could listen in on the conversation. He then transcribed the message onto the single sheet of paper, handing it over to the waiting hands of the General.

News of the assault

Captain Rick Lavender was forced to endure an 'informal' Investigative Review of the 'Standard Operating Procedures (SOPs)' used by his Command in the conduct of field research. This is about the navy's way of 'heaping' blame, finding someone to fault, should things go 'belly up'. His frustration tinged of humiliation was on full display in having to acknowledge that no such 'animal' existed: never had.

"This is where the 'warfighters' doctrine governing such areas as 'rules of engagement' are simply not tenable with the tenants of research, as practiced at the overseas forward laboratories."

Without losing his rhythm, he continued on: "For the most part, my sailors are left to fend for themselves with no ready access to communications, like a mobile phone, or transport; forced to make 'on-the-spot' operational decisions without the benefit of a 'fuckin' SOP. Why, because no such document could account for the unique challenges they confront, most of which we could not have dreamt up, never mind prepared for. 'Not in a million years.'"

Later, he would bemoan his 'choice of words', and predicament, as his 'second in command' listened on attentively, and not without sympathy. "Our 'rules of engagement' are more about the rigorous ethical conduct of medical research, especially among populations with little education and fewer choices in life. I should suggest they should go visit the Baliem Valley and get to know the Dani before passing judgement. But I think I said enough, maybe too much".

Of course, this was all but heresy to the two investigative officers visiting from Hawaii, the senior of which, Commander Marvel, repeatedly quipped that the navy could only function in 'good order' under such a code outlining relevant rules and regulations, while leaving out the part about 'engagement' and 'combatants'. To which Captain Rick could only shake his head and mutter to himself: "What the hell is he talking about?" But Commander Marvel, for all his bravado and, 'give me the facts, not excuses', no-nonsense approach to what was really more a 'fact-finding' inquiry as opposed to anything more sinister, was no idiot. He understood that Captain Lavender had inherited his Command, making all before him, and those senior at higher echelons, equally culpable. If blame were to be assigned, there was more than enough to go around.

More importantly, he would later conclude in his summary findings: "The Command has in no way acted irresponsibly and that the circumstances, the air crash was well and truly beyond the control or the fault of NMRC-Indonesia." He would have dearly liked to have added, 'shit happens', but decided to keep that sentiment to himself.

The navy's mark in infectious disease research is the stuff of legend, a history rich in anecdotes and fraught with danger made more understandable by the nature in which the mission is carried out. He cited the example from the Navy Medical Research Center (NMRC) – Egypt/Africa: a senior Egyptian field-hand losing an arm and eye when the vehicle he was riding in hit an unmarked land-mine in the Sinai; or when navy staff were forced to flee in the middle of the night on camels from a research detachment in Ethiopia, fearing for their lives. The photo of a long-ago retired Commander, a navy virologist, sitting atop a camel with his eyes aglow like a hyaena in the night, making a hasty escape in nothing but his underwear. Commander Marvel was not short of haunting imagery and yet humorous testimony to the inherent dangers of working off the grid: 'below the radar', so to speak. Speaking his mind, to his wife on the phone from his hotel room at the Borobudur:

> "While these sailors are so removed from the staid and starched Navy way, they represent the 'chutzpah' that sets the Navy apart from the other services; doing their job without fanfare, more often on their own in the most inhospitable of places: you would not believe; hunting down neglected tropical diseases with names too difficult I cannot even pronounce. I think they did not so much as defy navy conventions, as they were failed by them."

"'I guess you had to have been there'," implying him, "to make sense of it all," she jokingly retorted. But she did, as a 'submariner', Executive Officer no-less, onboard SNN Lone Wolf: as the name would imply.

In the departure hall, the Commander shared with Rick what he already transmitted to Hawaii; findings that would then be later send to Washington. Relief washed over him. "I know this does not make the loss of Commander Bonaparte any easier to digest. But yes, 'shit does happen'. You need to stop blaming yourself. You held yourself accountable before the 'big navy' even got wind of this. Now go and retire and look me up if you make it to Pearl. I will most definitely visit you at your Bali home. Who knows, I may just decide to become you next-door neighbor." Walking past immigration to his waiting Garuda flight to Singapore, he yelled back at Rick: "Stop beating yourself up!"

Rick now sat in the secured suite deep in the bowels of the Embassy's chancellery. It was lined with cushioned walls and supposedly immune to electronic eavesdropping. The Ambassador and his senior staff drifted in in no great hurry for a priority briefing by Colonel Dowdy. There was good humor all around, and Rick was coming off an adrenaline-induced 'high' knowing Commander Marvel was not looking to make him a sacrificial lamb, after seeing him off the previous night for his flight back to Hawaii. And yet he felt more than a twinge of self-loathing at how quickly he rationalized and reconciled the loss of Jacques. Captain Lavender did not have a lot of friends, and even fewer people he respected. And yet Commander Jacques defied expectations, everybody's, taking chances without the conventional regard of the norms that governed advancement. He thrived in proving the detractors wrong, taking on gutsy missions in which there was nobody but himself to rely on. Jacques stood out as a 'sore thumb' in today's navy, and for that, Captain Rick Lavender felt a deep, numbing loss wash over him for this kindred spirit.

He was shaken from his thoughts as Colonel Dowdy began to speak: "I learned from TNI contacts in the last few hours that Kopassus mounted a successful air and ground assault on the OPM stronghold of Geselama. All nine remaining hostages except for two Indonesians were freed after being tracked along with their captors, accounting for the four Britons and two Dutch nationals. I might add the two Indonesian captives killed were hacked to death by OPM. Also, one of the Dutch captives who is pregnant is being transported to Gatot Soebroto Military Hospital, having been wounded, by an OPM spear. Sick fucks!"

"How many of the OPM were killed?" asked the head of the Political Section.

"We have no firm numbers, but I was told that Kopassus took few prisoners." He continued: "And while we cannot confirm, there are reports that the lead chopper was painted white, possibly with the ICRC insignia."

The political section head, always feeling the need to be heard, interjected: "If true, such would represent a flagrant abuse of the Geneva Convention."

The Ambassador, who could not help himself, stared down his political officer, and rebuffed: "Well, that is not our problem. But from where I am sitting, that would be a pretty ballsy move, if true."

Captain Lavender, feeling now entitled to speak his mind with more abandon than he had felt in a long time, quipped: "Yes, Mr. Ambassador, pretty audacious if you ask me."

Days after the hostage rescue, Captain Lavender was still trying to make sense of it all. Sorting fact from fiction, with accounts 'bent' to either glorify or disparage the actions of the military, depending on geopolitical persuasion. There was still considerable speculation that had yet to be confirmed as the media picked up on the story; with reports of foreign assistance from British and Dutch forces, even mercenaries, to confused details concerning the use of ICRC markings in carrying out the rescue. *But hey, this was what legends were made of,* thought Rick, as he savored his cheeseburger at the Embassy cafeteria. "Some kind of crazy world this is, what with the hostage rescue."

The marine Gunnery Sergeant, going by the name of 'Gunny' – pretty original for a marine – sitting across from him managed a muted, "Yeah," as he nibbled at his less-than savory tuna salad: 'today's special'. Then more thoughtfully:

"This narrative has been hijacked by self-serving interests fueled by an international press; looking to sensationalize the plight of the Papuans, and their oppression at the hands of their Javanese colonial-like masters. There is nothing on the international networks about the two Indonesian hostages slashed to death with machetes at the end of the hostage siege by their OPM captors, or the pregnant Dutch captive now recuperating at Gatot Subroto Army Hospital. Not more than ten minutes from here, after being speared in the chaotic ending to a chaotic rescue."

"Telepathy," mused Rick, slyly flashing his white teeth. "Spoken like a 'true marine.'"

The river that gives and takes

Progress was painfully slow. It was as if this river had many minds on how to challenge us: from 'slow and easy to fast and furious', rocky and foaming to soothingly placid, from clear to mossy muddied more reminiscent of a swamp. In some places, thick and spongy green reeds with seemingly predatory intentions would writhe up and wrap around the protruding bamboo ends of our 'magic carpet', snaring the raft and making any forward movement impossible. We spent more time picking our way over partially submerged boulders than riding the rapids, so to speak.

Another iteration of our laborious river journey was carrying our now waterlogged raft over steep and slippery banks when the going got too tough, too rough. In the space of three days, our lazy float down the river had exhausted us more than any overland hike we had experienced so far. From the river, the lush landscape on both banks rose dramatically into steep green slopes. At times, the course of the river veered and returned like a sideways U, lending to the illusion that we were: protected; held captive; and threateningly exposed from all sides. All the same time. From upstream to downstream, and from side to side.

It all became 'too real' when Ramu was thrown from the raft as it plowed into a half-submerged boulder. He narrowly missed smacking head first into a smaller rock that resembled a sharpened arrowhead, but still managed to catch his shoulder on the grooved serrated edge. Ramu not so much screamed but howled. Bakri, who began our water ride with fear and trepidation owing to his lack of swimming prowess, jumped into the turbulent swirling waters, and reached for Ramu. "Always the hero," I yelled without malice or jest. Meanwhile, I clung dazed to our craft, holding on for dear life. I heard nothing but the roar of rushing water slapping up against the rock – and my prone body, which kept forcing my head underwater. The force of the water held the raft precariously in place, allowing me a moment of reckoning as I recovered my senses and reached for Bakri's extended hand. At first it seemed like I would succeed in dragging him, and by extension Ramu, alongside our *Titanic*, until the force of the water turned it sideways and around the boulder that had served as a temporary mooring. I instinctively leapt into the frothing cauldron, mostly out of desperation, and grabbed for the boulder that Bakri had managed to anchor himself to. I could just hear his unintelligible shouts, drowned out by the watery chaos that enveloped us. But it was clear we were in big trouble. I could not see over the rock we had latched onto but surmised our raft and what was left of our belongings were long gone.

After what seemed like an interminable period – more like forever – 'holding on for dear life' without a clue or plan on what came next, it was time for decisive action: I let go and pulled Bakri and Ramu with me. *Bakri is probably none too pleased*, I thought. We held each other tight as we became one with the current. We bobbed like three corks and were soon enough swept over a small waterfall of just a few meters' height into a deeper still pool of water. By now, we were completely exhausted and gasping for breath, but the river gods took pity and deposited us onto a smooth rocky shoal that extended from the bank like a submerged jetty.

I had playfully dug into Bakri on more than one occasion that his heavy black Japanese binoculars circa World War II that hung like an oversized pendent from around his neck conferred the 'dignified air' of a bird watcher. This time, Ramu had nearly drowned the both of them as he clung to and pulled Bakri's head underwater by the strap around his neck. But no matter, Bakri would not relinquish his precious binoculars that he wore as a talisman, and nearly cost him his life. I would later learn that his father had been gifted this precious heirloom from his grandfather, and his father to him.

After crawling on all fours through the shallow water and clawing our way up the grass embankment, we lay shattered; me on my back, eyes closed, taking in what warmth the late-day sun had to offer, ever so mindful that we were still with a heartbeat and just conscious enough. The words that best characterized our depleted physical state were 'wet', 'hungry', and 'sorely bruised'. And yet, Ramu rose above his 'own world of hurt' in recognizing the true nature of our apparent predicament and uttered in his 'now' familiar but still tortured Indonesian, "Maybe we should die here," or at least that was what I think he was trying to convey. I thought, *good, at least he has enough strength of mind not to fall into his own Dani language*, which I could still not grasp except for the odd word; even when of relatively sound body and mind. And there was Bakri, again, 'ever the superman', defying gravity, sitting up and vigorously shaking his head, exclaiming: "*Tidak, tidak, tidak.*"

Some of the flotsam from our long-gone raft had washed into sandy pools carved out of flat rock buttressing the shoreline. Innovation driven by desperate need, hunger, I put to good use my old jungle survival skills from my days playing 'marine' in the jungles of Panama and the Philippines.

I gathered the few empty plastic water bottles we had pilfered as we 'beat a hasty retreat' from the village, used in another life for storing kerosene by the smell of them. I had tied the few with twist caps to each of the four ends of our raft for buoyancy. And now I was putting to test my fishing prowess.

Bakri first sawed through each bottle using his trusty jackknife, making halves: the bottom, and cap-removed top. After a thorough cleaning with sand scooped up from the river floor, used as an abrasive, he then fitted the capped end, minus the cap, into the sawed bottom half, making for a tight fit. But not before adding 'chopped' grub bait mixed with the putrid remains of what was a fish, laced with a finger prick of 'my' blood and weighted down by pebbles. Our contraption proved the 'perfect' trap in capturing scores of small 'minnow'-sized fish darting about the shallows. Our prey was 'just' small enough to enter the neck of the top half, attracted by our chum: one way in and no way out, at least for most.

I was beside myself, boastful even, at my own ingenuity. The satisfying crunch of the fried minnows was beyond delicious. The crunch of brittle bone with every bite was equally satisfying. Even Bakri chimed in, feeding my ego with his praises. "Imagine that, it worked," I shouted up to the heavens as if 'standing my ground in defiance', like *Thor*, the mythical '*God of Thunder*', batting away bolts of lightning. The darkening sky foretelling of the coming rains that would soon leave us without fire. So much for my moment of joyous revelry.

Wamena seething

Icha made an early morning pilgrimage to the 'wet' market located alongside the 'main drag' in the town. Even by Javanese standards, the putrid smells emanating from decaying animal carcasses and rancid meats carried by the smoky fires spewing charcoal embers threatened her own sensibilities and left her stomach churning. Flies that swarmed like gnats into densely buzzing clouds added to the surreal scene she encountered at the local market.

But Icha was no fool. "*Geblek*," she whispered to herself. For today she was joined by Pak Nono in tow, who was now her responsibility, at least until the 'real' bank manager returned from Jakarta. Nono, now bored with his surroundings after only a few short weeks, decided that today he would explore the underbelly of Wamena; feeling the exhilaration and freedom that comes with the prospect of a long weekend holiday without his family, thanks to Indonesian National Day observances. For Icha, however, this was more than an imposition. And so, in her own Javanese way to end this silliness, she steered Pak Nono to this place.

The apocalypse-like scene that greeted Nono was reminiscent of a Marlon Brando movie he had once seen on television; the one about a renegade American soldier during the Vietnam War who went both mad and native (adopted as a god-like deity by a primitive jungle tribe), although he was unsure of which came first: going mad or going native.

A flustered Icha realized that Nono did not regard the sights and smells of the traditional Papuan market with the same revulsion as most of the non-Papuans she had encountered in Wamena. Indeed, he seemed to thrive and take in the fumes, 'so to speak'. As a flustered Icha picked up the pace with Nono trailing behind, she abruptly stopped, turned, and exclaimed: "I cannot do what I need to do with you hanging on and pulling 'invisible strings' to slow me down. I need to get back to my baby. Please excuse me, Nono. I will see you shortly at home."

She turned and quickened her pace, hoping that Nono would slither away and let her get on with her business. She had gone no further than the Padang restaurant sandwiched between a stall selling mostly used clothes and a dusty room from which the few intrepid travelers who managed to circumvent the hurdles, from necessary permissions to transportation in and out of Wamena, when that was even possible, could hunt down Papuan primitive and made-to-look primitive art, but really no less primitive, in the dank and dark confines of the cluttered space.

But no such luck! Nono navigated the odd soldier and sprawl of food stalls that spilled out from the market area and found Icha with her back to the street eating a concoction that little resembled his favorite: 'curry ayam', chicken curry; only chicken feet, nothing but skin and bone, sticking up from the watery reddish curry broth, giving the dish away.

"Things seem tense on the street with the military visible but making itself scarce at the same time." Icha ignored the uninvited interruption and silently fumed over this pesky man who should have better things to do than follow her around, like she was some sort of close confidant.

Finally, after enduring his insistent bantering, she dropped 200 rupiah on the rickety table, turned to Nono and exclaimed: "What is going on in your head that you feel you need to follow me." More statement than question. She immediately regretted her outburst and suggested that Nono might enjoy a walk to one of the local Dani villages, and that she was sure one of the soldiers might be encouraged to provide an escort, for a small sum.

Nono was famished, now wishing he had joined Icha at the *warung* for a meal. He reminded himself he was not starving, only hungry, as he chewed on the minty leaf, imitating his guide. The walk along the scenic, well-trodden path was uplifting. This was the first time he had ventured outside of Wamena since his arrival. He delighted in the greenery that could easily swallow you whole, and the mesmerizing river snaking its way through the distant valley, cradled protectively by steep canyon walls. Even more emphatic was the spectacle of the long-tailed birds with insanely colored feathered plumage as they fluttered in and out of the dense bush. Nono, while not a card carrying 'bird watcher', had seen pictures of the fabled 'bird of paradise', but never had the photos captured the exotic beauty of these creatures, as he now could attest to, in person, and in the wild no less.

At one point along the track, his guide abruptly stopped and pointed to an almost comic-book likeness of some prehistoric bird, and motioned Nono to remain silent and still as a flightless cassowary scurried across the path up ahead. It was huge for a bird, and while not the size of an ostrich, it had a fierce reputation when threatened, befitting is huge size, enough so to outrun and bring down any man, woman, or child. The dark, almost black, matted coat of feathers, and crown of cartilage adorning its head make for easy spotting, if lucky enough to catch a glimpse of this rare and endangered species. Its sharpened elongated claws attested to the slashing damage these creatures inflict, if so inclined. The guide whispered, "*Burung 'kasuari'*, this is not just a bird, but a dinosaur, that will rip your heart out if you are foolish enough to get too close." Nono stood transfixed, and praised Allah for this gift, and for Icha in pushing him to take in this enchanted place.[26]

Another interplanetary traveler as is author, Gordon Ramel shares his love of the 'cassowary'.[27]

Dwarf Cassowary

Returning home in the late morning, having escaped the clutches of Nono earlier in the day, Icha was met by Desi outside the gated entrance, with baby nestled in her cloth sling slung over her neck and fastened to her chest. "Maybe someone has broken in. I was passing on my way to buy some fresh sardines, just arrived by the way, when I heard a pounding, like someone taking a hammer to the wall, and glass breaking."

"How long have you been waiting here?"

Bowed and looking unsure of herself, Desi answered: "A while."

---

26 *Conservation of the Dwarf Cassowary for those so inspired; https://wildark.org/species/dwarf-cassowary/.*
27 *https://beautyofbirds.com/dwarf-cassowaries/.*

Both cautiously entered the yard, scanning for any sign of a 'break-in'. They walked around the house and spotted the glass shards and broken steel ribs among a pile of pulverized concrete to the back; Nono's window to the world, or garden to be exact, had been shattered, and the outside bars yanked from their mooring.

The policeman took notes. After all, this was home to the BNI branch head. While evidence of 'forced entry' was clearly indicated, there was apparently nothing missing, although Icha could not vouch with certainty since she was not so familiar with Nono's personal belongings. Sipping Icha's overly sweetened tea, the officer mused: "How odd that nothing was taken."

To which she added, "I will check again when Pak Nono returns."

Icha settled into an evening routine with a nagging guilt that she needed to make up for her sharp tongue with Nono, shooing him away. He had showed Icha nothing but respect since taking up residence in Wamena. She prepared a special treat of *gado gado*, a delicious Indonesian salad served as the main course, with a peanut-based dressing that her grandmother had taught her to make and swore would bring a smile to even the sullenest of her neighbors for she delighted in cooking for. "Pak Nono will appreciate this," she explained to her baby gurgling and cooing with delight in the crib that the former BNI Director in Wamena had built for her baby when her trader husband went missing; she was already well along in her pregnancy, near 'term' when she came looking for work. She felt better already thinking of how to make up for her rudeness. She would do what she did best: cook up something special.

Dusk turned to night, and Nono had still not returned, and Icha struggled to stay awake late into the night, holding her baby close. She awoke with a start as the rooster made his presence felt, crowing insistently, as he did every morning, shattering the still morning calm. Still in the dark, she gathered her baby up in her arms to feed her, and quietly made her way to the hallway corridor and gently knocked on Nono's door, sensing beforehand the futility of this small and yet somehow reassuring gesture.

Carrying her sense of deep foreboding as if balancing a heavy bag of rice on her head, Icha left her baby with her neighbor Desi as she did every morning and trudged off to the morning market with robotic determination; trying to bring some semblance of normalcy in calming her growing trepidation.

The 'no name'

Commander Norman Bates had a 'nose' for searching out
the hidden 'watering holes' tucked away among the floats and
warehouses along the Jayapura waterfront. He could impress
'Bacchus', the Roman god of 'wine and revelry', with the
copious amount of beer he could consume and still function
with meticulous precision. Tonight was no different as he sat
in the 'nameless bar', built upon slanting stilts looking ready
to collapse into Jayapura harbor; accessible by a lone wooden
plank extending to the shore. For Norman, the danker and
darker, the better. The accompanying stink oozed ambience,
reeking of piss, sweat, vomit, rotting food, and stale beer.
All making for an aphrodisiac-like sensory attraction, if not
addiction. Fortunately for Norman, Indonesia was a treasure
trove of nameless bars. Norman felt very much the cowboy in
some 'Wild West' saloon: going by the name of 'nameless bar'.
The wooden floorboards sagged under the crowded weight
of Sulawesi traders and ships' crews. Seemingly out of place
was the party of mid-ranking uniformed air force officers, who
acted less so as the night wore on.

Just as Norman entertained the thought of joining the
group, he was waved over and asked to join them. "You do not

remember me?" asked one of the officers. Norman was not sure if this was question or statement. But for the sake of appearances, he played along.

"Of course I do."

The officer, a Major by his insignia, slurred his vowels as he introduced Norman to the group: "This is the American navy 'mosquito' Commander from the laboratory on the hill!" Then turning to Norman, he managed in English, "We had the pleasure of meeting when you accompanied your navy construction crew, I think called 'Seabees', looking to build an airstrip on the coast." He continued: "Supposedly for malaria research." Norman was suitably impressed, especially given the inebriated state of the airmen. But he was also acutely aware that the inference, as many in the Indonesian security services speculated, was that the airfield was not so much about malaria research, but rather to collect intelligence on the growing insurrectionist threat to the island province.

Norman, in his relaxed manner and in fluent Indonesian, replied: "Yes, the villages we conduct research in are carved out of the dense jungle along the highly malarious northwest coast of the Papua and populated by recently settled Javanese families participating in the government's 'Transmigration Program'.[28] The purpose of our research is to evaluate new malaria drugs, for which we need immunologically naïve populations who have not previously been infected by the malaria-causing parasite. And so, we work with TNI and LITBANGKES to assess new drug therapies while caring for these Javanese immigrants." He went on to say: "The real

---

28 *https://en.wikipedia.org/wiki/Transmigration_ program#:~:text=The%20transmigration%20program%20 %28Indonesian%3A%20Transmigrasi%2C%20from%20 Dutch%2C%20transmigratie%29,Indonesia%20to%20less%20- populous%20areas%20of%20the%20country.*

beneficiaries being TNI soldiers, sailors, marines, and, yes, airmen, like yourselves, deployed to Papua."

The group sat with mouths open, but speechless, nevertheless! To Norman's surprise, one of the quieter members of the group, possibly more sober, inquired if he was 'one-and-the-same' Norman Bates from Hitchcock's cinematic masterpiece, *Psycho*? He even laughed at his own attempt at comical irony. Norman's first thought was he did not recall giving them his full name, or even his first. But the mood had clearly lightened.

As the night wore on, the major who first encouraged Norman to join the group, now just short of 'dead drunk', asked: "Was the navy doctor in Wamena who disappeared a friend of yours?" Norman simply nodded; suddenly overcome by an overwhelming sense of comradery with those at the table that he could not explain. *Alcohol will do that*, he thought.

"Yes!" Another officer continued in a surprisingly sober tone: "We have been flying missions for the past few months trying to locate your friend and his party. Sadly, with no success. We are still hopeful, but you could crash a 747 in those jungles and never even find a trace of the wreckage."

Norman got serious, fast. "Do you think they could have survived and maybe been taken in by one of the local Dani communities?"

To which the jokester responded: "Even if they survived a crash, the separatists are now no longer taking hostages, but heads. As a Papuan, if you are not separatist, then you are a sympathizer. Otherwise, you are considered a traitor, and your bones are 'ground to a pulp' and used to fertilize the garden."

Making their way in single file across the wobbly wooden plank and up the embankment to the harbor road, one of the airmen, a Lieutenant Colonel, who spent the evening nursing a single glass of 'Coca-Cola' without uttering a single word, caught up with Norman.

"Even though we have given up our search, there is always that chance that your friend will find his way, inshallah. We did find several possible crash sites using ariel reconnaissance photos, but we simply lack the 'lift capacity' to investigate but the most promising. I am sorry about your friend. Please to not take any offense for tonight. We lost some close friends today in a probable crash just north of Wamena and came here to let off some steam." Norman could only utter how sorry he was. *"Yes, as with your friend, we will be lucky to find even a trace of them. Our Indonesian 'Bermuda Triangle' likes to swallow up planes and people."*

"But your plane belongs to the military; can you not pick up any signal?"

"Ha ha, this plane was vintage." He smirked. "It belonged in a museum. Allah be with you."

Freakish encounter

On more than this one occasion during the journey, I had encountered a scene worthy of the movie *Apocalypse Now*, in which Marlon Brando strayed from sanity and served as the epitome of a mind and social order gone mad.

We had forsaken the raging river owing to the heavy rains that transformed the slow-moving waters into a torrent, fearing the river would soon overflow the banks. Drenched, Bakri and I managed to support Ramu as we trudged through the jungle up the steep grade, thrashed by spiney cactus-like needles that added to our shared but individualized misery. "I am not a 'pin cushion'," Bakri croaked, in between sniffles. "I think I am catching a cold".

"And that is a problem for you? A cold would be a welcome relief right about now."

We had become nothing more than sagging flesh on bone. This was it, sapped of all energy and willpower. I had managed after numerous tries to set Ramu's dislocated shoulder, yanking and pulling, fitting back into place, as he sat stoically, seemingly oblivious of the pain. I was not sure if it was just the Dani way, or his way, being able to rise above the all the hurt. All the while thinking: *I am becoming pretty good at this.*

We walked and walked, knowing if we stopped, this would be our ending. My fever now left me shivering almost uncontrollably. Maybe malaria, maybe something much worse. I fought through the fog clouding my thinking. Bakri said nothing. But I knew, as if an invisible tie bonded us together, that he too was on his 'last legs'. Our only consolation was the rain had eased up, giving way to something foreign, out of place here in our jungle. At first I dared not take notice, in case was now hallucinating; my mind playing a mean trick on me. But Bakri then caught the lingering whiff of acrid smoke, as had I. Perhaps? The tantalizing possibility of something up ahead now became very real.

I felt something sticky and warm underfoot. I looked down to see the earth smoldering, as we stood on the periphery of a burnt clearing. I inhaled the distinctive smell of diesel fuel. Bakri moved to free himself from under Ramu's good shoulder and half limped, half skipped up ahead. And then the broken fuselage appeared, folded like an accordion, taking center stage in a crowded debris field. The blades of one of the turbo propellers had imbedded into the ground. Twisted metal fused with barely recognizable body parts resembled a scene from some zombie inspired apocalyptic movie. Only this was real. The dead were too mangled, too burnt, to rise up anytime soon.

Funny how hunger and exhaustion can rob you of all sensibilities and inhibitions. I sat down cross-legged, the ground still warm and smoldering in some places, and picked up a piece of meat that smelled something akin to a Texas barbecue brisket. That is, until Bakri slapped the remnants of a forearm from my fingers. He was 'getting in my face', shouting at me. He succeeded nonetheless in bringing me to my senses.

Bakri, like most Batak, is a devout member of the Batak Christian faith, based on a transplanted German protestant heritage. So what happened next was no surprise, knowing Bakri; he wandered about the charred bits and pieces, mostly undistinguishable, stopping every few steps to mutter a prayer. I was struck by his inner fortitude. How he was now fighting through his own sensory deprivation to prove that the human spirit could rise above pain, hunger, and exhaustion, endured for what now felt a long time. At that moment, I felt more alive, more connected, than anything I had experienced in this and previous lives. While I could not quite fathom 'the father son and holy ghost', I knew we had not been robbed of our spiritual dignity. "How could you not love that."

Both Bakri and I turned as one in the direction of Ramu's distant and yet unmistakable cries calling out our names. We both had forgotten about our friend as we individually processed our gruesome discovery; Ramu had long ago stopped being merely our companion. Our pace quickened as we re-entered the densely packed maze of tangled underbrush, leaving the scorched wreckage and its horrors behind. As we drew seemingly closer to Ramu, other voices could be heard in an apparent back-and-forth exchange. Bakri was the first to break through into a large clearing as I followed closely behind. The source of all the commotion was now apparent. Ramu was ringed by a gaggle of angry, old, as in 'stooped and toothless', Dani women, gesticulating wildly in a pose that would have been comical if not for the rocks they clutched tightly in their hands.

News gets around

"I think you might wish to shut down our work in Papua, at least temporarily," counseled Dr. Narsiem, choosing his words with care. He had just returned from Jayapura, still exhausted, and disheveled from his long and bumpy flight, where he was overseeing a treatment trial for cerebral malaria at the Provincial hospital. Such an admission was not in character with Narsiem, especially so since his research activities depended on active clinical on-site supervision to insure ethical and scientific standards were met.

Captain 'wild' Bill Smarts was, above all, cautious. Not at all what his nickname would have implied. And while he came from the navy's medical research community, there was no illusion, including his own, that his experience in submarine hyperbaric medicine was transferrable to the dicey world of the navy's overseas infectious disease laboratories. But to his advantage, he did benefit from understanding the psyche of the navy's senior leadership, having served in senior-level billets tied to higher echelon Commands; and as such, his assignment as acting Commanding Officer made sense, at least from a headquarters' perspective. He understood, foremost, his task was that of damage control: a 'very' navy reference in keeping a damaged ship afloat. There were just too many questions following Commander Jacques' presumed loss; namely, what was he doing in the middle of nowhere, in the middle of a militant successionist movement no less?

"I think we are all on the same page," he whispered, barely audible. "Let's let things simmer down and see where we stand in the next few weeks. In the meantime, I will ordering a temporary drawdown of our operations in Papua as a precautionary measure, again, until things settle down. My understanding is that TNI is trying to keep up pretenses of normality, what with OPM running *amok*."

Narsiem smiled inwardly, while keeping with his outwardly serious persona befitting the mood, thinking: *I wonder if he knows the origin of the word 'amok' is rooted in the Malay, and by extension, Indonesian, language?*

As if reading his thoughts, 'Wild' Bill continued: "Doesn't 'amok' mean 'frenzied', as if possessed by a demon?"

Of course, Colonel Dowdy had thoroughly briefed him within hours of his arrival in Jakarta. Moreover, the Colonel had already made the decision to recall NMRC-Asia staff working out of the Jayapura laboratory, regardless.

What to do

Seated on the hard wooden bench, Icha could not help but wonder if she was making a terrible mistake in coming here. But she just knew that something was terribly wrong and carried her trepidation on her hunched shoulders. She had waited on Nono's return throughout the day, and finally decided to make her way to the army garrison on the outskirts of the town. After she had been shushed away, ignored, and openly denigrated, as to sully her reputation, by a 'bully' Corporal she had never met before, a Staff Sergeant rushed to the gate and apologized. The Corporal, a Papuan, was summarily called 'to attention' and verbally reprimanded. Icha was then ushered into a small, neat, green building on the compound, ringed by white stones; and led into the hallway leading to the Deputy Commander's office where she was now seated. She was told that Lieutenant Colonel Hassan was out, but to please wait for his return, the Staff Sergeant again apologizing. By this time, Icha wanted only to collect her baby and return home, hoping to restore some comforting normalcy to her life. But she had come too far and was resigned to seeing this through. Shortly afterwards, a group of officers rounded the corner and entered the room immediately opposite her with a lettering that read 'conference room' stenciled to the now open door. The trailing officer, a young woman, stopped and politely gestured for Icha to join them inside.

Still standing, Lieutenant Colonel Hassan introduced himself, and asked everyone to sit. "Do you wish for some tea or water?" Icha wondered if she should say yes. Instead, she shook her head slowly, back and forth. "Please, relax, and take a deep breath, and tell us why you are here." And so a visibly upset Icha proceeded to explain. She felt her heart racing, breathless, as she described not only what had happened, but also her resolute belief that she was responsible for whatever 'jahat' – evil – had befallen Nono. After which, Hassan asked First Lieutenant Rita to drive Icha home. "Please, Ibu Icha, know you are not responsible for any bad. On the contrary, you did good in coming."

First blood

Unable to make sense of the scene playing out before us, Bakri and I were momentarily frozen in the moment. The circle of women, at first glance too frail to pose a real danger, seemed to be constricting around Ramu, like a boa constrictor squeezing its prey. A few latecomers joined in the fun, adding their voices to the chorus of unintelligible but threatening language being hurtled at him. *Better words than stones*, I thought, recalling that childhood saying: 'sticks and stones may break my bones, but names will never hurt me'.

Bakri slowly began to approach crazed mob, ever so slowly, one step then another, at a time. I picked up on his movement and did the same. We were relieved of having to introduce ourselves as our presence was first sensed, then confirmed, as heads swiveled in our direction. I took a breath, held it, then exhaled: "Oh shit!" I felt that kind of 'out of body experience' you only read about, looking down on the scene playing out before us: thinking it resembled something akin to Spielberg's 1970 horror classic, *Salem's Lot*; something about witches.

One of the women stepped away from the rest, and deftly held up a gnarly looking homemade slingshot. I remember mouthing: "She cannot be serious." After all we had endured, to meet our fate at the hands of this 'coven'; a term referring to a gathering of witches. *My god*, I thought, counting 13 in the group. I burst out in laughter, uncontrollably. "Bakri, I think we have stumbled onto a movie set." Bakri turned to look back, as if registering my madness. I only stopped when the first stone struck my forehead; the first of many. All hitting their mark. Bakri fell backward and I fell to my knees. I tasted blood. My last vision was of being pummeled by claw-like fists, until I mercifully lost all consciousness.

Playing detective

Icha spent the evening and next day busying herself as best she could: cleaning the same clean floors, pulling weeds from the small back garden well into the night. The baby too seemed agitated with her insistent crying, sensing maybe that something was not right. She continued to prepare meals for herself and Nono; busying herself, taking out her worry on the linoleum flooring and heavy furniture with mop and broom in-hand.

"The house seems so clean, now with Nono away." Desi, her closest if not only friend, and neighbor, could not help but admire. Not exactly what Icha wanted to hear.

The following morning, she woke to the phone ringing, the landline, and rushed to pick up the call. "*Ibu* Icha, we understand that Pak Nono has gone missing and are being updated by the local military command. Do your best to keep up the residence. Please go to the bank and ask for Ibu Witaya, who is expecting you. She will give you money to cover all expenses." The call from Gindo proved like a calming balm for Icha.

She spent the next few days tidying up an already immaculate house. Her unanswered inquiries at the army garrison for any news left her deeply frustrated. But Icha was nothing if not resolute in finding Nono; when she set her mind to do something, look out! "But where to start," she asked Desi; more than twice her age, with whom she entrusted the care of her infant daughter on most days. Finally, they both came up with a plan: focus on the marketplace and nearby shops in picking up the gossip and rumors of the day. She was sure just about everyone in Wamena had by now heard of Nono's disappearance. And Wamena being Wamena, speculation was sure to be rife.

Icha also understood that the added military presence was more in keeping up the pretense that everything was under control; while in reality, she knew quite the opposite to be true. Friction between the local Dani and mostly Javanese and Sulawesian populous had been on the rise for some time, and now especially so following the taking of hostages and their subsequent rescue. She would need to be careful so as not to stir things up; at least more than they already were.

The lizard I am

The imagery playing in my mind is of a sleek reptile with toughened leathery scales adorned with a boney suit of armor, close to but not hugging the ground. Long hooked claws attached to short, bent appendages: enabling a speedy attack or getaway. A deeply forked tongue capable of sensing, smelling, compensating for poor night vision. An elongated tail, almost full body length, serves as both rudder and weapon that can snap most prey senseless. Fearing nothing but a larger version of the same reptile; and then, only to establish dominance. Feeling nothing except the urge to eat and drift into a restful but alert slumber, until ready again to test the waters: one claw at a time. A 'Komodo', no less, dragon-like lizard. Flies dance as if to a requiem on my rounded snout and hover like a mist, proving nothing more than an irritant.

I had lost all sense of self. Like the old silent 'Chaplin' films, edited so that a single image was merged with the next, and then the next, and so on. But at warp speed, making for an almost seamless projection. But the projector in my head was playing the reel in slow motion. So that this movie became a series of 'stills', one after the other. I was seriously frustrated that I cannot distinguish the lizard in my dreamlike state from myself. Was I that lizard?

Long 'forked' tongue, anvil-shaped head, with claws purpose-built for tearing, or better still, shredding, all held together by my elongated body that extended to my whip of a tail.

The endangered Komodo dragon from the Lesser Sunda islands, Komodo island, East Nusa Tenggara, Indonesia.[29]

I awoke with a sensation akin to getting tied up in the bed sheets during a high fever. Only I had no sheets, and a rough concrete floor for a bed. I first heard and then saw a very wrinkled goblin figure gesturing wildly, with beaded braids obscuring a face except for a very fleshy nose. But the face hovering above me was no aberration. It was an old, as in ancient mariner, 'prune faced' – deeply pitted and wrinkled, woman. Mummified came to mind. Slowly, my field of vision began to widen to take in the surroundings; or as much as my darting eyes would allow without moving my head but a fraction. I tried to utter the word: "*Air*" – Indonesian for water – which came out so softly that I could not hear the sound of my own voice. My parched throat felt like a vice,

---

29 *https://nationalzoo.si.edu/animals/komodo-dragon.*

hurting to even swallow. I ran my tongue over my deeply cracked lips, thinking only to relieve the sting, but instead, setting them on fire.

After lapsing into a deep sleep as opposed to an unconscious state, I woke feeling oddly rested, while still exhausted. Feeling droplets of water from a damp cloth pressed close to my mouth trickle down my throat was like a secret potion, a witch's elixir. Something to be savored. "You are okay! No need to talk," came a soothing voice. The language was English, and the accent was undeniably 'Aussie'. As I began to focus on the face staring down at me, pale and very freckled, accented by loosely hanging strands of red hair, I tried to scratch my memory: *did we get out, where are the others?* But I was safely ensconced in a better place, wherever that was. Closing my eyes, I was free-falling back into a deep slumber, less disturbed this time by the demons and spirits that had found their way into my head.

"You have been drifting in and out for the last ten days."

Well, that explains everything, I thought, somewhat agitated, still no more the wiser.

"My friends?"

"I imagine they are safe, but for now you need to stay quiet. Rest, we can talk later when you feel stronger."

The hard floor under my back had been replaced by bundled palms that now cushioned my body as would a soft mattress. "Can you help me sit up?" I felt many arms grasp my head and then neck and back, until I was sitting in a prone position. Only then did I realize that my 'Aussie' vision was not alone.

"We will bath you now."

"Thanks," I muttered, to no 'one', but 'everyone'.

My new family

I finally managed to hold down some food, nibbling on something resembling fried crickets, and dipping my fingers into a steaming sticky cassava paste with a little coconut milk for flavoring, served up in the fibrous husk of a coconut. My new tribe was eating the same in the far corner of the room; at least a dozen or so that I now counted as my newly adopted family. Or more apt, I was their newly adopted son. All women, all appearing ancient and frail. But looks are deceiving, as I had learned from my first encounter with a tribe. They engaged in animated conversation that felt familiar, like family. I felt safe.

As remote as their respective villages were from one another, from whence they came, their ancestorial home, most shared in the ubiquitous Dani practice of finger amputation(s). These women bore the cultural brunt of a tradition steeped in loss and anguish: a means of coping.[30]

---

30 *https://www.news.com.au/travel/destinations/asia/
inside-the-secretive-tribe-where-women-have-their-
fingers-amputated-when-their-loved-ones-die/news-story/
a25dc2605de1a87d28d8e4533d74247e.*

Contributor: Michele Burgess; Old Dani woman, gnarled hands, amputated fingers, Baliem Valley, West Papua, Indonesia – Image ID: BRXYF7 (Alamy).

I learned from Mola that Bakri and Ramu had waited until both felt fit enough to make for a village across the river and nestled atop a mountain range. Mola had urged them to stay, but Bakri was impatient, and felt that my condition warranted making the arduous journey without delay. "But I worry that the steady rains have made the going treacherous, and the deluge making the river impossible to cross. But your friends were adamant. There is a remote telecommunication tower adjacent to the village, which may enable your friends to signal for help." I asked Mola about the plane that had crashed, and more to the point, why nobody was searching for it. Mola only shook her head.

"The plane may have experienced some mechanical problem and was trying for the abandoned airstrip you may or not remember seeing when you came here, although it is now mostly hidden by overgrowth. The heavy rains obstructed the skies, so we only heard and saw nothing until the explosion. A few of us rushed to investigate. The only saving grace, that good to have come from such

tragedy, is that you would not likely have chanced upon us otherwise. I also do not understand why the army has not come looking for their plane, except maybe for the low clouds and drenching rains that may make any search impossible, at least for the time being."

Mola was an enigma. "Who are you, what are you doing here? You seem at home here, but how can that be?"

To which Mola simply replied, without rancor or condescension: "That is because this is my home."

We talked off and on for hours, days on end. Her story was as captivating as her person. She was older, but not old. A teacher and traditional healer, she had met her husband while studying for her master's teaching degree in indigenous education from the teachers' college at James Cook University in Townsville, Northern Queensland. He was a Dani from Jayawijaya, schooled by the Adventist Missionaries of Australia, and passionate about returning home and making his people strong. His passion became hers. And that was what they did: as husband and wife. They settled in the village of Kataya and, with the help of the Adventist Community in Australia, built a school and life for themselves. The MAF had even built a small clinic staffed by a local nurse, and an airstrip to service this growing missionary outpost. That all ended when someone in the village accused Mola of sorcery shortly after the stillbirth of her only child. The fetus would never have been viable, even if surviving passage through the birthing canal, given the severity of her deformities; so prompting the community to shun this red-haired interloper.

Her husband too had become a pariah among his own people for having brought this red-haired Mola into their lives. Shortly afterwards, the Indonesian military descended on the village and took her husband and many of the able men away for their rumored support of the OPM. When the Australian Embassy in Jakarta made official inquiries, they were told that the Indonesian military had no custody records of any such arrests.

The impact on the community was immediate and profound, with fear and distrust inciting a mood that could have easily turned openly hostile. Instead, there was an exodus; almost the entire community picked up and settled elsewhere. And so it was that the village of Kataya was no more.

Now, a decade later, Mola still called this place her home. She had long ago accepted that her husband would not be returning. But some of the older and elderly women of the village who had lost their men chose to stay with her. Over time, they were joined by others, who had been discarded by their respective communities for supposed offenses, mostly involving sorcery or mischief. Indeed, I had heard anecdotal accounts of women, mostly beyond childbearing age, being singled out and blamed for the 'wabah babi' that had decimated their villages, and paying for such superstitions, sometimes by the ultimate price: their lives.

I was learning that everything 'bad' in the Dani life could be explained, including such calamities as the death of a family member; infestation that destroys a garden; and yes, failure to conceive or give birth to a healthy baby. These women made for 'convenient culprits' for whatever misfortune befell their families and villages. I felt nothing but shame having imagined these women with pointed black hats and broom sticks, taking them for 'witches'.

Casting aspersions as such is by no means unique to the Dani tribe. That lethal cocktail of superstition and ignorance, fueled by those 'very' human traits of greed and envy, manifest into tribal warfare, ethnic cleansings, and genocides; leaving the ethos of that which is mankind in tatters. If not for this place, there would be no such sanctuary for these Dani outcasts, or societal 'throwaways'. "This feels like home." Thinking of Mola, and the refuge that is this place. Not unlike the 'discarded' old women, I too had found a haven.

Icha playing detective

Icha is 'steady' – not bound by 'highs and lows' that might otherwise make up her days; except for when she is cooking – bringing out her passion, unleashing her pleasure. She makes a 'mean' *kari ayam*, with enough heat – *panas panas* – to scorch earth. She prides herself in the simple tasks of keeping a clean house without being overly obsessive.

She wears her moods like tattoos stamped to her forehead: unhidden and raw. Subtlety not her strong suit. Her directness at times interpreted as confrontational. This earned her both respect and mocking growing up. Smart, her inquisitive nature and fearlessness left many in her Javanese community with the impression of an impetuous youth. But now, as an adult and mother, Icha has transformed herself in her search of Nono as a 'wolf in sheep's clothing'.

She wandered around Rasa Nayak, the local market, nibbling on underripe mango slices sprinkled with salt, unconsciously swatting flies that kept landing on her face. This was her third morning on the prowl, listening, trying to pick up any tidbit of news that might be relevant to her investigation. Desi had been a source of encouragement, someone Icha could confide in and plot the next move with. For her part, Desi relished being partnered with Wamena's star 'sleuth', a role she took up with gusto.

From the Dayak tribe, the original aboriginal peoples of West Kalimantan (Indonesian Borneo), much feared in previous times for their headhunting and cannibalistic practices, Desi had found her home, much like Icha, in Wamena; a *'pembantu'*, no less, for Pak Ali Sulimen, Director of the Regency's meteorological station; 'callings' both she and he had aspired over the last twenty years. He loved to jokingly refer to Desi as *Ibuku*, 'my mother', given her way of always fussing, looking after him. Not shy, and supremely confident of 'her place' in the household, she returned the favor by nicknaming Pak Ali Suliman *'petugas cuaca saya'* – 'my weatherman'; in private, of course. Theirs was a formidable relationship that defies conventional stereotyping, benefiting from and befitting the absence of normal 'familial' trappings. The director's wife died young, of complications following the birth of her only child, a son, now finishing his studies in Jakarta. He too referred to Desi as *Ibuku*. – as he would his 'real' mother.

> "He was introduced to a man from Ugem village who sometimes visits Wamena to sell 'kotekas' and fossils embedded in stones from the riverbed. It was the first time he was seen here in many months; not since the hostage-taking. Nobody is sure, but they guessed he was hired by Nono to take him to his village, located where the three mountains, 'Eroma Ugem Kurima', come together."

Icha then read:

> "The trek begins by Jeep, to Kurima. Passengers are jostled and pitched, back and forth, as the 4x4 navigates

the winding road and deep tracks usually muddied by recent rains, leaving them sore, just shy of whiplash; 'stops-and-starts', accompanied by an ensemble of whining engine and screeching gears. This is followed by a grueling half-day hike that offers glimpses of the spectacular Baliem River Gorge, partially obstructed on most days by low-hanging, rain-laden clouds. This tour is a must for the adventure-minded visitor who wants to authenticate their stay with 'the real' Dani experience."

"The brochure reads like an advertisement," commented Desi, mindful that Icha was in need of little encouragement.

"Yes, but I must follow".

Desi continued with: "You should take this news to the army garrison." To which Icha shook her head.

"We will find Nono. I think Lieutenant Colonel Hassan is a good man, but much too busy trying to 'keep a lid on the boiling water threatening to spill over.'" She smiled to herself at her own cleverness.

Desi asked if this 'rumored' guide had a name: "Was he young or old?"

Icha smiled for the first time in days. "I might think you are looking for a husband, or maybe for me."

Unwavering Icha

Desi tried to talk Icha out of taking to her feet and tracking down Nono. But Icha could be obstinate; usually was, once having set her mind on a particular course of action. "But the baby," Desi had invoked.

She now fretted and was consumed with worry as she rocked the infant back and forth in an effort to quiet her. "I should have done more to stop her!"

Icha was not at all enthralled by the beautiful vista opening up before her. Looking across a green valley floor cradled by steep mountains and bisected by deceptively 'calm' running waters; 'twisting and turning' around earthen obstacles, much like a contortionist. Her two guides had spoken little of the natural wonders before them, much to her relief. Icha was in no mood to make small talk. Afterall, she, they, were on a mission.

She struggled to keep her footing on the muddy trail, 'slipping and sliding', as they climbed higher and higher. Her companions seemed far more at ease, even as the youngest was nursing her daughter slung over her back. When Desi had suggested finding a strong male in making for the Ugem village, Icha pooh-poohed the notion that she needed a man; instead, she hired two Dani acquaintances who raised skinny chickens in a rickety pen next to a traditional dwelling, just on the outskirts of the town. She often spoke with the mother and daughter about the local goings-on. They were a reliable source of information, whom she could trust. More importantly, they were Dani, claiming patriarchal family ties with the destination she had intended.

She wiped the smudged laminated BNI ID card with her sleeve. She thought how austere he looked in his postage-stamp-sized photo, not at all like the Nono she knew. He took every opportunity to ingratiate himself with a smile, especially with strangers: no matter they be squatting on filthy mats in the market on 'selling days', trying to peddle old meat or fish that tasted as vile as it looked; or with the prim-and-proper staff he oversaw at the bank. He was curious, almost like a puppy, delighting in the attention and goings-on around him. These thoughts were running like film edits through her mind; all the while thinking back to the day she sent him scurrying off, because she could not be bothered. Icha then reminded herself that she could not think of Nono in the past tense. She would find and bring him home.

Following closely behind her guides, an impatient Icha 'willed' them to go faster, just as an exposed root on the path they were following reached out and grabbed her foot, sending her sprawling near the ledge of the deep ravine they were skirting. She would have easily gone over the side if not for the quick hands of her two companions, forcefully grabbing her by the arm. Shaken, she collected the contents of her rucksack that had tumbled out onto the ground and proceeded to berate herself loudly for the rest of the crossing.

"*Pernahkah Anda melihat pria ini*" – have you seen this man – she repeated over and over to anyone and everyone she encountered, holding Nono's photo between two extended fingers. Tami and daughter Kat, who had guided Icha to Ugem, politely cautioned that it was better to make proper introductions, first with the community leaders, then individually with members of the village.

Icha finally acknowledging with a nod that directness and forcefulness of her overtures was a bit excessive. Her zealousness was proving intimidating and putting those she hoped of engaging on the defensive. The Dani were proving resistant to 'her' charms, even with Tami and Kat in tow. The stone-cold stares that met her inquires was disconcerting; not so much a peak at Nono's photo.

Icha took notice that Ugem was surprisingly clean, at least from her frame of reference with the Dani 'quarters' in and around Wamena. Oval-shaped huts were laid out in an orderly fashion, the walls of which were adorned with decorative touches of tribal art. There was a stick fence reinforced with even larger sticks that could not be interpreted as anything other than a stockade, providing for a sense of protection and dimension to the village. The terraced gardens just beyond the walls appeared well tended, with sections demarcated by whatever was being grown, be it vegetable or legume. This was not at all what she had expected, defying her expectations as to how the Dani lived and worked.

By late afternoon, the setting sun finally managed to peek through the clouds over the expansive valley, illuminating the village with the soft glow of twilight. Icha and her small entourage gratefully accepted the offer of the 'guest lodge' and settled in for the night. "Tomorrow morning, it is better that you stay here, and let us ask the whereabouts of Nono." For that, Icha found herself relieved as she dug into the boiled chicken and sweet potato. She was famished. Shortly afterwards, as Icha drifted in and out of sleep, the suckling of Kat's baby tugged at her conscience.

"Am I so bad a mother as to leave my own child, even if for just one evening?" But she knew she had no choice.

Separated by water

The jungle spit an emaciated Bakri out into the clearing. There was little let-up in the rain, steadily falling since before the previous night had turned today. He sloshed his way up to the main structure sitting atop the knoll to where I had taken up residence. His entrance, sudden and unexpected. His appearance, more an aberration: pale and hunched, more cartoon-like, as in my childhood favorite, *Casper the Friendly Ghost*, in *español*. His clothes were soaked through, torn and tattered. The few women in the far corner of the room paused, momentarily distracted from their rhythmic pounding of cassava leaves, a step before boiling to rid them of their toxicity.

I looked beyond Bakri to the entrance, expecting Ramu to follow forthwith.

But instead it was Mola that then appeared, moving slowly up behind Bakri so as not to startle him, and wrapped her arms around his neck and hugged him from the back. Just in time, as he swooned, then collapsed backwards into her arms. She then scooped him up and lay him beside me.

Days later, Bakri was fit enough to talk. "Rarely had a day passed when we were not slogging through pools of stagnant water and wet undergrowth, feasted upon by leeches, engorged to the point of exploding. Each night, we pried them from each other's bodies as part of our daily ritual. Ramu worked his magic, extracting a soothing salve that oozed from tree bark. Who would have guessed. It was more than good fortune that Ramu possessed the wisdom of a sage in the ways of traditional herbal remedies. It was 'Providence'!"

Although devoid of any spiritual inclinations, I too recognized Ramu as a 'saint'. So often I had been spared the worst of fevers, rashes, and bloody 'shits', by his medicinal interventions.

"So, where is the cavalry?" I asked, knowing this 'Americanism' intelligible only if you had been brought up with and bought into the lore extolled by the old 'John Wayne' styled 'cowboy and Indian' movies. It was the notion that the forces of good would always prevail and come to the rescue. But for sure, the duplicity of this phrase was not lost on me; the Indians slaughtered by the thousands and forced from their ancestral lands, by the cavelry, no less.

Rain still beating down on the thatched roof, Mola led everyone in a prayer to celebrate Bakri's safe return. And while I am 'not' the praying type, I recognized the likelihood that our improbable survival could not be so simply put down to luck or grit, although we'd been generously gifted of both.

She even dipped into her 'stash' doled a small helping of coarse coffee grinds from a small satchel into a boiling pot of water. I took delight in letting the aromatic steam waft into my nostrils as I inhaled deeply; bringing on a sensory overload that sent electricity through my every nerve. The adjectives, 'addiction' and 'reawakening' come to mind as I conjure up the 'Nescafé' commercial illuminating the euphoric yet calming sensation, before even taking the first morning sip. And that is something, since I do not know the difference between an adjective and adverb. Ha ha!

Bakri recounted his separation from Ramu, who let himself be swept downstream holding onto a thicket of tree limbs wrapped in vines, in the hope of reaching the opposite bank. There was now no trace of the large boulders and debris that had snagged our craft and brought a quick end to our rafting expedition. There was also no evidence of the vines' bridge that Mola had steered them toward before seeing them off almost a week earlier. Bakri finally gave up trying to find a shallow section from where to ford the river, knowing that any attempt to do so would not end well.

Maybe most surprising was that Bakri had entrusted his prized possession, his binoculars, to Ramu. We did not need to speak of the bond that had formed between the three of us over the past weeks and months. We had now become a brotherhood, forever linked, no matter the final outcome; Ramu's absence only served to strengthen and remind us of that bond.

Looking first to Mola and then to Bakri, I really wanted to say what I was thinking: no longer feeling the need to be saved. But in doing so would have left me at a loss in trying to explain what I could not, and, more telling, reveal. That I had found some peace, here, together with my 'new family'. I felt the stirring that come with 'want' and desire: of Mola. Instead, I strung together words into a sentence to appease all our sensibilities: "Ramu will assuredly find his way to the village, without us like a 'ball and chain' holding him back." Maybe I said that more for myself, feeling a little guilty, paying scant enough attention to the welfare of this man who befriended, protected, and loved us, as we did him. My own feelings were confused, not sure whether to think of him 'as of this world or having passed on to the next. Maybe he was already sharing in a 'Pig Feast' with the ancestors.

Later that evening, sitting with Mola as Bakri slept the 'sleep of the dead' after slurping down our meal of pounded pumpkin seeds boiled into a facsimile of a mushy porridge, minus the oatmeal, milk, and sugar, I told her about John, and how undeserving he was of the 'pilot' title we had previously bestowed before his name. But since I was feeling a twinge of guilt, I figured I should own up to how we abandoned him to his fate back in the village from whence we came; of course, as we were forced to flee because of the very nature of his transgression. Mola said nothing and kept to a face that was expressionless, impossible to read. That night, and for the first time since being taken in by 'my new family', I found sleep elusive.

Nowhere to turn

Ringing, repeatedly, Icha kept calling late into the night. She had returned from Ugem and Kurima, finding no sign that Nono had visited either. She had spent the second night away in Kurima, hoping that maybe someone had seen him and his guide before setting out for Ugem. But like with the villagers of Ugem, Tami and Kat got nowhere. It was not so much that nobody had remembered them, but that their inquiries elicited only nervous stares. One old woman seemed eager to approach them as they were departing Ugem, calling out in 'not' a hostile manner, but she was quickly shushed away by a group of men that gathered like a shield in front of her. One of the community elders did come forward and spoke the word *gila*, as if to apologize for the interruption. Otherwise, they were paid scant attention, and even less succor in seeking out information.

Finally, her call was picked up on the first try, early the next morning. Pak Gindo coughed and attempted to clear his throat. "Icha, is that you? Only you would call me at this early hour," he said, but in a teasing manner. She stripped herself of that shroud of invincibility she used to cloak herself when absorbed in self-doubt and laid out before him an abbreviated version of all that had happened in her search for Nono over the past few day.

"Pak Gindo, I feel as if I have failed Pak Nono."

She continued, "I went straight to the army garrison upon my return to Wamena but was not able to speak with anyone on what I had learned, including Lieutenant Colonel Hassan. Someone needs to do something."

"Please, leave this to me for now. Please! I will speak with people from the bank who have senior-level connections with the military and can even place a call to the President if need be. You have done enough. Now, leave this to me." A relieved Icha was about to thank Gindo, when he interrupted her: "I am being treated for a condition that affects my lungs, emphysema, so I will not be returning to Wamena. My home in Jakarta is too big for just me. If you do not mind taking care of an old and sometimes difficult man, I want you and your beautiful baby girl to come and stay here. I would so appreciate if you would consider this as a favor to me. This is not about me helping you, but you me."

For Icha, making decisions was more about small things she could control in her life, like what to cook for the evening meal, or how to stretch the household allowance so she could tuck away a few rupiah for the baby. She allowed that Gindo's offer was more than she could have hoped for if she allowed herself such fanciful indulgences. So why was she left strangely unsettled at the opportunity to improve her circumstances, and that of her daughter?

Desi merely looked on as a spectator, letting Icha ramble on and on. After describing her failed attempt to find Nono and return him safe and sound, she recounted her conversation with Gindo. She did so while attempting to conceal her all-too-obvious anxiety, as she nervously plucked at the woolen strands of her fraying pullover.

Goodbyes

Despite protestations, Commander Norman Bates was resigned to being called back to Jakarta, with the rising tensions in the province now spilling into the usually tame streets of Jayapura. Yesterday's machete attack that left two soldiers with serious injuries took place in the light of day, and not by some alcohol-crazed Papuan. The details were sketchy. But enough so that the entire town and surrounding communities, including Sentani, were left on edge; with most shops and government offices closed for the day, a Friday, making for a long weekend. He made excuses to remain an extra week since the recall order was given, to oversee the few remaining Javanese and Papuan staff in securing the laboratory for what all presumed would be a temporary closure, or so Norman hoped.

The interruption would most certainly impact the scientific oversight of ongoing research activities, especially those focused on evaluating anti-malarial therapies in newly resettled Javanese migrant communities along the coast, accessible only by boat. Norman found his smile in recalling the consternation and obstinance of 'not just a few' navy 'bean counters' to the idea of procuring rubber dinghies to ferry staff across the coral-laden shallows, to and from shore. Norman laughed as he recalled someone raising the absurd notion that such a purchase might be counted against the navy's 350-ship congressional authorization. Fortunately, Captain Lavender intervened with an injection of common sense.

On Sunday, three days before their scheduled departure, compliments of Merpati, Norman, along with the two remaining Javanese research staff, checked into the Suni Garden and Lakeside Hotel in Sentani.

Norman occupied himself over the next few days hunting down traditional 'ikat' from some of the villages around Lake Sentani; 'ikat' being both process and finished piece, ascribed to the application of natural vegetable dyes to non-synthetic yarns of cotton or silk that are then woven into much prized textiles.

To suggest that these 'beyond intricate' art forms are merely local handicrafts would be a gross misrepresentation of the intrinsic worth of these patterned fabrics, highly valued by connoisseurs of the trade. So much so that a quality 'ikat' with the necessary pedigree can fetch tens of thousands of US dollars; with earnings going to the usual middlemen, and a pittance to the women who learn this craft at a young age and toil laboriously for months in turning the dyed yarns into works of art worthy of a gallery hanging. So distinctive are the designs, specific to villages, provinces, or regions, that someone with Norman's earned expertise from years of collecting could connect a pattern to a particular location. But what really sets 'ikat' apart as truly an 'Indonesian' art form, aside from just a handful of countries like Laos, is that there is 'no inside out', if fitted into dress, like a sarong, or just a wall hanging. The simple and yet intricate designs reflect local folklore and spiritually rooted mysticism, sometimes bordering on the frightening, as well as scenes of everyday life in the village, and of nature; so skillfully woven as to make it impossible to distinguish the 'front from the back' and the 'back from the front'.[31]

Laden boxes are stacked high in every room of Norman's Jakarta home, spilling out into the hallways, make for a collection that could easily grace the walls of the famed 'Smithsonian Museum'. Hundreds if not thousands of '*ikat*', each with their own remarkable story, making him: '*ikat* rich and dollar poor'.

Young woman from Kambera, Sumba, wearing an ikat garment and with the 'warp' for a cloth tied and ready for dying, 1931.[32]

31   *https://en.wikipedia.org/wiki/Ikat#.*
32   *https://en.wikipedia.org/wiki/Ikat#/media/File:COLLECTIE_ TROPENMUSEUM_Ikat_techniek_in_Lewa_Kambera_ Oost_Soemba_en_vrouw_met_haarkam_(hai_kara_jangga)_ TMnr_10014278.jpg.*

Collection Ann Hecht. Photo by J Marshall; detail of a warp ikat decorated hinggi from Sumba Indonesia – Image ID: AP776G (Alamy).

"Colonel Simanjuntak will meet with you now." A Staff Sergeant ushered Norman into a large anteroom, adjacent to an even larger office.

"Commander Bates, it is good to see you. Please, join me for a coffee or tea, or water if you would prefer."

"Coffee would be great. Thanks for taking the time to see me," replied Norman.

After the exchange of polite pleasantries with an informality born of familiarity, Norman explained that he wished to pay his respects to the Provincial Military Command before his departure the next day; although his visit was in fact choreographed from Jakarta, he deliberately omitted that from his introductions. Norman elaborated that the laboratory closure was only temporary, and hopefully research operations would resume in the coming months if not weeks, after tensions in the restive region had calmed. He went on to disclose that he would temporarily be relocating to Biak, an island to the northwest of Papua in the Pacific: 'only a skip and a hop away'; more of a stop-over for the Merpati flight flying in and out of Papua, to explore malaria research opportunities having to do with a recent surge of cases. Norman suspected the Colonel already knew of this plan, since the local Command would have had to sign off on the approval process, given that Biak fell within their administrative jurisdiction.

While Colonel Simanjuntak's consummate English-language skills were not to be derided, Norman continued in Bahasa Indonesian. "Is there any news from the Baliem Valley?" he asked, knowing full well that 'search', now 'recovery', operations had been called off some time ago.

"I am sure you heard by now that one of our planes went missing last week on a routine reconnaissance flight." And after a deliberate pause, the Colonel continued: "Anything is possible." And to interject a little friendly humor into the 'goodbyes', he asked Norman how his mother was, alluding to Hitchcock's *Psycho* thriller, in which the character 'Norman Bates' is cursed with dissociative identity disorder (DID) and assumes multiple personalities, including his long-diseased mother and her penchant for killing guests at the family's 'Bates' Hotel. Lovingly, Commander Norman to this day still resented his parents' whimsical indulgence in saddling him with a name that always drew smiles, and subtle and not-so-subtle references to his fictional namesake.

As Norman left the Command compound, he glanced at the departing C-130 taxiing to the runway, lining up for take-off, engines revving to a high-pitched whine, and then lift-off. The plane made a graceful arch once airborne and made off in south-easternly direction. Norman could only imagine the destination, but strongly suspected it was carrying additional troops to the now volatile Jayawijaya.

A river too high

The insistent rains were finally letting up, with peeks of blue sky and rays of sunshine unveiled through the prism of thinning clouds that continued to cast wide shadows. I was sensing, maybe owing to Mola's quiet reserve that was bordering on awkward silence, as of late, that we just might be overstaying our welcome. She was spending more and more time tending to everything but my insatiable and most obvious attempts to attract her attention; like a smitten schoolboy clumsily fencing for his teacher's affection. I was even drawing audiences of gawking women who were entertaining themselves by my silly amorous antics. This was so not like me. I had worked hard over the years perfecting the art of 'aloofness', or so I thought, having failed at the one relationship that mattered in my life.

Bakri and I began to confront our limited options: to stay or go. "Why would we be any more successful at crossing the river now? We would surely face the same dangers you and Ramu risked, not more than a few weeks ago. Yes, Ramu throwing himself into an 'avalanche' of cascading waters to cross over to the other side spoke to his resoluteness, courage, or maybe desire to join the ancestors. I am just not sure I am ready for the afterlife."

"We should have heard something by now if Ramu had managed to reach the far shore, or any shore for that matter." I purposely stayed clear of any connotation suggesting he may not have survived his plunge.

Thinking to myself: *now I am believing in the spirits of the forest. How could no one be looking for the downed wreckage and her crew?* I said as much to Bakri, who remained stoically optimistic. But while the question irked me, the answer was obvious. Our world, wherein lies what 'was' Kataya, is the proverbial 'needle in a haystack'; most assuredly so to those looking down from the skies at this vast and impenetrable expanse.

"There could be dinosaurs roaming the jungles, and nobody would know," I remarked to Bakri on more than a few occasions. Influenza, the probable culprit of our *'wabah babi'* outbreak, likely struck down at least a quarter of the Dani population in Jayawijaya, at least from our preliminary estimates in the field. So remote is this region that the introduction of a human or swine influenza virus, or a combination thereof, 'could have, would have, should have', devastated this vulnerable population; especially so having never been previously exposed to either the virus or the soldiers who likely brought this 'gift' with them from distant Java.

Nagging me still was the possibility that we were completely off track, drawing on conclusions from 'assumptions', that could easily fall like a 'house of cards'.

It was no different than the horrific toll wrought upon the indigenous peoples of the Americas by the scourges of smallpox, measles, and, of course, syphilis; in the benign genocide to which European colonizers were most culpable. America's 'manifest destiny' was no less advanced by these same diseases during successive military campaigns intended to rid the 'Wild West' of its 'original' inhabitants, even more so than bullets. This, and similar stories played out with little to no fanfare throughout much of the North and South America continents.

The decimation of newly discovered tribes in the Amazon basin during the 20th century tells a similar story, that of contact with peoples' living in extreme isolation deep in once impenetrable jungle communities. Not so much unlike the Dani, tribes once 'untouched' by outside influences made more vulnerable to the scourge of disease by their exposure to pathogens not previously encounter, accompanying invasions of explorers and latter-day plunderers.

Time to go

Mola is no 'mother hen' roosting over the women who make this settlement home. She tends to those around her with empathy and respect. I have never heard her speak out in anger or raise her voice above the din. She exudes neither authority nor controlling tendencies. And yet she is revered by the community.

"Mola, please accept our thanks, and thanks to God that we came upon you." Bakri was of late falling back on the deities for all the 'good, bad, and ugly' in his life; less of a reawakening and more of a revivalism.

She once alluded once to her place in the settlement, amongst the community: "I have not stayed on here under false pretenses, looking to fulfill any spiritual calling." She then quickly changed the subject, elaborating no further.

We prepared ourselves, both in spirit and body. Bakri and I had put on weight and added a little 'spring to our step' as our window of departure drew nearer. Now it was time to go.

As we followed the worn trail, accompanied by Mola and two of her flock, I could not help but wonder: *what if?* I found myself second-guessing our decision to leave; not only as to the 'why', but to the 'where'. I was thankful that our path bypassed the wreckage and body parts that had been likely scavenged by the creatures of the forest. Maybe we should have buried what was left of those onboard, done more. I composed myself. I had not given in to contemplating their last moments, until now.

The sound of rushing waters grew louder as we traversed the rocky terrain running parallel to the river, catching glimpses of bright sunshine glinting off the waters through gaps in the dense foliage. We finally came to a stop and proceeded to pick our way down the steep embankment. At this point, I was on shaky legs, and felt my newly found energy ebbing away. I really did not want Mola to see me like this. I stood up and steadied myself after crawling past the edge of a deep crevasse and felt a hand reach out, taking mine in hers.

The waters swirled around the large boulder that easily accommodated the five of us. The noise of the roaring river was now deafening. "This makes no sense," Bakri yelled above the roar. Even at this safe distance, looking out onto the river was like a premonition of doom. I imagined myself a wet rag, 'tumbling' in a washing machine. This made no sense. We were shortly drenched by the spray and spit of the foaming waters. Our plan to cross the river by lassoing a rock on the far side no longer seemed daunting, but suicidal.

The women had spent the last week fashioning twine from vines hanging from the towering trees. Made me wonder if this was my *Tarzan* moment. They even wove small hand loops into the improvised rope to hang from in pulling ourselves forward, hand over hand. The only alternative to this foolhardy attempt would be following the river downstream; but we had neither the stamina nor the prospect of finding any villages anywhere nearby, in that direction. What began as an eagerly anticipated gambit when starting out this early morning, finding our way out of this endless maze leading to nowhere, had gone 'belly up'.

Bearing witness

Ramu was no creature of solitude. He had family, a village, and his friends, not least those left behind in that place of 'old women'. But he intuitively knew that now was not the time to show himself. Quite the opposite, he wished to run as far as he could from this place. He had seen enough!

He was well ensconced on an adjoining peak, offering good vantage of the entire ridgeline. His attention was focused on the village, adjacent to the twisted steel remains of a tower; felled not so much like a tree but toppled by some kind of explosion. Ramu figured it was used for communications, as was the tower back in Ninia.

Able to forage for food easily enough, even finding mushrooms that grew among slippery mosses carpeting the rocky outcrops. There were no 'picky eaters' to contend with. Jacques could be especially difficult when it came to food.

He arranged stones into a small walled structure and affixed clumps of twigs, mud, and moss; a reasonably dry shelter offering protection against the rain and wind. A cushiony layer of moss fashioned as a mattress provided adequate insulation from the cold ground. He resisted the use of fire for cooking or warmth, not looking to draw attention to his presence.

Ramu 'clicked' and silently scolded himself in failing to notice earlier the 'watchtower' on the far end of the plateau, near to where the women of the village toiled in the well-tended gardens. He instinctively laid himself out flat on his back, pulling brush he had collected for his shelter over himself, hoping to blend in with his surroundings. The 'climbing' Dani 'warrior' pulling himself up using interwoven vines ringing the tall stalk to grip onto; carrying his paraphernalia – that which to make war with – on his back. He would have to be more careful in staying out of sight.

Photo Contributor: Paul70128; Yai Mabel, Anemaugi Village War Chief, Kurulu District at Baliem Valley, Papua, 2006.[33]

His precautions were well warranted as he spied an armed group, men, women, and even children, sporting long guns, bows and arrows and other killing implements. They dressed in tattered clothes, some in army fatigues, and carried themselves as 'Big Men', roaming about the village at will. Were it not for the sequence of events he observed over the past few weeks, Ramu would by now have introduced himself and his plight. After all, that was the purpose in making for this village; a quest that nearly cost him his life.

---

33 *https://en.wikipedia.org/wiki/Baliem_Valley#/media/File:Kurulu_Village_War_Chief.jpg.*

An old man, a Dani villager, took to using his fists one day in striking one of the interlopers, for which he was repeatedly struck about the head and shoulders with what looked to be a heavy stick. Ramu had turned away, not willing to 'lay eyes' on such a cowardly act: not those of a warrior. He feared the 'ancestors' would almost certainly take their revenge, even on those like himself, mere spectators to such an affront. The man's prone body was still on the ground when he dared look again. But now absent were those who had perpetrated this crime. *They cannot be Dani*, he thought.

Some days later, Ramu heard the distinctive 'swoosh, swoosh' of rotary blades as the chopper made a descent, drawing near to the toppled tower, then settling down beside it. Ramu counted eight men wearing bright orange jumpsuits capped by white helmets. There were also three heavily armed TNI soldiers that joined in the exodus. Large gear bags followed, along heavy sacks that looked like rice, tossed from the sliding door. Over the next week, a heavy-lift helicopter made numerous deliveries of equipment and supplies. Steel girders were flown in, attached by thick cables tethered to the underbelly, and expertly lowered and maneuvered into place. Ramu watched through binoculars, mesmerized.

He was finally ready to introduce himself; thinking these foreigners, but still Indonesian, would understand and help Jacques and Bakri. But again, he inexplicably held back, sensing it better to wait a little longer.

The 'men in orange' had set up camp just a short distance from the village, near to the fenced terraced gardens. The children took cautiously at first to the newcomers. But their curiosity won out. They dared each other in innocent play to run in circles around the 'men in orange'; who reciprocated by sharing sweets and handing out plastic whistles.

The discovery of a blueberry patch made for a scrumptious treat of juicy tartness; a definite improvement from the fragile diet of tubers, mushrooms, and assorted grubs, that had long lost their appeal: even to a Dani from Ninia. So preoccupied was Ramu scraping the berries from the dew-brushed bramble in bunches, filling his leather pouch and belly, that he was slow to pick up on the screams and gunfire from where the 'men in orange' had set up camp. The scene now being played through his binoculars told of a massacre.

The lapse of only a few minutes between the first shots being fired, reverberating against the rocky canyon walls, until he was able to safely position himself to take in the slaughter that unfolded was enough to spare Ramu of the worst. But what he saw through his 'glasses' was enough to leave an indelible impression that he would never be able to shake free of. While he missed the initial barrage of gunfire, he was not so lucky to escape the spearing and cutting of the 'still moving' bodies, as the ignoble 'freedom fighters' finished what they had begun.

Surreal! The newly planted OPM flag with its distinctive white star set against red backdrop and blue and white horizontal stripes lent unsettling pause and explanation to all that Ramu had witnessed. And while he was not prone to overthinking the aspirations of the 'freedom movement', the flag stood emblematic to the future of his tribe, his people. Ramu caught a fleeting glimpse of a lone man only partially dressed in his bright orange jumpsuit, running, falling, and sliding, his way down the mountainside, seeking out the protection in the dense flora on the valley floor.

Ramu's understanding of ritualized, small-scale warfare, was both prescribed and ascribed to by Dani custom: spoken from elder to warrior; and father to son. Much is about the 'righting of an insult, by returning an insult'. The 'art of warfare' requires much preparation and posturing, with warrior prowess put on display and celebrated in traditional dance leading up to hostilities. There is honor to living and dying by the 'old ways'. And while there are token deaths, most battles are over before they have begun, with notably little bloodletting. But as if defying traditional expectations where a battle was proposed and agreed upon by both aggrieved parties, this act of savagery left Ramu feeling only empty, his culture defiled.

News of Nono

"Are you there?" Desi shouted, while banging on the old pot hanging from the gate with the heavy mallet tethered by a leather strip knotted through a hole bored into steel. "I am not sure where she is," she said, turning to Tami and her daughter Kat, who demurred in calling attention to themselves as they hung back in the tight alleyway winding itself through the neighborhood of walled properties. "Can you come back before noon? She is usually home by late morning."

Tami looked hesitant and stammered: "It might be better if Ibu Icha met us at our home. She may wish to buy a chicken and some eggs."

Desi replied that she would inform her friend, while trying not to 'give away' or 'give into' her excitement; her curiosity now clearly piqued.

Icha drew in a deep breath and slowly exhaled, as if it might be her last. The scrawny chicken she came back with was stewing away, the smell wafting through air, wreaking sensory havoc on anyone so fortunate to catch a whiff of her 'special' dish, her grandmother's version of a Javanese favorite, *semur ayam*. Shallots, garlic, tomatoes, ginger, and lemongrass are first sautéed in oil, followed by the chicken, potatoes, and nutmeg. After being brought to a boil and then allowed to simmer until tender, the whole is poured onto steaming rice.

She and Desi knew they needed to pass on the information shared by Tami and Kat. Icha even bought three chickens to encourage the two to share all they had learned. When she failed to reach Gindo with the news, Desi came up with the idea of a meal featuring Icha's 'pièce de résistance'.

The difference between preparing and hosting a meal was not lost on the two. That the invitations were accepted created near panic in the kitchen, leaving Icha to fuss and fidget nervously in getting the 'right' balance of spices to a boil. Desi had haggled at the overpriced grocery stall that catered to the small non-Papuan community. All the while, Icha lorded over the cooking, making the most of the ingredients on hand: improvising and substituting as necessary. Gindo had often chuckled at her creativity in 'making something from nothing'. She was masterful! Desi meanwhile excelled in taking directions as her apprentice chef.

First Lieutenant Rita joined the Lieutenant Colonel and arrived promptly, while Ali the 'weatherman' was late as usual: "I had to bathe and change clothes first". They were later joined by the Grand Police Commissioner Adjutant of Kepolisian Negara Republik Indonesia contingent for the Jayawijaya District, Lieutenant Colonel Kumi-Krispe Kuri. A Papuan raised in the picturesque Javanese city of Bogor, where his father taught at the Bogor Agricultural University, he was close to both Ali and Gindo. When all were seated, Icha offered a nod for the feast to begin. But rather than wait until mouths were empty and stomachs full, she took a breath and held it, then launched into a spiel of all they had learned, especially since yesterday, following their visit with Tami and Kat.

"And how did you come to learn this," probed Kumi-Krisp; not in an unkindly way. Icha had anticipated this line of inquiry and was ready with a practiced response, until Desi got there first.

"That is not so important as to what you do with this information. Our friends learned from their friends, so it is impossible to know the source of this news." Desi clearly relished wearing her newly minted badge marking her as master sleuth, figuratively of course: a role that fit her perfectly.

"Icha's *semur ayam* should be honored as a national treasure," Kumi-Krispe offered without prompting.

Hassan laughed. "You have been here too long." The two strolled together on the darkened road, with Rita holding back, in the company of the police escort who trailed the Grand Police Commissioner Adjutant, whenever and wherever. His was a posting intended to soothe long-simmering tensions in the Regency and distrust between police and local inhabitants, especially so in Wamena. But of late, his supposed 'calming' presence only seemed to stoke the passions of Papuan and non-Papuan alike. That the OPM had now embarked on a strategy of raising their profile through increasingly violent exchanges was exacerbating the tensions all around. More ominous was that dissent to Jakarta's rule, expressed but not acted upon, had now risen to open defiance.

The night was silent, except for their quiet conversation. The only interruption was the dogs yelping behind high walls, sure to discourage trespassers. "What should we make of their story?" asked Hassan, showing his deference to the Grand Police Commissioner.

"I think we need to pursue any and all leads. Nono is gone now for over two weeks. We have already known that Nono departed Wamena with a guide from Ugem. We too visited the village as did Icha; and as Icha, learned nothing. The guide who goes by the name of Baiya has not been heard of since he first traveled to Wamena some weeks past, or so say the villagers. With no other leads other than what we learned tonight, it is imperative that we get some reconnaissance on the ground. No easy feat." Hassan questioned if they should not first interrogate the informants. "We cannot risk frightening these women into 'silence'. Yes, Icha and Desi are much better suited to manage the trust and confidence they have earned, certainly more so than the military or police." Hassan nodded in agreement, rubbing his hands together for warmth. There was a noticeable chill as temperatures plummeted in the dead of night, as was the season.

Retribution

With heart racing, he felt a tightening in his chest forcing short and rapid expulsions of air, to the point of hyperventilating. His every instinct was to run, and as far away as possible. But his circuitry was wired to override the impulse and stay put. The weather had again deteriorated; what began as a light drizzle had turned into steady rain. But he hardly noticed.

Ramu knew with certainty that there would be swift repercussions for what he had witnessed, but he was not prepared for what followed. The first helicopter had broken through billowing cloud formations that shrouded the highest reaches of the twin peaks. Hovering as if caught in a time warp, first over the campground, then village, before rising and making off in the direction from whence it came; like some predatory 'big bird', scared off before it could swoop down on its prey. There had been no attempt to retrieve to the bodies since the OPM left. The village too, emptied out shortly thereafter. But there had been a slow return of the inhabitants in the last few days.

It was not yet first light when he heard the swishing sounds of rotor blades directly above him. He braced himself in his small earthen fort, expecting the worst. Ramu had been schooled by Christian missionaries whose underlying motivation was to 'save souls, spread the gospel'. But he never abandoned the Dani belief that in death, the spirit lingers and can be counted on to sow grief and despair among the living: the cause of all misfortune, except maybe for witchery. Described as a 'malicious maggot' by translation, such evil must be driven away; hence the tradition of 'finger amputation', or *Ikipalin* in the Dani language; long since outlawed in Papua (and neighboring Papua New Guinea), but still practiced in the Baliem Valley.

Ramu wondered if his family, extending to most of his village, had already given him up as dead, and if so, had performed the customary funeral rites: smearing fresh ash and clay over their faces and bodies. But he did not want to die alone. "Not here, not now," he repeated, over and over. The spotlight emanating from the chopper hovering above moved back and forth, side by side. His cocoon which protected him no longer felt safe. The rotor 'wash' than kicked up the earth around his fortress creating a cloud of dirt that served to further disguise his presence. The helicopter descended further, spinning, around and round, then took off down into the valley.

The rat-tat-tat could be heard from a distance, followed by incendiary explosions, until no more. Ramu had no sense of time, and only left the cover of his shelter following an interminable period of silence. He squinted as an early morning sun peeked over the horizon. A light breeze made for an idyllic start of a promising day; except the smoke billowing from village across the way.

While not jaded by Western constructs like 'no good deed goes unpunished', Ramu knew better enough to stay put. He alone could explain to the Kopassus soldiers, in their distinctive camouflage uniforms and red berets now milling about the smoldering remains of the village, all that he had witnessed. But Ramu had experienced first-hand how soldiers treated the Dani in their own villages. They would come to Ninia and look upon every person with derision and suspicion. He also feared 'his' story would not be believed. Surely someone from the village will come forth in describing the events that had taken place, and the role of OPM, he hoped, if only to excuse his own inaction, assuage his guilt in doing nothing. There was no question in his mind as to the dangers of venturing into the wilds, mostly lying with chance encounters with roving OPM or Kopassus forces, especially now. "Yes, I will wait a few days, and then make my way back to the settlement, to Jacques and Bakri," he thought aloud. He could not help feeling some relief with the prospect of returning to his friends. Only they would understand. "Yes." He smiled.

Bliss is never lasting

"Maybe I am losing my mind," thinking, as I pondered my obsessive behavior working in the garden. I was using an improvised hoe, nothing more than some scrap metal, the end of which was roughly forged into a cylinder that the whittled end of a tree limb snuggly fit into.

Fortunately, I had Lela, my mentor and tormentor, who was always hovering over me, cackling at my expense. Way past her childbearing years, she sported braided hair that kept hidden her face; her sagging breasts reaching below her bellybutton. I 'not once' saw her when she was 'not' chewing on betel nuts, referred to as 'green gold' in Papua, or 'buai' in the local vernacular, leaving her mouth, gums, teeth, and all, the color of bleeding red. An animated Lela, through repeated pointing, poking, and prodding, taught me how to apply the white oozing sticky substance leaked from the skin of the underripe 'matoa' fruit – from the *Sapindaceae* family – same as the better-known longan, still hanging from the hardwood trees in a nearby grove. With its glue-like adhesive qualities, I was able to firmly secure the stick into the tube.

My rows of buried sweet potato 'slips', the rooted sprouts of mature sweet potatoes, were perfectly straight, spaced eight to ten inches apart. Only a thin dusting of soil was necessary to top the buried root. My real challenge was the vermin, who mocked me with their nightly antics with total disregard of all my best efforts; leaving me to clean up their mess every morning. Invading snails and slugs in particular created havoc in my garden. But I returned the favor: collecting them for Lela to boil up or cook on 'red hot' embers; a ready source of protein.

Bakri had decided to leave me to my gardening, and instead took up the Papuan tradition of crafting arrows for the bow he had found in one of the long-abandoned huts that had fallen on hard times. Underneath the grass thatched roof, collapsed under the weight of time, the elements, and just neglect, he chanced upon a sleek elongated naturally curved bow, minus a bowstring. He rummaged through the natural debris hoping to find an accompanying set of arrows, only to stir up a scrum of mites left over from some nesting birds: the most recent occupants. Despite having been ravaged and left with an itch that no amount of scratching could relieve, and a bright rash over most of his body, he persevered to make his bow 'whole' again; in the absence of arrows, he would simply make his own. Days into his enlightenment, he was still puzzling how to craft collected bamboo into arrows. Fortunately, he had better luck in gathering bamboo shoots that made for a welcome addition to our communal meals, served up in steaming broths flavored by smashed ginger root; a surefire 'cure all' for whatever ailment.

While my garden was not exactly flourishing, my relationship with Mola was, at least for me. We spoke, and held one another close, as I rediscovered the wonderful abandonment that comes with losing oneself to someone else. I had discovered bliss in the 'here and now'. Not that I wasn't mindful that such contentment was, from my experience, only fleeting; I just chose to ignore such just chose to ignore thoughts.

Bakri too seemed beguiled, lulled by natural rhythms of daily life in the settlement. He began to absently whistle to himself, of course, 'while he worked', as the saying goes. Watching him one day so engrossed in whittling his bamboo stalks and fitting them to shards of broken stone as arrowheads, I dared myself to think that maybe his was more escape than finding solace. All the while, playing into the same fanciful illusion that everything was 'okay'.

My fitful nap in the early afternoon was interrupted by an insistent tapping on my chest. I opened one eye, followed by the next, to Lela. I reached for my face to wipe away bleeding 'beetle nut' red spittle, as she excitedly mouthed something unintelligible into my ear. 'In the moment', her face looked every bit the 'scary mask', the kind you would wear to a Halloween party. Her blood red mouth accented by the absence of all but two remaining teeth.

Mola suddenly appeared standing over me, alongside a breathless Bakri. Both frantically collecting up our few belongings into a woven thatched grass bag. Hissing like a snake, she yelled for me to leave immediately: "Like right now!" Her tone and words conveyed an urgency that got me up and moving, 'faster than a speeding bullet'.

We made off in the direction leading to the back of the settlement, and a steep slope leading into a thicket of mulberry bushes, crisscrossed by worn footpaths. 'Slip, tumble, and fall', trying to catch myself. "*Déjà vu*," I gasped, panting like a dog as I gulped for air, trying to catch my breath. More injurious, Mola's stinging words caught me out like a slap to the back of the head. I replayed them over and over in my head: 'run, and do not come back here'.

As we further retreated into away from the settlement, our pace turned into a crawl. After a few minutes' pause to catch our breaths, I could not stop but think: *Funny! How oddly satisfying, back to relying on one another, just the two of us.* It was if a 'spell' cast by a 'coven' of witches, had been broken, as we distanced ourselves from their 'covenstead', witch's lair.

But as in all good things, my newfound clarity proved fleeting as dusk approached and the mosquitoes feasted, while we went hungry. It was all I could do in thinking: *what would Ramu do?*

Speaking of Ramu

The bright orange contrasted with the sea of green. Ramu had finally left his perch, with the intention of making his way back to the settlement, eager to return to Jacques and Bakri. He had tempered his excitement and slowed the pace, enough so to avoid any chance encounters with OPM or Kopassus. He cautiously made his way over to the berm running parallel to the river; making the grisly discovery of a man sitting against a tree. His orange overalls were in tatters and caked with blood. He had bled out: here, and alone. The gashes to his scalp, chest, and arms, bore the marks of machete-made cuts. Ramu felt an intense grief, so debilitating as to drag him down like an anchor. He had dared hope this man would have somehow made his way back to his family, his village.

As he turned in the direction of the headwaters, a tributary he spied when making his first crossing of the river, he felt blood, his own, oozing down the side of his face. The axe, a traditional stick carved from an iron wood and fitted with a smooth elongated stone attached by tree vine, had grazed the side of his head. Ramu eased woozily against the same tree cradling the dead man. Whack, again, this time taking the impact on his side. He felt the old strap choking him, as someone was pulling to free the binoculars hanging from his neck. Instinctively, he lowered his head and let the leather cord slip off, taking with it the binoculars he had been entrusted with.

A Dani axe: from the author's private collection.

Ramu summoned his ancestral warrior spirit despite his dizziness and made off. He ran and ran and ran, until he could not run further. He furiously dug out, from the soft earth under a large fallen tree, a small depression to snuggle into, pulling the loose soil and natural detritus into his tomb; lying camouflaged, and perfectly still.

Making no sense

"We need to leave this place, now!" Bakri was usually not so emphatic. But I needed some kind of validation for what had happened. Lela had slipped grains and bananas into our carryall, or rather pouch, as we fled the settlement. Now practiced in the art of gathering, we were managing quite okay, three days out from being chased out.

I crawled behind a reluctant Bakri, who wanted only to make distance between us and the settlement. We planted ourselves just below the grove of mulberry bushes; hoping nobody would be making mulberry pies that day. I still managed to surprise myself with being 'oh so' witty. We were able to catch whiffs of roasted pig, as loud banter mixing with laughter filled our ears. "They are having a party." I nodded my head quizzically, in agreement. More than that, men's voices rose above the chortle.

"We need to move closer, from a different direction," I whispered.

"No!" Once again, there was Bakri being atypically emphatic; like maybe he had caught a 'grow me some ball' virus.

"Please, Bakri, stay here, I want to get closer to the

gardens, while keeping out of sight." But Bakri would have none of it. Instead, he hunched down and slowly made his way thereto, as I followed closely behind.

Keeping low, we now had partial view of the festivities. The scene was as advertised: men and women milling about, while maintaining some division. A group of young girls sat together in a huddle, shouting back and forth with the men congregated around smoking pits. "Well, mystery solved," I said to which Bakri smiled. Then I caught sight of Mola, with a man sporting a bushy gray beard, hand in hand, walking down the knoll on which the huts were clustered. I took in his T-shirt with the emblematic OPM flag emblazoned on the front. I was too focused to notice Bakri's stare riveted on the man. I too caught the glint against the man's chest, and slowly exhaled. As if reading each other, we both backed off and retreated to our mooring.

I said nothing, waiting for Bakri to react first. We were both trying to digest the same vision but through different lenses that now rendered both of us weak; without being overly dramatic. For me, it was all about Mola. I felt like I had been irrevocably stripped of something vital to my being. But for Bakri, it was that connection with his father, and his father before him, now broken. Seeing his binoculars tethered to the man walking side by side with my Mola left him in tears. We both also realized the implication: that they were taken from Ramu. He would never have given up what was so precious to Bakri and connecting him to us. Not alive he wouldn't.

All too obvious, and yes, most frightening, were the 'fighters' toting oversized weapons to their chests and over their shoulders. How could we not feel 'ambushed' by what we saw. Some, no more than children, pointing assault rifles at one another in play. I thought back to when I was a boy, playing soldier. I always played the 'marine'. But this was no game.[34]

We plotted our next move over the next few days. Not that we had but a single option open to us. We would make our way down river following the bank, sticking to our side. Looking for Ramu made no sense. Especially now, having seen the prized binoculars that we knew he would never have given up voluntarily.

It was Bakri who recognized the drone of engines overhead, growing steadily louder. He jabbed me with his finger, and I followed his stare, catching sight of a turboprop plane banking in and out of sight, making repeated passes. There was something birdlike and deliberate in how the plane now circled: lower and lower, as if in slow motion; so slow, it was a wonder it could keep from stalling. I was reminded of a hawk with wings flapping furiously in maintaining lift, circling, homing in on some unsuspecting prey and swooping down with outstretched talons.

There was no way we could signal our presence given the dense overgrowth we were hidden under. "This is our first plane sighting since getting lost." I had to pause before completing my thought. "We got into this mess."

But now we were faced with a dilemma. If the crash site is spotted, then TNI would surely mount a recovery mission. But with the OPM now in our midst, it was better to heed Mola's words: "Run, and do not come back here." Bakri and I staked out a spot further downstream along the river, well enough hidden by the natural flora and far enough from the settlement, without being 'too far'.

---

34 *https://www.bangkokpost.com/world/1701592/indonesia-military-use-of-child-soldiers-a-rights-violation#cxrecs_s.*

Revealed

"The before and after satellite photos confirm the aerial sighting of the Fokker crash," read the Colonel. Reconnaissance of the valley and ridgeline adjacent to the mountain range of the 'tower' massacre had by chance picked up a possible sighting of the Fokker wreckage; the search for which had ended in the previous month. His Senior (tech) Sergeant dragged the small fold-out magnifier over the photos laid out on the Major's desk. *"Mungkin"* – for maybe!

The Baliem Valley was littered with dozens of crash sites waiting to be discovered. Committing additional resources at this time to investigating a crash site would require some 'leap of faith'. But the Colonel rationalized: "The wreckage looks 'fresh', given the impact zone has not been reclaimed by the surrounding jungle." To which the Senior (tech) Sergeant nodded in agreement. But it was the date-time-stamped satellite photos that made easy the decision to 'pull the trigger' and mount a recovery operation.

The (tech) Sergeant added: "We heard back from the provincial authorities in Wamena that there used to be a small runway nearby, just shy of the wreckage, servicing the village of Kataya. My guess is that the 'pilot' was in trouble and trying to make for it. Here! You would not recognize it as such if you did not know about it." He circled the X marking the spot with a paperclip. The likely approach and relative proximity of the downed plane to the airstrip made such speculation both plausible and probable.

"And Kataya?" questioned the Colonel.

A young Lieutenant (intel) officer stepped forward smartly and replied: "We are gathering information now. Apparently, Kopassus responded to an OPM threat in the area. But that was many years back. Shortly thereafter, the village was abandoned by most of the inhabitants. Since then, we know next to nothing." Then, pointing to a spot on one of the photos, the Lieutenant added: "But look here. These gardens look well-tended." The Colonel looked at him quizzically. The Lieutenant continued: "We have requested some additional satellite photos to gather any evidence of recent human activity," sensing the Colonel was not entirely satisfied.

After the Lieutenant left the room, as smartly as when he had entered, the Colonel looked to his tech Sergeant, smiling wryly. He mused, "He seems so young. Too young!"

The 'gift' of Nono

Icha's infant daughter had taken nicely to the wrapped batik sling: cooing and looking wondrously at the world around her. Gurgling noises gave way to small bubbles forming around her lips, which added to her delight. Her mood was contagious, as Icha and Desi strolled to the small complex of government offices, and beyond to the Resort Police Headquarter and Military District Command 1702/Jayawijaya. Their excitement at being called to the office of Lieutenant Colonel Kumi-Krispe Kuri was tinged with nervous anticipation. "Surely, this is about Pak Nono," Desi offered, when first getting the written invitation, hand delivered no less.

"This is no summons," commented Ali Suliman, when the policewoman delivered the message in the early hours of the morning.

"The Grand Police Commissioner Adjutant is asking you both to lunch."

Seating was for four, the table simply set, the food was anything but. The fish was fresh, so fresh that Icha guessed it had been fished out of the river earlier in the day. "Fresh and steamed, what a treat. Thank you for this special meal." The same policewoman who had delivered the invitation had taken over baby responsibilities with a warm smile and gentle touch, hefting the baby to her shoulder; seriously taken with her surrogate role.

"Let me introduce Colonel Agus, who flew into Wamena this morning from Timika. I invited him to listen and learn from you."

"Thank you, Lieutenant Colonel, I am honored to meet the two of you, and cannot thank you enough for your dogged efforts to help us secure the release of Pak Nono." Both Icha and Desi immediately picked up on how the Colonel had phrased his remarks: 'secure the release'. Icha was buoyed. Nono was alive! Clearly, he had been taken, and TNI would do what it needed to do in bringing him home, at least to Wamena.

"I do not want to know your sources, but we believe them to be 'reliable'." The Colonel continued. "But there have been 'developments', and we ask if you could continue to ask questions of those you trust. But you must be careful so as not to bring attention to yourselves." And with emphasis: "And certainly not sharing our conversation or that we are now working together."

To which Desi blurted out: "What developments?"

Ali sipped the overly sweetened tea, now cold, likely from the same pot he had drunk from that same morning. He had returned home early, eager to learn about the luncheon. Desi was busying herself in preparing a mutton broth that looked less than appetizing from where he was sitting. Usually, she over seasoned to compensate for her culinary shortcomings. But it seemed to Ali that on this afternoon, she was manically focused on the spices and herbs: smelling, washing, and tasting, before throwing into the 'too hot' pot of boiling water. Ali could not help but smile as he imagined Desi in a pointy black hat, riding a broom, brewing up some witch's potion.

"I cannot tell you anything, except that the food was *enak enak* – so delicious," Desi volunteered, if only to move on from what was foremost on Ali's mind.

The phone rang and rang. Nobody usually called at the house, at least since Nono had disappeared, and certainly not this late at night. No good could come from such an intrusion that mocked the calming illusion that the night brings; that all was alright with world. Icha was struggling to balance the news of the day as shared by the Colonel Augus with the now-imposed expectations that threatened to undo her predictable world. Finally, she succumbed to the insistent ringing and picked up the heavy receiver. To which Gindo uttered a ,"Thanks God."

News that Nono's replacement would be arriving in the coming months, after completing the training program in Jakarta, made even more real that nothing would go back to what was. In the meantime, Gindo said that, although semi-retired, he had been asked to return to Wamena during the interim period to, to 'mind the store', so to speak, "Since my condition has considerably improved". Icha sank to her knees on hearing this, her salty tears stinging her face. She tried to control her voice that betrayed the emotions she felt, failing miserably.

Early the next morning, Desi poked her head into the kitchen where Icha was busy boiling eggs for a breakfast porridge. "I had to tell Pak Ali, he had to know," she said, as was her way in blurting things out; more so when carrying about a guilty conscience.

Icha took a few steps forward and wrapped her arms around her:"Of course you had to."

She then proceeded to tell Desi all about Gindo's planned return; such was her relief as she, word for word, gave an accounting of the call from the night before. But not before voicing her worries: "It is wonderful that Pak Nono is alive. But to ask us to collect information on where he has been moved to is wrong. We are not police. That is their job, not ours. We cannot continue to play 'detective'. Someone is going to get hurt."

Desi slowly nodded and followed with: "Pak Ali said the same thing."

The match is lit; Jayapura erupts

Spreading like wildfire, the protests claimed the fragile peace of the town and surrounding neighborhoods. Marches and accompanying calls for independence, buoyed by charges of racism, escalated into spontaneous rampages through the streets of Jayapura. While students from Cenderawasih University were the first to heed the call, anger and pent-up rage soon washed over to engulf the local populace.

Best-laid plans awry, the Colonel scrubbed all aerial activity in and out of the airport, except for essential military flights, mostly bringing in TNI reinforcements from Java. "How did we not see this coming?" he demanded of his visibly shaken (intel) officer. Of course, he knew that it would only take a spark to set off this eruption, a long time in coming, sending the illusion of calm on a fiery trajectory into the sun. "Of course, the recovery mission will have to wait," he snapped at his (tech) Sergeant, standing alongside his desk; instantly regretting his outburst. "I apologize for that." He mumbled something about frayed nerves with all that was going on.

Time to move on

The waiting was made all the worse, stretching into days – as we anticipated being rescued. Funny how I was now underthinking our situation, with 'rescue' coming to mind. "How could the plane not have spotted the wreckage?" Bakri kept repeating, only adding to our shared sense of frustration. "We need to save ourselves. Enough of waiting for a 'big hand' to scoop us up and out of this mess."

"The river will surely lead us to other settlements." More question than statement. Mola's mention of a 'missionary' outpost held out possibilities, although her recollection was just that: something she heard from her husband years ago. The one sure thing was the river would eventually deliver us to the sea, eventually. Problem was, I had no idea which sea; there was 'Cerum' and 'Halmahera' to the west, the 'Arafura' to the south, or possibly emptying into 'Cenderawasih Bay' to the north. Mola had once referred to the Mamberamo River, but never elaborated further on the 'course' of the river, nor the hazards downstream. As for Bakri and me, we were clueless. So much for our preparation prior to undertaking our 'investigation', now only a distant memory.

My sandals of bark and vine, gifted by Lela back in the

settlement, were already frayed. Bakri's were no less tattered and worn. Regardless, we began picking our way along the bank, with Bakri of course taking the lead.

Navigating a river while on the river can be perilous enough, as we had already discovered. From its banks: a nightmare, none the less. Our river zigzagged, making passage slow-going, having to contend with the curves and bends of the channel. The underbrush made treacherous our way, disguising gullies and cuts carved into the earth from flooding and run-off erosion. We were entering 'Lower Course' of the river, transitioning from Middle Course; notably not as steep, with large 'meanderers', large flood plains, and oxbow lakes. I kept my distance behind him after getting slapped a few times from low-hanging branches brushed aside and vegetation 'snapping back'. If only Ramu and his machete was clearing our way forward. After no more than a few days, we were both ready to abandon ourselves to the river currents.

The force of the overflow had taken large bites out of the riverbank, creating small harbor inlets that we had to ford or trapse around. We entered a section, the 'Lower Course', that was 'swamp'. "We need to stop before it gets too dark," offered Bakri; for which I was grateful!

"Let's first move to higher ground, inland. There!" I pointed to a grassy slope in the distance. "The mosquitoes are devouring us here."

We kept to the relatively tame grasslands overlooking flooded marshland for the next few days. It felt like we were finally making good time, putting distance between us and the settlement, and hopefully OPM. "We are really exposed here," Bakri mentioned more than once. We both understood without giving way to our fears; OPM treated their Indonesian captives as 'occupiers from the east' and deserving of their fate.

The channel was lost to an expansive floodplain, making

difficult in following what was now more a lake than a river. "Have you ever seen the *The African Queen*?" he quizzed.

I paused, and asked, "The movie?"

He continued, as if not really interested in hearing my answer: "Yes! I remember seeing it as a young boy on the big outdoor screen set up in our town. A ritual attended by my family and neighbors every Saturday night. President Sukarno attempted to bring the country out of hibernation from our 'deep sleep' under Dutch rule. Movies became a favorite of the fledgling government in introducing us to the modern world. A practice that continues to this day on many of the smaller islands; absent electricity and powered by generator." Not sure how or if to reply, I said nothing. "I barely remember the story but will never forget Humphrey Bogart and Katharine Hepburn."

To which I could not resist adding my own two cents' worth: "They were opposites, the drunken adventurer and captain of his own broken-down steamboat, plying up and down the Congo River, and the 'prim-and-proper' spinster: half missionary – half 'superwoman'. They came together and saved one another. A love story."

Bakri turned and looked at me with the first non-fanatical smile I had seen on his face in a long time; eking out some humor from the moment with the rejoinder: "We are the same!"

I joined in: "Yes! And for sure, you are Hepburn, and I am Bogart."

We continued our trek, keeping with the rim of the shoreline. More than once the stagnant water, smelling of sulfur and rotting boiled egg, left me fighting nausea, ending in gut-wrenching heaves. Of course, Bakri fared better, using a porous pouch of tightly interwoven vines as a make-do filter, while I could no longer be bothered, scooping up the greenish water into my mouth.

The rains had long past, and sunburn was seriously contributing to my nightly teeth-rattling chills. Although skirting the still-flooded plain, the *Anopheles* mosquito still manages to swarm our camp setup on the overlooking ridge. This dawn-to-dusk 'biter' is neither stealthy or subtle, sinking a needle-like proboscis into the skin, drawing a blood meal, and then sharing their 'Plasmodium' parasite load with whomever is close at hand.

Not so much a lottery, or 'Lotto' as it is known throughout Indonesia – but the odds of winning at the 'roulette' table at almost 50% greater than getting malaria, even in a highly endemic area. Of the 3500 species of mosquito, only 30–40 (of the 530 belonging to the *Anopheles* species) transmit the disease; and only 5 of over 200 Plasmodium parasite species are responsible for malaria in humans. Of course, these numbers belie the true impact of malaria globally: the number of new infections worldwide each year, well over 200 million, attests to the terrible scourge of malaria as a disease to be reckoned with.

Frankly, I am no expert, but living (in the same building) and working (on the same NMRC-Indonesia compound) with Commander Bates all these years has certainly rubbed off on me.

This photo of a feeding An. Farauti mosquito from the region that includes West Papua (Indonesia) and Papua New Guinea is from James Gathany' collection and brought to the attention of the author by Neil Lobo and Kevin Baird: getting 'up close and personal' with these malaria-transmitting vampires.[35]

Bakri concluded the obvious after my first febrile episode: "You may have malaria!"

To which I replied, "No shit, *Dick Tracy*." Bakri frowned, thinking for sure I had lost my mind. Seeing his expression, I then yapped a most unintelligible rant, describing this famous comic-book detective, a fictional sleuth; always on the side of law and order, the right side, putting the bad guy away,

---

35   *https://phil.cdc.gov/Details.aspx?pid=18751.*

and making the streets safe again for the good citizens of 'Tracyville', of course. The phrase, a true 'Americanism', simply implied: 'Of course' – you idiot – 'how could it not be?' I knew my humor was wearing thin on my friend, and so left out the 'you idiot'.[36] But in fact, there was 'little' evidence of malaria in the highlands of Papua, both Indonesia and PNG.

Although my friend Norman told me once: "You just need to know where to look."

Bakri borrowed from Ramu's traditional remedies and hunted down an assortment of roots and bark from young saplings, seasoned with a 'god awful' odious-smelling paste squeezed from the stems of flowering plants growing in the shallow wetlands; it was smashed, boiled, and stirred into a oatmeal-like mush and fed to me with an improvised 'two finger' spoon. For Bakri, it was hit or miss. "If this does not work, we will try something else."

The African Queen. Humphrey Bogart, Katharine Hepburn. Date: 1951 – Image ID: K350P1 (Alamy).

36 *https://openlibrary.org/works/OL15830183W/Dick_Tracy.*

"Ha ha, that is comforting to know," I croaked out. He cradled me, cajoled me, and yelled at me. He only managed not to curse or pummel me with his fists. Not his way!

Running a fever, high enough to fry my brain, or an egg, I dreamt. Not this time of lizards, but of breezy conversation among shipmates: Dick as Dick, Rose as Katharine, Charlie as Humphrey, and me playing myself, as the ancient boiler powered our steamer down the crocodile-infested Congo River.

I woke up to a star-studded night sky, and no fever. I turned my head and found Bakri staring into the same sky, thanking 'his' God. And while making no claims on 'his' God, I too gave thanks.

No more a game

Wamena is like and unlike any other small provincial town in Indonesia: news spreads fast, rumor faster; and most of the population, the Dani, come from a world apart from any other found in the archipelago. For that matter, the planet. The relatively small, non-indigenous, Indonesian community comprised of mostly traders and civil servants takes comfort in actualizing the 'manifest destiny' of the *Republic*, the 'tip of the spear', so to speak. But day-to-day interface with locals is akin to avoiding puddles of dirty water on a muddied, potholed street.

Icha, an early riser, was woken still earlier by a resounding pounding on the front door. The baby stirred and purred, and thankfully fell back into that place where babies go when they close their eyes and drift off to la-la land. Desi could barely catch her breath as she shared what she had just learned. "Two Papuan teachers from the primary/secondary school were killed overnight in the house they shared, and a third is at hospital. There is lots of talk, but TNI is blaming OPM and OPM is pointing the finger at TNI. Whatever, we have been told to stay home today, everyone. Pasar Nayak has been ordered closed. The same for all businesses and government offices. Ali thinks this is OPM trying to rally its supporters and start something like in Jayapura."

"Yes, what would the government have to gain in committing such a horrible act?" replied a now wide-awake Icha. "As if Wamena needed more tinder to kindle a fire."

Gindo heard the early morning commotion, still exhausted from his travel onboard a lumbering C-130 military transport plane out of Halim Perdanakusuma Air Force Base in east Jakarta, followed by an interminable wait on a hard bench for a military flight out of Jayapura; taking him first to Timika, and then onward to Wamena. All in all, he felt pretty good, except for the wear and tear on his backside. Desi caught sight of his head poking sheepishly around the corner into the darkened front room and 'jumped' in surprise. His disheveled appearance giving her a 'start', appearing like some ghostly aberration stepping out of a Japanese horror flick. "Oh, Desi, forgive me! Pak Nono arrived late yesterday. I should have told you. I know that Pak Ali will be so happy." Within a nanosecond, Icha caught herself: "I mean Pak Gindo."

With restrictions in place that were now accompanied by draconian 'shoot on sight' orders for anyone foolish enough to stray outdoors, the afternoon meal was to be a 'make-do' affair. Icha and Desi busied themselves in the garden patch picking out green tomatoes and stunted celery stalks; Gindo was left to chip away in a valiant attempt to free the frozen anchovy from Kabui Bay from their icy tomb in the small but noisy freezer to the back of the house. Meanwhile, the always affable Ali was responsible for wandering about and lending commentary on how best to pluck and pick.

Icha was still able to make do, transforming the basics into culinary artistry. "I missed Wamena, not so much, but your cooking!" Gindo let his words hang, then nodded ever so slightly: "I need not say more." There was laughter at the table, catching up. The tensions outside their front door were cast aside, and of course, Gindo came bearing gifts. "It is likely I will be here for some time, since the candidate in training set to replace Nono has decided such a move would not be reasonable given family considerations. It seems there are no new 'takers' for the position left vacant by Nono's disappearance." The mention of Nono had immediate effect, sucking the oxygen from the room and suffocating all conversation.

Following an awkward pause, Desi volunteered: "*Terpujilah nama Allah*, 'in the name of Allah', give Pak Nono a way home."

Fast-forward: the lifting of curfew. Lieutenant Colonel Kumi-Krispe visited his old friend Gindo for cinnamon tea in the early evening, joined by Ali. Icha was in the next room trying to lull an irritable baby to sleep while Desi had her ear to the door; or more accurately, to the open end of the drinking glass held up to the wall, a trick she used in magnifying conversations. Icha silently mouthed, "Stop that," all the while encouraging Desi on with her eavesdropping: arms extending out, elbows bent, palms facing skyward, head tilting to the side, imploring her.

"As we approach a new kind of calm in Wamena, the search for Nono will continue. We missed him by no more than a few days when a 'special police unit' entered the village of Aikima. A few of the villagers suggest that he was moved to the southwest, but nobody is sure. It is probable that this is not the work of OPM, but rather one of the 'gray gangs' that prey more on their own. He is likely a captive of 'convenience', rather than an 'intended' hostage. He was simply in the wrong place at the wrong time. Nono will likely be got rid of quickly if our experience with these outlaws is anything to go by."

Seeing those around the table visibly upset by his last remark, he immediately corrected himself: "I mean release him, not kill him. They are not so much looking for any confrontation with the security forces or being burdened with the care of a hostage. Rather, this is about creating mayhem and stoking fear in the local communities; this rabble of misfits are no longer welcome even among their own. It is not in their interest to harm him, any more than he has been already terrorized. But the demons, he will carry into the next life."

Gindo could be contemplative given the right ambience. He knew he was among friends and feeling with purpose for the first time in a long time, and so described his feelings flying over deeply scarred copper excavations just outside of Timika; in the area managed by Freeport PT, with TNI's blessing. The massive Grasberg mine cone-shaped excavation defied imagery but was no less imprinted into the soft tissues of his 'amygdala'; that part of the brain responsible for memory.

The massive Grasberg open pit mine from an aerial view – Image ID: 2R63D50 (Alamy).

"We are both cursed and blessed by our reliance on copper and gold. The immense revenues generated by the mines have made hostage our national interests. The Republic needs to take this wealth and reinvest in West Papua. Make the Papuan take pride in their ethnic distinction and appreciative if not proud of their Indonesian heritage." And then, almost as an afterthought: "And then there is the environment."[37]

"OPM would lose advantage of 'pride and progress' in calling for a Free Papuan State. Just look to Papua New Guinea, where the corrupt politicians are equally despised along with their Australian masters. Australia would be the main beneficiary to profit in doing so here under a west Papuan flag." Gindo blinked! He had never heard Ali this 'emphatic'. Ali never 'voiced' strong opinion, about anything, never mind interest in the geopolitical goings-on of West Papua.

"Not bad for a 'weatherman'," he remarked.

---

37 *https://www.theguardian.com/global-development/2016/nov/02/100-bn-dollar-gold-mine-west-papuans-say-they-are-counting-the-cost-indonesia.*

Into the arms of...

Tender and succulent, the small fishes skewed on the pointed stick made Ramu weep, as he sucked the savory juices from charbroiled flesh and crunched down on the spiny brittle bones. Such was his hunger that nothing was wasted, trying to slowly chew each morsel against the temptation of 'inhaling' his meal-on-a-stick. The small creek feeding into the tributary that fed the river was plentiful with darting shadows against the shallow silted bottom, and crawling with freshwater crabs. His wooziness and blurred vision had left him retching up whatever he was able to put into his mouth for the first days after getting wacked. Ramu could still taste the soil, smell its lingering musty scent, half-burying himself to escape detection by the OPM goons, now long gone.

He tied the braided vines to an overhanging tree limb and tested both to support his full weight. Then without a pause, he committed himself to swing across a narrow stretch of the river. Jacques had spoken many times of 'Tarzan of the Jungle', and how he traveled, swinging from one vine to the next, all the while shouting and beating on his chest. Only Ramu was no Tarzan. Not only did he fail to let go when reaching the end of his forward momentum, but he also succumbed to the pressures of gravity when finally letting go. Being the swimmer he was not, he thrashed and clawed his way to the churning surface; with the current doing most of the work, spitting him onto the opposite bank.

Mary Evans Picture Library Ltd, Stock Photo – Image ID: 2K802K0 (Alamy).

Ramu had enough of 'white water' thrills and vowed never again to jump into a river, any river, with such perilous abandon. Much less play Tarzan. Yes, he was now closer to making his way back to his friends. But he was not so sure what he would find returning to the 'once' Kataya settlement.

Passing the crash site, he approached the nearby clearing with caution. The trusting Ramu had become much less so after his first encounter with the 'old women', and the events of the last few weeks. His entrance was met with a subdued reception, with a few of the older women greeting him as if welcoming a long-lost child. There was a sense that something was not right, that the good energy of the place had soured, as if bad spirits had invaded the sanctity of this refuge.

He couldn't really make sense of everything that Lela and her crew were saying in between slurps of a watery carrot and sweet potato stew. All together, they babbled on about a string of events, making no sense to Ramu. His only interest was in deciphering from the barely intelligible but excited bursts about the whereabouts of Bakri and Jacques. *This is no good,* he thought dismissively of the insistent banter.

The Dani family of languages comes to the market in three flavorful sub-families: Wano of Bokondini; Central Dani consisting of Dugawa valley and Dani Barat accents; and Nggalik. Understanding the linguistic nuances particular to each village, universes unto themselves owing to topography and the insular view that outside influences pose an existential threat to survival of the community, inevitably raising the hackles of the aggrieved ancestors, made challenging even the simplest of communications. Kind of like speciation; a byproduct of evolution. And so it was that Ramu struggled to comprehend; especially so when words loosely strung together were sputtered in frothy 'beet-red' betel nut drool.

Ramu was nevertheless exhilarated by the human contact, as it seemed were the women. He was poised to act on what he had gleaned from the spirited discussion. Head spinning, he surmised that his friends left the village. And so, he would follow the river downstream, as surely they had done.

He also learned that soldiers had come to the settlement to recover the human remains from the wreckage. They were respectful, and brought bags of rice, and hoes and seed for planting. When they learned that only old women inhabited what once was Kataya village, they gifted vitamins and other supplies. Yet there was a palpable angst expressed as Lela recounted how Mola had been taken away on their 'bird'.

But for this night, he would allow himself to be lulled to sleep, both exhausted and satiated. Only sleep was anything but calming, as thoughts and images racing through his head made for a long night.

News of a possible sighting

The office was devoid of any personal effects that might provide a clue as to the current occupant, except for the 'white-on-black' name slotted into the clear plastic holder in the corridor. But Captain Rick was not planning on staying long as his retirement date loomed ever closer. His navy-imposed exile nevertheless made each day passing feel like a 'snail's pace'.

The navy loves to assign blame to a name, even for bad juju raining down from the heavens. While he was initially held responsible for failure to exert sufficient oversight for policies and practices critical to the mission and enacted long before assuming Command, his 'verbal reprimand' was nevertheless a vindication of sorts. But in true navy fashion, without apology to the insult inflicted. Rick was in good company along this hallway; generally reserved for the more notable pariahs whose transgressions made them contagions, but who could not be so easily disposed of, by virtue of their senior rank. But for Rick, exile was nothing short of a blessing.

True to form, Rick stepped into his office and scanned the open folders containing busy work to keep him occupied and out of everybody's way. He was buoyed on this early morning by the beautiful spring weather; even in his windowless, broom-sized closet of an office. Coffee in hand, he scanned his inbox filled with routine training and administrative navy dribble, until catching an email with the 'Subject' heading of 'Possible Sighting', from his good buddy Colonel Dowdy.

Rick,

I wanted to share news from my counterpart at the Australian Embassy. An Aussie woman found living in a remote village in the Baliem Valley was forcefully taken by TNI and handed over to the Australian Embassy for immediate repatriation, lacking any immigration documentation. She was almost immediately put on a flight out of the country. My understanding is that she was amongst her adopted Dani family for well over a decade, 'ruling the roost' as would a mother hen to a group of adoring old women. To the point, she mentioned having met with 'your' Commander Jacques and two others, not more than a few weeks ago. There is some question as to the veracity of this sighting. The Australian DATT suggested she may be a little off in the head but gives credence to her story. Yes, maybe 'mad as a hatter', but we are looking to follow-up. I will let you know when I know something more. There are plans to reach out to her. But we were warned she feels aggrieved and is in no mood to talk with anyone at this time, not least the Australian authorities whom she holds accountable in supporting the illegal Indonesian occupation of West Papua.

Heard you are planning on returning and taking up residence on your Bali retreat following your retirement. Looking forward to the visit.

Winny

'Dr. Livingstone, I presume?'[38]

'*Geschenk van god*' was how the Dutch missionary referred to Abraham following the death of his young mother during childbirth. Premature by three months, he should not have survived but a 'moment in time' following his delivery into the world. Destined for the priesthood, he was schooled in the teachings of the Catholic faith.

But Non-Commissioned Officer (NCO) Master Sergeant Abraham Kambuaya had a different calling, joining the 'Autonomous Papuan Constabulary' service as a 'young buck'. His early posting to Wamena was warmly welcomed by the locals and a source of Dani pride. Unlike Lieutenant Colonel Kumi, who had spent his youth in Java, Abraham was home grown and bred. A Dani boy from the Baliem Valley making good. That all changed following his transfer to the National Police and his reassignment to the 'Special Reactionary Force' for Jayawijaya Province; he was now a 'Judas' among his own people.

His mostly Dani police platoon, augmented by a squad of indigenous army scouts, was quickly mobilized and dropped upriver; slithering down swinging ropes tethered to the skids of 'big birds' placidly hovering in place like female *blue-winged*

---

38   *https://en.wikiquote.org/wiki/David_Livingstone.*

'digger' wasps in the early morning heat tunneling for grubs to sting and lay their eggs within. Without casting aspersions, it is notable that when hatched, the larva eats the infested grub from the inside out. Less ominous would-be wasps search for a sweet treat of mountain nectar.

Charcoal-blackened faces numbering into the dozens filed quietly through 'bush', making their way to Kataya; at least so named on the relief map tucked into Abraham's huge hip pocket. Arriving unannounced and by surprise was critical, as was explained to all assembled at the police 'operations center' just a few hours before boarding the choppers. Nothing was being left to chance. Lieutenant Colonel Kumi-Krispe Kuri was equally adamant that under no condition were any of the women in this village of 'old women' to be harmed. Not so much as a scratch!

As the force approached the settlement, they divided into their respective teams, to cover all entry and exit points. Such was their well-practiced stealth that the women working in the garden did not even take notice, until surrounded by one of the teams. A few cowered behind others, while most stood tall with an indignation that surprised Abraham. And then, in unison, they emitted a cry that shattered any remaining semblance of normalcy of the early morning.

Mopping up the remnants of the community consisted of sweet talk and treats. Abraham had never encountered such a group; a place where these women, abandoned and discarded, could come together, and seek solace in one another's company. He had read about the 'very Western' concept of retirement homes, which he felt beneath the dignity of any human being. But here, he felt a relief that such a place existed, thrived. Knowing no mother or family growing up, especially as a ward of the church, he sometimes felt estranged from his cultural roots, his Dani identify. And so, he took silent comfort in this place, vowing to keep those who found a home here from harm. These were, after all, 'his' people; they were 'all' his mothers.

The platoon Commander, a young Javanese Lieutenant who knew 'just' enough to trust his NCOs, provided a preliminary report over a static-riddled comms channel, short and sweet:

> "Sighting confirmed... But long gone... Need to monitor for possible OPM presence in the area... But currently no related activity... Permission to send Alpha team via helo extraction downriver, and track subjects back upstream to this location... At the same time, Bravo team will make their way on foot downstream and meet up with them." After a lengthy pause, the radio crackled: "Affirmative... Pickup tomorrow at 0600 hours... The rest of platoon stay on station until notified otherwise..."

Catching up

Resolute, Ramu plowed ahead. Sure-footed, he made haste, 'short work' of the obstacles he faced making his way downriver. The seemingly insurmountable head start of Jacques and Bakri would have discouraged most 'mere mortals', but not Ramu. He felt invincible, protected, and guided by the ancestors. Their perceptible presence, reflected in the sheen that glimmered off the waters, the palpable 'vibe' emitted by the quivering of plants and swaying of trees rooted in the dark rich soil, propelled his legs forward, as if carried along the spirits looking out for him.

There was no mistaking the two 'stick-like figures', even in the glare of a late afternoon sun. "The binoculars," he lamented. Even more distant was a slow-moving procession marching in single file, barely visible to against the horizon. Crossing what was a narrow range of hills, heading for an escarpment, where a steep slope meets with plateau, he was reminded of a caterpillar, its elongated body slinking forward, each segment independent of the others, but all working in unison. Ramu intuitively knew what he most feared: the caterpillar on a collision course with Jacques and Bakri.

Without even momentary pause, Ramu gathered up

all his strength and broke into a run, making for his friends to give warning. He needed to reach them before they were intercepted by OPM.

Running toward Jacques and Bakri waving and shouting caught their attention. Both glanced up in his direction. Neither believing what they were seeing. The incredulity of Ramu running at them like that of a crazed 'wild man' was unnerving; certainly, like no Dani they had encountered. Each was left wondering if they were witnessing some mystical aberration; readying themselves for whatever was coming their way.

Back together

The three were running, again, as brothers. No less an 'act of defiance' in the face of 'no mere threat'; staring the damsel in distress, the villain, and of course the hero, as the fast-moving train comes barreling down the tracks towards the our heroine, all tied and defenseless, of the 'silent' movies era. Survival instincts kicking in. Just how they had come together was now left behind as 'survival' began blurring memory. Each actor would offer a different recollection if asked. That 'wabah babi' had brought them to the 'here and now' was testament to the power of the spirits, so thought Ramu. Jacques only knew that they were in 'deep shit'. The centipede slinking its way down the rocky slope of the far peak was making slow but even progress, gaining on them.

Disappearing into the ravine separating their ground from the surrounding hill, Bakri barked out orders, as commanding as any Jacques had heard in the navy fraternity. "To the marshes, and into the trees beyond."

"Any crocs, you think?" asked Jacques, knowing there was no turning back. Bakri could only laugh, trying to extract some humor out of such a crazy notion. *Maybe not so crazy*, he thought, *just another perilous anecdote to our survival.*

Putting up their hands, waving a 'white flag' of surrender, was not an option. All three knew this race would end badly if they lost it. Jacques and Bakri trusted Ramu with their lives. And believed to be truth without any doubt his account about what he had witnessed back on the twin peaks, and the massacre; all delivered between gulps for air in the span of a few 'short' minutes. Bakri's only comment was, "It makes sense," when connecting it with what had happened back at the settlement. Jacques also now understood in a flash of recognition that Mola's betrayal, or so it seemed at the time, was intended to save them. He felt stricken that he had so misjudged her.

Jacques gingerly dragged his now-bare feet through the chest-deep waters, swollen and crusted, skin ripped and torn, looking more a piece of old meat, ever so fearful about stepping onto a jagged-ended branch unseen through the silt, or worse, something slithering on the muddy bottom. Notwithstanding, the forward movement in taking a more hurried approach would have been equally impeded by 'Newton's Laws of Motion': a simple matter of physics.

African Queen, (The African Queen) USA 1951, Regie: John Huston, Humphrey Bogart, Katharine Hepburn – Image ID: H85RKC (Alamy).

Digging deep into his endless reserves, Bakri confronted this swarm of 'bad juju' with an armor of humor: "We must look like geese out of water, waddling from side to side." *Talk about 'grace under fire*, thought Jacques.

What seemed like a simple wade across the swampy expanse was taking, well, 'forever'; but Bakri kept that to himself. We three resisted the temptation of looking back, moving in an orderly queue with Ramu taking point. I again conjured up scenes from *The African Queen*, blurring real from imagined, trying to lose myself in movie's narrative.

Every waterlogged trunk and tree limb bobbing in water, was a croc 'in waiting', or so I imagined. I was becoming dizzy with concentration, trying not to let my 'inventiveness run free: keeping a head clear and my imagination on a short leash. The fading light brought cool relief from a 'hot' sun. But there was no time to rest, as OPM was surely following closely behind us. And still, we held the bright fiery ball falling behind the towering reefs with awe and wonderment, still able to appreciate something so simple as a setting sun.

Alluvial deposits in the marsh clouded the waters with silt, but also gave us solid footing; we were making good time. But as the fading of light signaled the coming of night, we entered a bog that swallowed me up to my ankles. I managed a short distance, my legs now 'dead weights': encased in 'wet' mud that could have passed for newly poured cement. The 'mire' claimed both my sandals and stamina. Every step, lifting one foot forward to gain traction in pulling the other free from the vice-like suction, stripped me not only of my clothes, but sanity. I could go no further.

"Okay then, stay here. Better yet, you should lay down and take a break. But Ramu and me, we do not have that luxury. I will choose the time and place, and this is neither. Next month is my daughter's birthday. And I will help her blow out the candles. You should be there. We 'Batak' throw a mean party."

The rhythm of our march became mesmerizing, like a cadence. The glitter of moonlight through the dense canopy of trees was the only thing going for us as we 'slogged' onward. I could only hope we were not going around in circles.

Daylight brought hordes of mosquitoes looking to make a meal of us. While ever so tempting, stopping was not an option. Ramu, still in front, was using an 'invisible' rope, 'willing' us onward. Finally, we broke into a small clearing and that led to a rock-faced wall. We all took measure of this obstacle before us, all the while looking upward. It soon became apparent that we had no other option but to climb. It was up, or nothing. We were hemmed in but three walls – there was no going forward: only backwards.

As if on cue, Bakri, broke into spasms of near hysteria that left him lying on the ground trying to catch his breath. Finding nothing funny about our situation, I joined him. Like a contagion, our laughter spread to Ramu. "We gotta do what we gotta do." The absurdity of my impromptu remark left us again in 'stitches'.

Bakri finished with some 'proverb' that only he could come up with at a time like this: "A fit of laughter is always better than a fit of rage." Then smiling, he added: "I needed that!"

Returning from the spirit world

An uneasy 'peace' was the 'new norm'. Markets were now open, and restrictions except for a late-night curfew lifted. Kumi-Krispe sat staring at the wall in front of his desk, adorned with the 'rough' tapestry his mother had given him so many years before, on the occasion of his graduation from the National Police Academy. The intricately woven hemp tapestry, colors long faded, lent a coarseness to the surreal pictorial of 't' figures wielding hoe-like implements in a terraced garden; the scene set against a backdrop of a steep rocky hill shrouded in a blur of gray. He would often let his gaze linger on this symbolic reaffirmation of his Papuan-ness; whenever feeling the conflicted pull in being of two worlds, and of neither. Doing what he did whenever he felt this 'tug' threatening to undo the precarious 'order' that thinly veiled an internal chaos threatening to well up, he sought out his two close friends.

"No fire, just smoke: yes, smoldering," he described the tenuous state of calm that hung over Wamena: "Like a wet rag," he shared. Gindo and Ali had remained silent. But they understood very well. Looking at the banker, Kumi-Krispe pivoted: "Your Batak friend, along with his American companion, may still be alive. But please, keep this to yourselves. Do not ask me more because I have already said too much."

The baby had been fussy with colic all afternoon, leaving Icha in a frenzied state of anxiousness. She found reprieve tending to the three while Desi did her best to soothe the infant in the next room. The little bit of homespun wizardry had not yet had the desired effect: a concoction of castor oil sweetened with young coconut milk and honey.

Gindo could not help but ask: "And Nono, any news?" To which Kumi-Krispe could only shake his head. All the while, Icha strained to listen in on the conversation among friends, pouring freshly squeezed lemon juice sweetened by the gooey drippings of pressed honeycomb in a cheesecloth of sorts, served up piping hot. She had promised herself to stay out of the detective business since being asked by that Colonel Agus to spy on her Dani friends. Tami and Kat had posed no risk to anyone. They were simply just that, friends, who she bought chickens from, gossiped with, and they helped her without asking anything in return; and by doing so, put themselves in jeopardy. Not only with the local authorities, but with their own people: the Dani.

But she did have news that she kept to herself, beating down the urge to share with even Desi. She learned that Nono might be in a village to the south of Wamena, hidden away in an impenetrable highland jungle. But she could not, would not, part with this information, at least not yet, for fear of again implicating Tami and Kat. She resolved that this time she would not fail Nono. Her mind had been racing for days to come up with a plan, the gist of which relied on help from the most unlikely source: the Grand Police Commissioner Adjutant, Lieutenant Colonel Kumi-Krispe, no less.

Sleep had eluded a restless Icha until the 'wee hours' of the morning; and so the insistent barking of the neighbor's dog failed to stir her. Blurry-eyed, she forced herself to gather up her crying baby for a feeding, swaddled against the chilly dawn air.

Making her way to the cooking area, she barely took notice of the sliver of paper sticking out from under the door. After taking a moment, her 'antennae' told her something was amiss. She gently pulled at the corner, but it did not yield. She unlatched the chain and turned the lock, letting the door swing open as if by magic, as it did every morning, squeaking on its hinges. A crinkled ball of paper now wedged against the backside of the door thanks to her handiwork spoke clearly and loudly to Icha: 'pick me up before anyone sees you'. And as if 'on cue', the baby began crying and Gindo could be heard entering the kitchen area, exclaiming, "It is so cold this morning," as he proceeded to rummage around for a pot to warm up water for his bath. All this as she snatched up the balled paper and placed it in her apron pocket.

For the next two days, Icha camped out in front of the provincial police compound, waiting for the opportunity to ambush Lieutenant Colonel Kumi-Krispe, and enlist his support in the plan still percolating, whirling about in her brain like some dervish 'sufi' dancer spinning around in a long and flowing robe, all for the sake of achieving the right hypnotic state in communing with the divine; or in Icha's case, to rescue Nono. It was Kumi-Krispe who caught sight of Icha wandering a corridor leading to the 'kamar mandi' – or bathrooms, as he strolled to relieve his mind and urge to pee. "Icha, nobody told me you were here. Come to my office and take some tea. You cannot think of going. I will arrange…"

Icha surprised herself and the Grand Police Commissioner Adjutant with an emphatic: "No," before he could finish the sentence. "I must go, and I cannot, will not, share the information I have unless I have your word. You must promise me." She continued: "The instructions are clear, that nobody else must know. I believe you are a good man, and I cannot do this alone. I have not even a name for the village, only numbers."

"Coordinates," corrected Kumi-Krispe. "Let me think about this."

Icha now shouted out a, "No," although she did not mean to yell. "I must know now, and you cannot tell anybody else." She stood resolute; arms folded across her chest.

Kumi-Krispe, drawing on some inner strength, tinged with resignation, finally replied in a whisper: "Okay," looking at her as if for the first time, aware that *pembantu* Icha was much more than what she seemed.

He followed her with a 'thousand-mile stare', taking in her poised and assured gait as she passed through a small metal door to the back of the compound, opening into an empty field, across from the strip of dirt road that circled the complex. Kumi-Krispe understood what was at stake, and not just the life of Nono.

There are times when you set aside all self-interests and put it all on the line, including career, maybe life: my life, he thought. *This is one of those times.* His mother, yanked from her Dani existence to tend to the new home of her husband on Java with six children in tow, stood as a selfless totem by her own sacrifices. She often told her son that the ancestors would always protect him, as long as he honored their spirits by protecting those who needed protecting. He hoped this was so!

Turning up the heat

Brigadier General Radolfo Putri fully understood the implications of what was now entering a new and most dangerous phase of OPM aggression, or struggle, depending on one's persuasion; a distinction that ideology and political leanings tend to blur with simplistic euphemisms like 'good' and 'bad'. The targeting of government institutions including schools and health facilities had jolted the 'powers that be' into rethinking the separatist threat posed, from Merdeka and Bogor Palaces to the Armed Forces General Headquarters – Markas Besar Tentara Nasional Indonesia in Cilangkap, east Jakarta.

The General's communications to the 'three-star' (Lieutenant General) serving as Kepala (Head) of BAIS, short for Baden Intelijen Strategis Tentara Nasional Indonesia (Indonesian National Armed Forces Strategic Intelligence Agency), were unequivocal, and devoid of any sanguine expression of a quick 'fix'. "This escalation is nothing short of a reign of terror intended to create fear and panic among locals, Papuans and non-Papuans alike, now painted as 'fair game': in the OPM crosshairs."

The burning of three schools and killings of a student and two teachers in Boega District, whom OPM claimed were government spies, brought the General to Dambet village, located nearby in the same district. Rising through the ranks of Kopassus, he reveled in taking to the field, leading by example; in this case, on a dirt bike with a small contingent of soldier 'bikers'. This was not about hunting the perpetrators, but rather calming the population with a show of bravado. The message being: 'everything is under control'. That narrative lost as Radolfo Putri took a bullet to the head.

The repercussions are swift in coming. Reason and restraint 'out the window' as assailants are hunted down, and non-judicial punishment meted out with little distinction as to actual complicity. It is enough just to be Papuan.

Time of reckoning

Intended to restore order to a restive Papua, the impact of this new campaign proves quite the opposite. Like a lightning bolt igniting a wildfire during a 'strike', so is the reaction of the indigenous Papuan population. Timika is under siege. Even well-armed troops cede to the mobs running 'amok': laying waste to the town and surrounding villages. Frightened Indonesians and foreigners working for the international mining company PT Freeport-McMoRan Indonesia (FCX) become hostage in their segregated and protected living compound(s), replete with amenities like a golf course and movie theater. Even a Sheraton hotel. A facsimile of 'little America' in the wilds of Papua.

Strike action at the numerous mining sites operated by FCX now threatens to disrupt the very economic lifeline of TNI, which sources more from industries under their control than through government appropriations, not least the largest copper-extraction operation on the planet. Equally worrisome for the architects of this amazing amalgamation of peoples, tribes, religions, oceans, and islands, is the potential loss of revenues from this mammoth mining enterprise flowing into the national coffers. Without such, subsidies for critical essentials like rice and petrol will simply not be sustainable. All in all, putting the integrity of the *Republic* at risk; never mind fueling separatist notions from across the 17,000 islands united under Jakarta rule.

Chasing down 'the three amigos'[39]

The radio set was more vintage than antique and fitted snuggly in the green rucksack with 'Property of USN' stenciled on the pocket flap. The din of the static whited out most of the words. Abraham could barely string out enough to make intelligible the garble. The words of *pertempuran* (fighting) and *pemimpin tim turun* (team leader down) nevertheless caught his attention straight away. The distinctive clatter of small arms fire lent audio clarity to the scenario being played out, in real time. Attempts to raise Bravo team following the initial 'burst' of transmission proved futile. Abraham knew they were now in a race, his team, and that the mission had radically shifted: from finding the 'three amigos', as the Lieutenant back with the remainder of the platoon in Kataya had 'coined' the subjects of their search, to the rescue of Bravo team.

The intel gleaned from the 'old women' in Kataya was of a band of mostly young people finding their way to the settlement shortly after the departure of the two 'boulays'. They came in search of fertile land to settle and plant gardens; their hilltop village no longer able to sustain a community that had outgrown itself. But there was never any mention of guns, let

---

39 *https://en.wikipedia.org/wiki/Three_Amigos.*

alone OPM. 'Mother hen' Mola would have been proud as they all followed the script as practiced.

Abraham now recognized that the story told by the women questioned was a tad too uniform. So focused was the operation on finding the 'lost' amigos that they missed the obvious. This oversight was nothing short of tactical failure, overlooking and underthinking the threat at hand. And now they were paying the price.

With no coordinates to fix their position relative to Bravo team, Abraham scrambled to close whatever real or perceived distance there was between the two. One of his team, a Corporal who was tasked with the 'comms' owing to his technical prowess in keeping the radio in some semblance of working order, quickly proved laggard owing to the excess bulk and weight he was carrying on his back. "This damnable radio is an abomination," he barked. Abraham frequently shared his frustration at being shackled as if by a chain to this 'more-often-than-not' useless appendage, even in the capable hands of the Corporal. He made the decision to position the Corporal along with another member of his team beneath a rocky outcrop affording both protection and 'eyes' as far as the river below, with the rest stripping down to essentials for the long haul ahead.

Rude awakening

Jacques was not even aware of having dozed; he was suddenly spitting out the frothy bloody mess that kept pooling in his mouth. Taking little notice of the spilled teeth on the ground, although aware that they were his. He oddly imagined himself gluing them back in place. "Just out of reach," he said, trying as he did to sit up and latch onto some invisible handhold and yank himself back to reality. He felt himself teetering between unconsciousness and wishing he were dead.

A dull blade ripped rather than cut the lobe from his ear, or nearly. He tried to gather his arms around his head for protection as he turned onto his stomach, just as his torment was interrupted. Screaming erupted from whomever was standing over him: one sounding of anguish, another of fury. He rolled over as Ramu thrust, again and again, the jagged end of a long bamboo stalk into the writhing form now lying beside him. As the life of his attacker ebbed away, carried by the retreating tide of bright red blood pooling under his torso, they could not avert their eyes from his blackening stare, gazing at nothingness.

Ramu dripped water from his leather pouch onto Jacques' face, wiping clean the sticky blood smears with his thumb. The blood oozing from the torn earlobe was already beginning to congeal. Bakri was not so gentle, and splashed coconut milk on his face after Ramu had his turn; tugging him by his arm slowly to his feet. "Take this," Bakri demanded of Jacques, offering up a halved, filled coconut that was no less than the 'elixir of life' at this moment in time. Jacques swished the white liquid around his mouth, puffing his cheeks in and out like a blowfish. Feeling lightheaded as he savored the thirst-quenching liquid; in addition to proving antiseptic to his rearranged mouth, now minus a few teeth.

Serving notice that he was still alive and planned to stay that way, Jacques welcomed the searing pain emanating from his right jaw and now-swollen cheek. Not so much his ear. A sense of calm enveloped him as he felt less wobbly on his feet, wishing now for 'the more pain the better.' "What happened?"

"Not sure, but we prepared. Ramu collected some rocks and mature bamboo stalks and young pliable tree saplings while you took a leisurely nap. We fashioned some slingshots with vines, and even added a cradle for the small stones intend as projectiles. We were sitting there" – he pointed – "in the thicket of 'black' bamboo, when this crazed child came running at you, to where you were lying, and began to pummel you with his fists. Ramu was able to reach him as he tried sawing at your ear with a sharpened flintstone." Jacques staggard upright and reached for his 'brothers', hugging the 'crap' out of them.

The three gathered themselves in mind, body, and spirit, ever so mindful that others would soon be following and armed with more than bare fists and sharp stones. The attack only made more imperative what they must do next. "Stay here and wait for me to reach the first perch that should support the three of us. There!" Bakri and Jacques looked up, following Ramu's gaze. "I will then lower the vine-rope and first pull

Bakri up, and then you." He nodded to Jacques. "Then we will do it all over again, and again, until reaching the top."

It had been decided that the three segments of braided vines would be 'made one' using a conventional 'square knot'. But less certain was the best knotting for pulling what Ramu hoped would not be 'dead weight'. A smooth rope would have favored the 'prusik knot'. But Jacques worried that the knot, intended to cinch on the line during an ascent or descent, would meet with too much resistance using the roughly hewn vines-turned-rope. *But what the heck*, he thought, it was not like they were in possession of an iota of climbing acumen: never mind even the most basic of gear. "Bakri, 'damn', you know I am scared of heights. Even standing on a stool leaves me shaky – unsteady." He now had to put his life 'in the hands' of Ramu, quite literally.

Plan gone awry

Alpha team had cleared the ridge skirting the elevated mountain range, having made good time in moving upstream, while avoiding the twisting and turning contours that would have made passage by way of the riverbank nonsensical. The lake that came into their field of vision was fed by the same river that it was emptying out into, not so unlike a snake with a large bulge in its middle of some half-digested meal.

Abraham 'followed his nose', flitting down the grassy slope with a 'naked eye' to the water's edge; taking in the deceptively serence landscape that gave nothing away. He pulled his binoculars, holstered on his webbed belt, and scanned the wetlands, just outside his visual reach. The green 'camos' were a dead giveaway, as were the bodies now bobbing listlessly, mostly on their 'not-yet' bloated stomachs.

The scene that unfolded as they approached the marsh resembled a macabre horror show. The mutilated remains of Bravo team told a story of unbridled savagery: *maybe intentional*, thought Abraham, *so that the ancestorial spirits would not recognize the fallen; and the flurried act of humiliation. After all, these were Dani warriors.* The onslaught must have come from all directions as evidenced by the dead attackers scattered in two quarter-moons, almost linking up with one another. Most certainly outnumbered by this ragtag force, Abraham conjured up images of desperation and fear as, one by one, Bravo team sank into the murky waters.

A Sergeant on his team waddled up to him, weapon raised above his head, with his scouts scanning the marsh, from front to back, and sideways, with rifles 'at the ready'. Abraham understood their own vulnerability as they now waded through tall grasses following a barely discernable channel. "This is bigger than us. Did you notice the bodies, theirs and ours, stripped of any firearm? So, there are more of them out there."

Abraham confronted this mayhem, especially the butchery that left the corpses disfigured, in some cases beyond recognition; at first with revulsion followed by an unbearable anguish, for these were more than the sum of Bravo team. They were every bit 'his' family, as was the church that took him in and the sometimes irritable but always forgiving straggly bearded missionary who raised him as his own. His own self-inflicted pride in being part of TNI, albeit the National Police, now 'kicked in', and in a moment of weakness, or maybe self-awareness, he understood that he wanted revenge, hungered for it, and was willing to risk all to get it.

"Return downstream with the team and send out a message. You must describe what we found here. Leave me two scouts. We will pursue the perpetrators of this crime. I cannot say that this is OPM, at least not for sure. But the similarity to the attack on the repair crew at the sabotaged communications tower is obvious, in that all were severely mutilated. Some likely while still alive. Maybe the work of some crazed renegade faction of OPM."

As Abraham and his scouts pressed on, he began

connecting the dots, both in time and space: from the events at the communications tower; to the 'visitors' who wandered into the settlement; with the here and now. *Yes, he thought, they were likely 'one and the same'.*

Saving Nono

Not devout, a Muslim, nevertheless. Only the slightest movement of her lips and quivering fingers, keeping count, betrayed the calming mantra: 'Subhan Allah' (Glory be to God), 'Al-hamdu lila' – Praise be to God, and 'Allahu Akbar' – God is the greatest; silently repeating each thirty-three times. She was not so devout as to rely on the ninety-nine stringed 'prayer beads', or 'worry beads' to those so inclined, referred to as 'misbaha' in Arabic. For Icha, they were more incantations of the worrying sort. Her way of coping.

Icha sat stiffly as if to brace herself against the vibrations that ran from the soles of her feet and up through her body, like an electric current. Her stoicism was etched on an otherwise blank canvas: her face. Her rigid expression gave nothing away, at least outwardly. Icha was 'digging deep' to control her fear. And yet, she had never felt more alive.

As the yellow Bell 407 helicopter carrying the PT Freeport logo swooped through the air, bucking downdrafts, and then soaring to frightening heights, Kumi-Krispe took Icha's hand in his and offered a gentle squeeze. She turned and looked at him, mouthing a 'terima kasih'. It was the first time he had seen Icha so much as crack a smile.

The past twenty-four hours had been dizzying, to say the least. Kumi-Krispe marveled at the 'quick' response when he fielded his request directly to Colonel Agus. He supposed General Widodo had personally sanctioned this mission. He was equally sure there would be a price to pay, since bypassing his own Command hierarchy: the National Police. His reputation was for playing fair and sticking to the 'regs'. "But sometimes…!" He knew with absolute certainty this was 'that' time, his moment, conjuring up the universal military credo: 'better to ask for forgiveness than permission'.

A dozen or so children 'hooped and hollered', trying to reach for the long stick with the white cloth knotted at the pointed end. The young woman and old man had emerged from the treeline, together waving their improvised flag. *Practiced*, thought Kumi-Krispe. The 'wash' from the rotary blades as the helicopter gyrated into a descent 'kicked' up the loose earth into a swirl, obscuring the almost comical scene below.

Icha had been instructed to wait until given the 'thumbs-up' signal by the 'pilot', in his yellow shirt also bearing the PT Freeport logo, before exiting the craft. "Remember to keep your head low so you do not lose it," Kumi-Krispe shouted against the deafening whine of the engine as the skids finally grabbed hold of 'mother earth', but only after a few bumpy 'bum-jarring' attempts.

Kumi-Krispe steered Icha clear of the slowing whirl of the blades and toward the flag bearers and their entourage.

Greetings are symbolically important among all Papuans, and more so among the Dani. Sporting shorts and sandals and a T-shirt emblazoned with the 'LA Clippers', Kumi-Krispe slowly yet purposely strode up to the group with Icha in tow, in a manner that could only be inferred as non-threatening. His smile was not overdone nor undercooked, conveying an integrity that could not be faked. With head lowered, not bowed, he extended both his arms and gently reached for the old man. That so simple a gesture could make for such a powerful bonding without expression of words between the two strangers 'spoke' to the honesty and sincerity conveyed in the human touch. Kumi-Krispe, while under no illusions, was nonetheless humbled in the moment.

Icha had played out a hundred scenes as she imagined how Nono's release would unfold, just since embarking on this foray; now she stood momentarily 'dumbstruck' on seeing him emerge from the tangle of densely packed vegetation beyond the clearing, supported by a young man at the waist, using a stick to control his own unsteady movements as his body shook with jerky spasms. She had remained in the shadows as Kumi- Krispe and the old man talked, not understanding a word between the two. Until now! Icha could not help herself. She ran to Nono, covering half the distance between the two in a 'flash', then abruptly stopped and turned to face the old man, as if seeking his approval. She seemed to regain control over her vexed emotions; walking to him with arms outstretched, repeating, "*Terima kasih*," over and over again. The old man did not so much as flinch at this display of affection, disguised as gratitude, feeling the warm tears that ran down her face onto his bony shoulder.

Nono was ill, there was no doubt. Emaciated and shaky on his knees, he was helped into the helicopter. He showed no emotion, not even the slightest suggestion of relief. Once safely ensconced between Icha and Kumi-Krispe, he remained in a trance-like stupor. His 'thousand-mile stare' to nowhere giving nothing away except for the high mental toll exacted from his suffering.

Don't look down

"You can do this," shouted Bakri, feet dangling from the ledge of the precipice. Ramu had made 'short work' of the climb to the first of three overhangs we had mapped out before tackling the steep cliff face, substituting 'paper and pen' for 'ground and stick'. More surprising was watching Bakri scurry upward, digging into crevasses carved into the rock wall canvas. Our crude dirt drawing eerily resembling a 'Picasso' etching I had once puzzled over in an Amsterdam museum, in a failed attempt to impress no one in particular, except maybe the Japanese 'goddess' who I could not help but notice doing the same. I vaguely recalled the name of this work that meant little to me at the time: *Seated Man Reading a Newspaper*, circa 1912.[40]

"I can do this!" Trying to convince only myself, psych myself up: maybe both. I stuck my swollen toes in the first fissure, while reaching for the next. "Umm, maybe, just maybe." I had little upper body strength left by this time and had to extend my bent knees in moving from crack to crack. All trussed up in my improvised harness of braided vines that ran under my

---

40   *https://i.pinimg.com/*
     originals/16/7d/30/167d30a8080898dc7a402e31d7a08b36.jpg.

arms, I felt like a roped steer, minus the horns, ready to dangle from the lasso, with Ramu playing the part of the cowboy. I managed to keep my panic in check, except on those occasions when looking down to the ground. Yes, this was one of those life-or-death times in which you trusted yourself to never let go. In my case, of a rock wall.

All went quickly 'to shit' on the last leg of the climb. "We need to haul him up, now!" Bakri knew I was going no further. Not on my own. He tied the end of the intertwined vines around his waist and braced his outstretched feet against the boulder: a human anchor.

'Leaking blood like a sieve' from vine-made incisions that sliced through palms and fingers to the bone, tendons bulging from sinewed arms as if ready to burst, Ramu pulled, hand over hand, with me at the other end screaming like a banshee.

The vine-rope, just peeled strips of bark woven together, proved remarkably resistant to breaking under the strain, yielding, loosening, and tightening, with every pull. But the lifeline was now fraying badly, hanging over the cliff's jagged rock edge and threatening to splinter altogether from the heat of the friction and added dead weight: I flailed madly below. Finally, 'up and over', and just in time.

"Tarzan would be proud," spoke a 'spent' Ramu.

"Yeah, just switch the loincloth for a 'koteka,'" Bakri chimed in, smiling at his own comical contribution to the thought.

The flayed skin on my upper body, particularly under my arms, looked as if someone had taken a whip to me. My feet by now a bloody mess, swollen and rotting. "No wonder you could not manage even a foothold," Bakri continued.

Still 'high' on adrenaline and drenched slick with sweat, nerve-endings temporarily oblivious to the damage done, I added to the subtle levity: "You sure are talkative."

Ramu's Indonesian was rudimentary but entertaining

in creating a relatable 'imagery' to his words, roughly communicating: "They will swat this climb like a pesty mosquito buzzing the ear and finding a meal in the nose. We need to leave this place."

Bakri delighted in Ramu's mastery of *Bahasa* and could not help himself: "Makes me want to scratch my nose."

"Our women are expert at weaving, using '*pisak gagalek*' – knitted bark yarn – in making '*sali*' and '*yokal*' – traditional skirts for unmarried girls and married women, respectively. I am sorry my skill is not so good. It would be better if we had a girl with us."

To which Bakri replied, "Maybe a wife for you, of marrying age of course."

"Yes," answered Ramu, "maybe Jacques and I can find sisters, and become brothers," with the utmost sincerity.

But Ramu continued to impress as he gently unfolded his pouch to yield a clutch of eggs taken from one of the many birds' nests nestled into the 'nooks and crannies' of the cliff just scaled. After he had disappeared for a short stint, his way whenever searching out food and drink, a feast was had; taking the time to build a small fire for a banquet of tubers, grubs, and eggs. I could not help thinking that 'hunters and gatherers', no matter tribe or geography, could not afford long-term aspirations, since survival was really a day-to-day affair.

My near starvation was punctuated by cravings that ring true of the cliché: Americans love to eat fast food. I think not a day has gone by since the beginning of our ordeal when I have not had 'Pizza Hut' on my mind.

Package delivered

Colonel Agus had been waiting on them at the military airfield when the helicopter touched down. While Nono was whisked away by ambulance, Kumi-Krispe was taken aside and the two disappeared inside a small antennae-laden building adjoining a reception/departure terminal. In the deserted arrival lounge, Icha sat and sat until she could no longer keep her nerves 'at bay'; at which point, she found herself pacing back and forth, her restiveness on full display to the onlookers not hiding their curiosity on the other side of the large plate windows looking out onto the airfield.

When they finally emerged wearing faces masked of any emotion, Icha was sure she had gotten herself yet again in 'hot water'. After all, this was the story of her young life. *Did they not understand I am nothing more than a* 'pembantu'?

Colonel Agus spoke first: "Do you know what you have done?" Maybe letting his words 'hang' a little too long before continuing. "What we could not!" Kumi-Krispe then surprised her, taking a step forward and embracing her. "You, Icha, are much more than a *'pembantu',"* he said, as if having read her mind.

The hotel room at the Timika Sheraton was more fitting

for someone else, not so much for her. She felt almost in a dream, one she could never have imagined. Except for the heavily armed soldiers just out of sight, she could have been a *'panguian'*, a sultan's wife.

Icha could not help smiling. She never looked for confirmation of her ideas or actions. Her family back in the 'village' only recognized 'the girl', never the woman: obstinate, sometimes fickle, single-minded, and unyielding once she got a notion in her head. Her *'nenek'*, or 'grandmother', often scolding: "No man will marry you; just: *Terlalu keras kepala, sama anjing gila*" – too stubborn, same as a rabid dog." But that fierce determination now brought her a sense of peace. She could now turn her attention to her baby girl, whom she suddenly wanted to hug to her breast and protect from all the craziness around her.

"*Pujilah Allah*," she spoke aloud, and not for the first time, thankful that Desi was caring for her daughter. Truth be told, she just wanted to get back to being the *'pembantu'* she was; although she knew in her 'heart of hearts' that she was so much more.

For three days she waltzed with different partners, going over the events that led her first to Kumi-Krispe, and then the two of them to Nono. Her tepid inquiries about Nono had gone unanswered, although assured he was getting the best care possible. A General Widodo had visited her that morning, for the sole purpose of thanking her. "Your contribution in securing the release of Nono was recognized by the President himself, for which you should feel proud. We are grateful for all you have done." His perfunctory words were not intended to evoke a response.

Notwithstanding, Icha replied, catching a surprised Widodo off guard: "It was I that put Pak Nono in danger, and so I had no choice but to act."

"How is that?" asked a quizzical General, genuinely puzzled by her remark. And so Icha told him the story.

The setting sun and approaching twilight brought a surreal feeling that this time and place was of another world; a moment she wanted to savor. Tomorrow she would be returning to Wamena and the life that was her own. Impulsively, Icha wondered if anyone would mind if she took a stroll by the pool and maybe dipped her toes in the clear turquoise-blue waters.

A tall tale

"Impossible!" Narsiem shook his head, making an equally emphatic gesture; emitting a discernable clicking noise for added effect.

Captain Smarts continued: "Our sources are considering the accusations as a fanciful version of the facts. But we are obliged to follow-up, if for no other purpose than to clear the reputations of Commander Jacques and his Indonesian colleague."

Narsiem could not hold back. "His name is Dr. Bakri Ginting, and you will not meet a more honorable and caring human being. As for the Commander, my understanding is that you have never actually met him."

Choosing his words carefully, he continued: "Sir, respectfully, this makes no sense. And regardless of the truth, this 'inquiry' will only serve to bring into question their integrity, character, based on what is in all probability a self-serving distortion of the facts from the one person who is likely more 'villain than saint'. This army wash-out crashed his helicopter for no reason and was medically discharged based on his mental health." Actually, Commander Norman had only just learned of this 'tidbit' from none other than an incensed

Captain Lavender, shouting into a hands-free speaker phone from 'half a world away'. Norman was quickly on the 'horn' passing on this news to Narsiem and a select few others, knowing full well that Smarts was using every opportunity to sully Jacques' name, and use as fodder in his crusade to shut down the Jayapura lab, but for good!

On the call, Norman shared: "MAF screwed up badly in not asking for official documentation pertaining to his service record when they brought him aboard," speaking of course of John, the pilot.

A tired-looking Colonel Dowdy was seated to the left of the Ambassador, sitting at the head of the long rectangular table when Captain Smarts was ushered into the meeting room. From there, nothing went as 'Wild' Bill had imagined. It lasted just a short while, but an eternity to the dapper navy Captain in his pressed summer whites uniform; the Ambassador had effectively reprimanded him for initiating an investigation without so much as providing the embassy with notification, never mind seeking consultation. When Captain Smarts suggested that this was a navy affair, an incredulous Kile 'shut him down'. "Captain, I am responsible for everything that goes on here. Or maybe you would rather speak with the PACOM Commander back in Hawaii, with whom I spoke earlier this morning. Your rush to judgment in this case, given the circumstances, makes clear you are interested more in 'finding fault', even going so far as to impugn the integrity of a 'missing' naval officer, than uncovering the truth. To undertake such an action is preposterous, beyond judicial sense, especially so when Commander Jacques has yet to even surface." Not normally given to tirades, he now looked to his Defense Attaché.

Colonel Dowdy, or 'Winny' to the select few that included his Rick, was still 'smarting' from his verbal 'shellacking' at the hand of a very perturbed Captain, one in the same: 'for not doing enough'.

"I arrived at Halim airport this early morning, returning from Papua on a TNI passenger jet. I, along with the RSO – Regional Security Officer – and some of his Indonesian staff, interviewed the pilot. Furthermore, we managed through TNI interpreters, making our way by army helicopter to the remote village where he was found, to conduct random interviews among the locals.

"Not only did the pilot's story change repeatedly with each 'telling', but not one was remotely plausible given that he was found with a young girl, pregnant, described by the villagers as his wife. We learned that his marriage was forced by the community after he was discovered having his way with this 'child'. Given the circumstances, we can surmise that the Commander and his group probably fled, fearful for their lives, as I would mine, following the discovery that one of their own was a sexual predator, a pedophile, defying the hospitality and societal norms of the very people who had given them sanctuary.

"You do not understand Papua or the people who live there! The village elders, coming from the Dani tribe, in-all-likelihood would have meted out their own justice, in the absence of any other authority, government or otherwise. You need to understand that most encounters with their Dani neighbors are 'few and far between', much less with outsiders, 'boulay', including non-Papuan Indonesians. The only authority they recognize is their own, and that of their warrior ancestors."

'Wild' Bill looked as he felt, like someone had stuck a 'shiv' up his tight ass. He had not even mentioned the Reuters reporter he spoke with the previous evening looking to confirm the the'story' now freely circulating in the stratosphere; defying gravity, all but giving it 'a leg to stand on'.

The next morning, the local press was full of itself, regurgitating the many stories perpetrated by the 'pilot' using an unwitting accomplice, MAF, as his mouthpiece. The tabloids were trying to outdo each other with sensational copy. Even the more reputable news media bought into the hyperbole: 'hook, line and sinker'; taking a line from the fishing adage. The 'string' running through all the reports was in attributing comments by Captain Smarts attesting to the veracity of the claims being made.

Echo, echo, echo

Lolling on the long grass, matted and made warm from our body heat, we three, bellies full, made little effort to stir, luxuriating for a few minutes of mindless wonder. The setting sun offering a welcoming shade from what had been a 'scorcher' of a day.

"Go go go," I whispered while gritting my teeth for effect. Still sore, I managed to stand, just, my right foot threatening to betray me. Rot had settled into calluses, cracked and deeply rutted, oozing yellowish pus: a dead giveaway of the infection that had set in. Ramu grabbed my left arm and draped it over his shoulder, as Bakri took the lead. I was able to hobble, each agonizing step bringing tears to my eyes. All the while thinking that the searing pain was a 'good thing'. "At least I can still feel them, wiggle my toes."

Shouts reverberating off the canyon sides were distant and close, coming from somewhere and going nowhere, words impossible to decipher. Ramu stopped and turned to face the cliff's edge, listening intently. The 'barking' commands bouncing off the rock walls were no more. "They will not climb tonight. We too need to rest." Unexpectedly, Ramu hoisted me onto his back, wrapping my arms around his neck and holding them in place with his iron grip, making for 'still' higher ground with Bakri trailing close behind.

As first light suddenly broke across the horizon, lifting the veil of darkness, so did the echo of gunfire erupt: *tat tat tat*! The pinging of bullets could easily be heard ricocheting off stone as volley after volley silenced the usual jungle chatter accompanying the start of a new day. The rapid-fire exchanges soon became more refined, to single shots fired, and from the same weapons. Intermittent screams could be heard above the din.

Life goes on

As the violence abated in Timika, an audible sigh of relief could be heard across the island nation, all the way from Jakarta; and no more so than in Jayapura and Wamena. The rage-fueled rioting, 'taking to the streets', was 'spent'. At least for the time being. Analogous to a tropical storm morphing into a typhoon, drawing energy from warm surface sea waters, so too could the mood of the province turn ugly under the right conditions.

A 'show of strength' by TNI was no longer viewed by the security apparatus as having the desired effect. Quite the opposite! The presence of troops acknowledged to be fomenting local resentment, no less than an occupying force. But to BAIS TNI, there were 'no good' options.

There was something undeniably 'settling' in falling back into her daily routine, that inexplicable sense that all was okay with the world, at least her world. Icha promised herself to never again 'give in' to the 'fanciful thinking' that she could be a different person; 'robbing her of her child', and 'her child of her mother'. Gindo had again brought up the idea of coming to Jakarta, putting a roof over their head and food on the table, a chance at a better life, certainly for her daughter.

Noncommittal, 'on the verge' of ambivalent, Icha made no attempt to disguise her mixed if not contradictory feelings. So Gindo let it drop.

She understood that Nono had been moved to Jakarta, along with his family; grateful that he would be properly cared for. Kumi-Krispe had returned to Wamena, with 'Adjutant' stricken from his new title, 'Grand Police Commissioner', befitting his promotion to a 'full bird' Colonel.

Following a Thursday evening at the game table taking on Gindo and Ali, as was their custom, partaking in *teh*, sweets, and gossip, he confided to Icha who saw him to the door, and out into the night to his waiting escorts: "My immediate superiors wanted me 'court-martialed' for having bypassed the 'chain of command'. If not for General Widodo's intervention, I would have been executed rather than promoted". Icha's immediate reaction was that of 'dismay, then anger'; fiercely clenching her teeth and fists, as if poised to fight a 'dragon'. "Woops! Please, I was only playing with words. You would make a good Dani warrior."

To which Icha put to Kumi-Krispe: "As was your mother?"

Icha had been told during her last night at the Sheraton that she could never talk about the events leading to Nono's rescue, or her time in Timika. Kumi-Krispe reminded her of this, and the same of any confidence shared between the two. Icha could not help but buzz with a 'tinge of pride' in feeling worthy of such trust.

Slaying the dragon

What bullets could not accomplish, or at least finish, bludgeons to the head with heavy rocks did. The thickly bearded leader of the pack, wearing shorts and torn OPM-flagged T-shirt, lay mortally wounded. He was only able to lift his fingers as he traced the arc of the first blow with his fading vision. Abraham and his remaining scout were more methodical than frenzied as they went about their business, taking their vengeance out on the remaining band of marauders without hesitation: whether they be dead or wounded.

It was by no means a fair exchange, as Abraham and his scouts did most of the giving. The pre-dawn surprise had caught the ragtag bunch wholly unprepared for the inevitable onslaught. Even the bullet that ripped through the Moluccan scout's chest had likely ricocheted off the three-sided face.

His remaining scout, also from the Moluccan islands, scanned the steep walls of the boxed canyon leading to a 'dead end'. He supposed that the flat, sand and pebbled ground turned into a riverbed during heavy rains, by waters cascading down 'near'-vertical waterfalls; flooding the muddy bog they just came from, and eventually feeding into reed choked marshes they had waded through. As if instinctually, he looked up to the sky, hoping for cloud free skies in the hours ahead.

Both Abraham and his scout 'jumped out of their skins', taking cover behind a large boulder as shouts rained down upon them from above. "Help us, we are not with them, we are running from them," could be heard. A filthy brown rag sheepishly 'inched' its way from the brim of the cliff wall facing them as if suspended midair, except for the long stick it was knotted to. Confusion soon turned to that 'aha' moment as Abraham made sense of it all.

"The three amigos," he whispered hoarsely.

It was then that from out of nowhere a young boy bounded in their direction, pointing a crudely homemade wooden gun with a long barrel at the pair; actually, more slingshot than pistol, powered by two taut elastic bands. The searing pain as the bullet ripped through flesh proved the lethality of the weapon. This was no toy in the hands of a child at play.

Both scout and Abraham immediately pounced on the crazed, wild-eyed assailant. Subdued, the child continued to thrash about and try to break loose of his binds. The young boy was now on his stomach: wrists tied together behind his back, facing up, with elevated arms pulled straight back by the rope wrapped around his ankles, allowing for almost no 'give'; looking like a trussed-up pig fit for carrying to the slaughter. Scrappy and tenacious, the youngster was not taking well to captivity.

"You are bleeding," ventured his scout, just noticing a bloom of wetness spreading across his camouflaged jacket and seeping to his loose-fitting khakis, both still bunched up against the rock. He helped Abraham into a sitting position, undoing buttons and easing fabric off his shoulders. Rolling up his green T-shirt revealed the source of the flow: a 'angry' deep crevasse weeping profusely. "You have been grazed; but a lot of blood. After taking needle and thread from the first-aid kit pocket sewed into his web belt, the scout began to stitch the wound to stem the bleeding. For his part, Abraham grunted through gritted teeth, otherwise making no fuss.

'Mexican standoff'[41]

We had finally reached this perch that gave us advantage over our pursuers: a chance to make haste and create distance between 'them and us'. But Ramu and Bakri would hear none of my protestations. They sounded weak even to me. After an attempt at flag-waving, Bakri took the bold move of peering over the ledge. Two distinct voices bounced upward against the canyon walls: 'we are TNI' and 'come down to us'.

Had my head been held on by screws, I would have 'shook' it loose from my shoulders: "No way I am going back down there. No fuckin' way."

To which Bakri scolded me with a mean scowl etched on his face. "It is good that you can still find your anger when I am not mincing words." And meaning it.

The back and forth between 'us' and 'them' was turning

---

41 A Mexican standoff is an almost comical reference; imagining three parties holding a pistol to the head of another, so that each of the three has a gun pointed at their head. If any one of the three shoots, then a chain-reaction will result in all three with a bullet to the head. So, each is left with no 'good' options: to shoot or lay down their gun. The Mexican stand-off is more a scenario played out in the movies, and rarely ends well.

into a 'Mexican standoff', minus any third party, alive that is. Neither of us was budging, trust being in short supply. To retain advantage, we insisted 'they' come to 'us', and just one for starters.

Ramu had witnessed first-hand the brutality of our OPM nemesis. It did not take a 'great leap' to assume 'treachery' was also within their moral reach; no matter the absurdity of trying to stamp some ill-conceived notion of 'right versus wrong' to somehow justify such the 'means'.

Not sure what the yelling between Ramu and 'them' was all about, I tried to utter a few words seeking out some explanation, only to be 'shushed', Bakri drawing a finger to his lips. Finally, Ramu explained: "One of two is wounded, but not seriously. But he is too wobbly to climb."

"Wobbly?" I asked quizzically, finding how incongruous such a word, almost comical, taking any part in the conversation between 'us and them'. Bakri was quick with another 'shush'.

"We need to wait here," Ramu continued.

Bakri added: "They also have a prisoner, otherwise, the OPM 'dogs' are no more."

"So now what?" Although I already knew the answer.

Adding to my myriad of physical woes was a creeping lightheadedness. Beyond mere thirst, dehydration was taking its toll, leaving me unsteady on my feet. Bakri recognized the signs, and the imperative of finding water. We had ensconced ourselves on the rooftop of the canyon, with no access to river or stream, and little in the way of the vegetation-like bamboo grass and other plant life from which to extract the sweet, stored water. "Help, if that is what this is, better come fast," was all I could add.

Revelation

No good could come from the pounding on the front door, certainly not in the 'wee hours' of an early morning still clinging to what was left of the night. The roosters had not even begun their 'wake up' cackling. Icha found herself staring at the police Corporal, a Dani named Isaac, who always accompanied Kumi-Krispe on his Thursday night visits with Gindo and Ali: waiting outside, keeping vigil.

"*Selamat pagi*, Ibu Icha, I have been asked to fetch you and Pak Gindo."

Gindo, almost 'on cue', poked his head from the small hallway leading into the front room, looking as he felt: disheveled, having been roused from a deep slumber. "What is going on?"

Lips moving, emitting no sound. A hissing rush of air filled her ears and silenced the world around her. She stood stunned, leaning on the chair to keep from toppling over. Gindo had taken the baby, seeing how Icha had taken the news. Distraught, she began hyperventilating, trying to catch her breath. It took a 'force of will' to regain her composure, upon which she reached for her daughter.

The police Major – she did not catch her name, or much

cared – was more manikin than human, wearing a staid expression that revealed nothing. All she knew was she had to see Kumi-Krispe.

At first light, she and Gindo, under escort, boarded the Cessna, maneuvering so as not to step on the canvas stretcher filled with the new police commissioner. An oxygen mask strapped to his face, bandages plastered to his neck, the sedated Kumi-Krispe lay motionless, except for a gurgling sound accompanying his every breath. Icha held his hand in hers, no less than an embrace, refusing to let go the entire flight: sixty-five minutes that felt like forever.

The bungalow in the secured military enclave, in the larger-still TNI residential compound, was no Sheraton. But neither was her stay intended as a holiday. At least she had her baby with her this time. Having Gindo ensconced in nearby quarters settled her nerves but did nothing to allay her worry for Kumi-Krispe. She had no news of his condition since being whisked off and dropped at their accommodations. Until now!

Polite, but all business. Perfunctory introductions made. Icha took no small comfort in the presence of Colonel Agus. The policeman holding the rank of General officer smiled, and nodded to the Major at his side, waiting for his cue. The intel officer nodded, and proceeded with what felt a well-rehearsed narrative:

"Firstly, our apologies for all the secrecy, but you will come to understand why the both of you are now under our protection. To be sure, this is only temporary, and you are in no danger: not here, not now! Colonel Kumi-Krispe, as you know, was shot. He is at this moment undergoing surgery at Gatot Soebroto Rumah Sakit, in Jakarta. The doctors in Makassar did not want to chance removing the bullet lodged close to the cervical spine, where his neck meets his skull. He has the most skilled surgeons in the country attending to him. Of course, we will let you know what there is to know as we learn more.

"As for the 'here and now', we believe that whoever carried out this assassination attempt may also have sights on you two."

That was enough to cause a shudder finding its way to the base of Icha's spine. Before either of them could utter a word, the Major continued:

"We have some new information of Nono, who is now recovering from his ordeal, that may shed light on events over the past few months that may not seem related at 'first glance' but may tie everything together.

"I cannot say much at this time. But at this very moment, we are conducting an operation that we hope will be the end of this."

The plastic-coated sofa cushion squeaked as Gindo bent forward to ask, implore, for just a sliver more information. Looking first to the General, who reciprocated with a slight nod, the officer continued:

"We believe the Deputy Superintendent of Primary and Secondary schools in Wamena might somehow be involved in all this. Pak Gindo, we understand that Nono found receipts for the emptying of accounts maintained for the Regency by the Ministry of Education, Culture, Research, and Technology, at 'your' bank. But on close inspection, the signatures of the superintendent appeared forged, and her deputy is now missing.

"The deputy is a local, from right here in Timika. We believe he may have funneled monies to OPM."

To which Icha, also leaning forward to keep from sinking into the deep, soft cushion and disappearing into the sofa altogether, asked, "But what does that have to do with Pak

Nono's kidnapping and the attack on Kumi-Krispe, or us, for that matter?"

"Ha ha! Good question. We are still figuring that out. But we now believe they are somehow related. Maybe the kidnapping was designed to keep secret Nono's discovery, and he was held hostage to exact a reward from BNI. We also suspect the kidnappers never intended to release him. But when you and the Colonel returned with Nono, alive, you both became targets. They assumed it was only a matter of time before their secret got out.

"We also have the police report of the burglary that 'wasn't', nothing taken, the same day that Nono wondered off to a fate he could not have anticipated."

The Major looked again to the General, worried that maybe he had said too much. Again, the General nodded, signaling an affirmative. The General made to get up from his chair, but not before Icha blurted out: "No! This was not OPM! OPM took Nono from his captors, and worked through me, and I with Colonel Kumi-Krispe, to take him back. Could this be nothing more than a corrupt deputy trying to hide his actions and lay the blame on OPM?"

Icha was on a roll. "And could not have the killing of the two teachers been nothing more than a way to confuse, and point fingers in the direction of OPM?"

The General slowly sat back in his seat, as if caught trying to flee the scene of some indiscretion. All three uniformed men could not help but register their collective 'awe' as evidenced by their open-mouthed stares, taking in this 'pembantu' who defied all expectations. "I now understand what Kumi-Krispe saw, I mean sees, in this young woman," the General murmured, just barely recovering from his misspeak. At the same time, a creased 'quarter-moon' grin broke ear to ear across the normally deadpan face of Colonel

Agus, who had remained silent throughout the briefing. His smile said it all.

Having absconded the clutches of the law, the vice-superintendent was still considered a threat, but one not likely to pose any further danger to either Icha or Gindo. 'The gig was up'! 'Great minds' had concluded that criminal greed was the more likely motive, and not any sinister plot on the part of OPM; no matter being the 'bogyman' of choice, much like a favorite uncle. It took Icha to elucidate this logic. Both had given 'official statements' to the National Police before being allowed to return to Wamena.

Return of the Jedi
(from the *Star Wars* trilogy)

Returning from his banishment to 'his kind of town', Norman soaked up the humidity that only accentuated the briny fish smells of a Jayapura that had not changed 'one iota', not since his last stay. His mission this time was not in identifying new mosquito vectors for old diseases, adding to his collections, populating his breeding facility back in Jakarta, but rather to provide 'ears to the ground' as to progress in tracking down the elusive Commander Jacques.

Captain 'Wild' Bill, recently departed, was now in navy purgatory, albeit in sunny Hawaii, waiting on his expedited retirement following a 'letter of reprimand': the 'navy way' in rendering a career-ending scolding. A collective sigh was clearly audible at both the Embassy and on Jalan Percetakan Negara (the home of NMRC-Indonesia) when he skedaddled to the airport under cover of night from his lodging at the famous 'old' Borobudur hotel, having not yet moved into his permanent residence.

Strangely, the current 'peace' was more ominous then when the mobs had taken to the streets wielding their fists, and not without the machetes and axes for good measure, as Norman recollected.

After three restive days dusting the shelves and contacting local staff that the satellite laboratory would soon be back in business, his phone pinged the messages: "Colonel Simanjuntak has news. Can you join him for lunch this afternoon". The request as such left little wiggle room to interpretation. It was not so much an invitation, rather a summons.

Back to his 'old haunt', the Suni Garden and Lakeside Hotel on Sentani Lake, Norman refrained from ordering a beer, at least until concluding his business. The Colonel brought a guest, who was only introduced as Major Mugdi, with the Pakistan air force.

"An exhaustive ground search of area around from where the MAF 'pilot' was located, moving in concentric circles extending outward from the village, we have managed to locate the wreckage of the helicopter that carried Commander Jacques and his companions. Actually, not so much a wreckage. The Major here led a team to the site and examined the PK-YBB with our technicians. And while resting on its side, there is no evidence that the aircraft experienced any technical malfunction, or that its airworthiness was compromised. The tail rotor was twisted, but we believe from the impact of the landing. Major!"

"Thank you. Yes, we believe the helicopter was put into a steep dive, then tailspin, just prior to impact; landing on one skid and toppling over on its side. Impressive flying. But it is likely this was a controlled crash, a 'deliberate act', if you would. We examined the fuel lines and wiring, and there is nothing to suggest a stall."

The Colonel continued:

> "What made no sense was that the radio had been wrenched free and removed, the brackets holding it place shattered. There as a hammer wedged under the seat, possibly used to break it free of its mooring. A search of the area yielded nothing: no radio. I cannot speculate too much on this. But why would the radio if still in good working order have been removed from the craft? To enable repairs? Maybe a question for the 'pilot'. Nevertheless, I expect you will report back this information to your Embassy."

"Is there any additional news on the whereabouts of Commander Jacques and Dr. Bakri?" followed Norman.

To which Simanjuntak replied: "None that I am aware. But you understand that is out of my 'bailiwick,' not my responsibility."

As the two exited the large double doors of the empty dining room, Norman thought aloud: "And they did not even buy me lunch."

Robbed of the moment

Making for the dense jungle brush at the top of the rise, Ramu set off at sunset. I had an uneasy feeling as I watched him disappear into the tangled thicket, as if entering through an *Alice in Wonderland* looking glass, a portal to another world.

Bakri took the remaining water, counted in drops, no longer cups or even sips, and mixed it with the shallow dirt that dusted our rocky resting place; painting my face with the reddish clay mix, trying to cool my fever. Bakri called out from time to time, trying to elicit a response from the canyon floor. None came. The only positive sign was the gathering of storm clouds, the first in weeks. Rolling in, sheltering us from the sun's powerful rays; we were thankful. But salvation came with a 'catch': a return of rains. "We should look for shelter," I volunteered.

Agony! It only took a little poking and prodding, gentle as Bakri was, to set off every nerve ending, like firecrackers. I yelped! My foot was a mess. It was obvious that I was not going anywhere, anytime soon.

The day wore on. For the first time in a long time, we talked. Bakri of his family, his daughter. I of my few loves, all lost. "Sometimes I feel damaged. My need to feel loved, but also finding 'at peace' with my own company." I was not sure if that made sense to Bakri. It made little to me.

"Jacques, I have faith in you, that you will come to learn the greatest gift you can give yourself is to simply accept who you are, for a change, and never stop searching for 'that' one: and your capacity to love, and be loved." Feeling the wear on both body and soul, I needed to know, as if seeking reassurance for a life lived.

> *"What are we doing here? I mean, how did we come to be in this place? It is forgotten, torn between conflicting interests, and none particularly noble. We saved nobody! I had visions of coming to the rescue. Doing good. But we will likely leave nothing, not even a footprint as to our passing through. As if we were never here."*

Bakri was always a good listener, but never much for talking. Maybe it was because of the coming rains or utter sense of helplessness, but he spoke with a reverence I would associate as the providence of some 'bible-thumping' preacher.

> *"I have no answers! But your question hints to something swelling up inside of you. Maybe you just want to know that everything we have endured has meant something. I too feel as you. We came riding a white stallion to the rescue, without even a clue or care about the Dani themselves; forsaken by all sides. Funny how we never even thought to better learn about the place, the people, before setting off on our quest. Thinking our 'good deed' was enough.*
>
> *"But nothing is without consequence. Whatever happens, I truly believe we will have lifted a veil, a*

consciousness, about these precious people. Just by our being here!"

His words soothed and lulled me into a sleepy way: more a daydream.

The commotion roused me from wherever my consciousness was hiding. Or maybe it was the smell. Oh my God! Smoke was rising from a pit covered with a layering of banana leaves. Ramu held a chopped stalk of bamboo to my lips, letting the cool water play on my outstretched tongue. I abandoned all cares, slurping down the clear liquid, feeling it slide down my throat. The pressure between my ears, unnoticed until now, slipped away. Much like the 'popping' that comes with a rapid descent in altitude.

Ramu had struck 'gold'. Bringing down a juvenile wild boar with nothing more than a camouflaged hole in the ground and sharpened stick was masterful. He took no credit, though beaming with pride. Although far from Ninia, the ancestors would take rightful credit for this life-gifting prize. The revered tusks bundled together in a vine netting hanging over his shoulder would serve as testimony of this 'hunt'. Maybe Ramu would later fashion the bone for a nose piercing, or simply as an adornment, in memory of this 'moment'.

We tore into our feast. Skin crisped to a brittle perfection, succulent meat that bore a scrumptious deep earthy flavor: nutty; not suck off enough of the juices dripping from our hands and fingers; beyond scrumptious. Bakri, never forgetting his humanity, threw a few chunks over the edge of the cliff, yelling out: "These are for you."

I knew sure enough that with each morsel, my shrunken stomach would soon be in revolt. And sure enough, 'sooner rather than later', it did.

I was not sure which registered first, both imprinted in

my memory, my forever: the shot, or the look of surprise on Ramu's face. He looked down toward his chest, knees buckling, and fell face down. Not jerky, but also not fluid. The scene playing out in my head felt 'make-believe', if only it was. Bakri's stunned expression, frozen, was followed by a high-pitched wailing, not unlike an animal caught in a trapper's snare. As I reached for Ramu, Bakri draped himself over the 'still' body. "We are still 'the brothers three'," he said, in between sobs.

A 'bird's eye'

The view from the hill to the back of the laboratory gave Norman and recently arrived Hassan a perspective like none other. Small fires, at least from their vantage point, billowing black smoke and ash, could be seen creeping toward the city center and harbor warehouses, from all directions. Norman, not normally prone to shying away from just cataclysmic events, maybe even attracted by their 'scent', was genuinely scared. While not the 'garden-variety' volcanic eruption or tsunami, the mobs rampaging through the streets were no less 'a force of nature' defying all reason: headless and reckless.

Nightfall brought no reprieve. But the laboratory stood untouched. With the approach of dawn, the moonlight still shimmering off the harbor waters, Hassan ommandeered one of the lab's vehicles and made off with Norman. They circumvented the road passing through the center of town, opting instead for a residential government complex. Except for military lorries blocking the entrance, they encountered no obstacles.

Waving them to the side of the road, the young First Lieutenant was adamant: "You cannot be here."

To which Norman asked, respectfully, but with a notable trace of sarcasm, "And just where should we be, where is that?"

"I will send two of my men with you. Make your way to Sentani."

Revving up the sputtering Toyota Kijang badly in need of an oil change, maybe a new carburetor, the officer motioned for Hassan to open his window. Looking directly at Norman, and in schooled English no less, the officer exclaimed: "I am sorry you are so inconvenienced. It has been a long night for all. You have nothing to lose. We have everything."

Smarting from the sting as if slapped across the face, Norman bit down hard on his tongue, ears ringing. 'The Javanese way' with language is to render it free of insult; never to challenge or cause the 'loss of face'. Rather, words are carefully crafted without adding insult or humiliation to 'idiocy', as in word or deed – not purposely anyway; an enviable trait that is all about respect, no matter deserved or not, and living in harmony.[42]

The First Lieutenant's words were not lost on Norman as they drove away.

---

42 *https://www.arcjournals.org/pdfs/ijsell/v4-i12/5.pdf.*

'Where there is smoke, there is fire'

An attentive Desi shoveled rice into her mouth, pausing only to sip from her *Teh Botol Sosro* (bottled tea soda) to wash it down, all the while bouncing the baby on her knee. Touching elbows with Icha on the stool beside her, seemingly lost in her own thoughts, she playfully chided, "Wake up you, silly girl." The family-run 'warung' was most certainly not famous for the food, rather, the matronly shop owner who held sway in the community; a heavy-set woman who could spin every rumor and tidbit of gossip into gospel.

"How will I get supplies? My son needs to return to Makassar for school; I know the hospital is running short of medicines," she prattled on. The gist of her rambling was to announce that flights into Wamena had 'again' been suspended, at least from Jayapura.

"Yes, we heard the same on the radio," added Desi. "My 'Ali' says that we should be okay, that whatever is going on in Jayapura will stay in Jayapura."

The 'matriarch of the *warung*' leaned across the counter and intoned as if plotting with fellow conspirators.

"This is different. I hear some of the soldiers from the garrison have left for Jayapura. Many people have been

killed, although the radio will not tell you that. We would leave for Makassar, if only that were possible. Go to the airfield, you will see that all the MAF planes have left. You know that this is a long time in coming. The first sign of trouble, we will go to the garrison. I am sure 'our' women will be in great danger. You know how it is. I think the Church is somehow involved. Those priests in Jayapura have become the voice of OPM and are stirring things up."

Icha shook her head and sternly countered: "I do not believe that". She could only think of Gindo and Kumi-Krispe: Christians! And while only a *'pembantu',* she knew better. The matriarch simply shrugged and went about collecting their plates and wiping up the spills.

Long time incoming

My eight 'spindly legs' moved as one, as I raced the short distance across the felled tree that was my bridge, in short bursts. Just as I reached the thick stump, a violent shaking caused me to teeter and fall, awaking from my troubled sleep. "Are you still alive?" Bakri's way of lightening the mood.

"I was a spider. You think it means anything?" I was shivering, my drenched clothes clinging to my skinny frame. I 'felt' deathly pale, as if that is even possible. I had slept, if that is the word for it, for who knows how long. I tried to 'read' my temperature, putting hand to forehead, feeling hot and clammy to my own touch. "We need to get you on an 'IV drip' of antibiotics."

I managed a, "Fat chance here."

Looking around, I realized we were no longer where I remembered us to be. I was being jostled on a poncho, stretched over long poles. Bakri was trying to keep pace with my pallbearers, the slippery ground slick from rain that had since passed.

The next time I awoke, I tried to make sense of my new surroundings. Maybe I was still dreaming, or worse. Oddly, I knew this place. It was then, in a sudden fit of clarity, that I remembered Ramu.

Except for a lone gecko deftly snatching at flies on the wall, I was alone. But I could hear muffled conversation creeping through the opposite wall from where I lay. When I tried to sit up, I realized there was a needle in each of my arms, held in place by a tightly wound gauze bandage. Clear plastic tubes plugged into rubbery fluid bags fed steady drips of what I supposed were antibiotics and saline rehydration fluids. *Bakri got his way*, I thought.

Falling back onto the burlap sack, filled it seemed with sand that shifted whenever I turned my head, nicely fitting the contour of my skull. "People pay a lot of money for these kind of pillows," I heard myself say, as sleep was winning me over.

The interruption of footsteps caught my attention: drawing closer, the patter of 'little feet'. Lela had a way of giving off a 'vampire vibe', what with her 'blood red' betel nut-stained teeth and gums. But before I could make sense of her presence, possibly in a dream, I thought of 'Dorothy' from *The Wizard of Oz*, the movie, clicking her heels, wishing herself back home in Kansas.

My 'second awakening' was more a homecoming. Lela was fanning me, stirring the still air, keeping the flies 'at bay'. There was a loud clap of thunder, and not distant. My 'family', the old women, were in their favorite corner, chatting and eating a sticky cassava broth by the looks of it, with chunks of spam floating on the surface, or so I infer from the 'familiar' 'hormel' label on the peeled back 'can' left to the side. Yes, I was famished.

The TNI medic came prepared, as he should. Bakri stood beside him, waiting for his turn. "I am going to change the dressings now," he said as he peeled back the gauze pad from my foot.

"Still looks like you took a plunge in a hot oil vat, but

at least the smell is more tolerable," the witty Bakri added, smiling.

The inured medic was skilled. He had clearly attended to these kinds of 'foot rot' before. "You will be hopping around in no time," he offered, by way of solace.

The Lieutenant heading up our rescue expedition was 'matter of fact' in describing our status: "We are all stuck here for the time being. Nothing is flying, or at least available. But we have all that we need. Hopefully, we will have you out of here in a few days." I had the impression that there was more than he let on. When I asked Bakri about this, he too was perplexed.

"It is like we are being kept in quarantine, afraid that we will carry back some new disease. But okay, use this time to heal."

Over the next few days, a procession of notables graced my corner of the room. I learned of the events leading up to our rescue, although Ramu's death took the 'shine' from what ought to have been a momentous occasion. He was mistaken by one of our saviors from Alpha team for an OPM foot soldier; taking no chances, having witnessed the savagery inflicted upon their 'brothers-in-arms' from Bravo team. 'Seeing red' might be more apt a description. And yet, I could only think that our ordeal was no less about such a fraternity, comprised of just us three: Ramu, Bakri, and myself.

We spent endless hours talking, each realizing some unsettling truths about ourselves. Abraham a Christian, and I the heathen. Once entertaining the priesthood, he had not abandoned the sullied notion of 'right versus wrong'. He was no 'saint', 'rough around the edges' for certain, but still aspired to live a 'worthy' life, a 'calling' from long ago that he had never forsaken. Neither of us came out the 'wiser' from our ordeal, but profoundly change us, it did.

"Can you believe this?" Bakri's breathless excitement was palpable. He had sprinted up the hill from the clutter of OPM belongings picked and ferried from the canyon floor, to be used for whatever the forensic rationale. It was the swinging leather strap that proved the 'giveaway'. He lifted his arm skyward, pumping his fist into the air, celebrating the return of his grandfather's binoculars. "Halleluiah!" But that is coming from me.

In and out

The manicured gardens of the hotel had given way to large military tents and long lines; army engineers trying to maintain some semblance of order. Queuing 'not' so much a national virtue, there was no let-up in the rush for food, toilets, and basic supplies, making for a lot of 'pushing and shoving'. Norman, after three days now hunkering down with the masses, had joined the exodus to get out. His powers of persuasion in getting himself and Hassan 'bumped up' in the evacuation queue made no impression on those responsible for allotting space for evacuation. "To anywhere would be nice, thank you," he dared the 'giant' staff sergeant taking names.

Hassan had suggested contacting the Embassy. "A call would do the trick."

"Not going to happen!" That was not Norman's way.

His was a virulent antipathy in dealing with the Embassy, or any Embassy for that matter. A trait common to long-time navy researchers working in remote field locations; relying on their own wits and resourcefulness to get by. This aversion was not without reason: State – for State Department – staffers being prone to throw their weight around, 'huffing and puffing'; a persona derided by locals and met with cool ambivalence.

Their C-130, the 'Hercules' of the skies, swooped down and pounced, grabbing the asphalt runway. Biak had become a staging area for troops and materials being moved into Papua proper. But also a temporary haven to many of the displaced – Norman and Hassan being counted among their number. The 'guest house by the sea' made space for the two; as good a place as any to wait out the 'storm'; the damage of which was yet untold.

Wamena is not Jayapura or Timika

"Jakarta is preoccupied. There is little chance of relief for Wamena. Not with the 'cooking pot boiling over' in Jayapura and Timika. Good news is of the progress Kumi-Krispe is making following his surgery."

"Ha ha, yes, I understand he is anxious to return as quicky as possible. That Corporal Isaac is coming to the house regularly, giving Icha updates."

The chatter between Ali and Gindo as they exited the compound felt forced, as if their usual lighthearted banter was out of place given the seriousness of what was going on all round them. The meeting called for by the 'Acting' Police Commissioner was intended to calm the leadership in the community. But her 'poker face' was anything but reassuring. She appeared preoccupied to say the least, letting her subordinates do the talking. There was also a notable absence of Dani in the conference room. Gindo interjected early on as to 'why' this was so, to which the Police Major, the 'Acting', dismissively 'waved away' the question.

"You know me," whispered Gindo, conspiratorially. "I am no sexist. But her antipathy in having to deal with people, respectfully, has me very worried. She has no interest in what we in the community have to say. Just how can we keep the 'rice from burning, sticking to the cooker', by denying the Dani a voice, especially here and now. We need Kumi-Krispe back, and now!"

"We have no chicken or eggs to sell you," Tami spoke, in her Dani language, not in her usual shy but pleasant *Bahasa* Indonesian style. Both Icha and Desi stood outside the welded wire mesh fence, trying to make sense of her words; the hens in plain sight, their cackling drowning out the ensuing silence. As they began walking away, almost reaching the bend in the road, Kat caught up with them.

"Of course we have chickens and eggs to sell you. I think Tami was confused. She is not herself these days." They left mother and daughter to hash out their differences, face to face. Desi's bag bulged with not the usual chicken, but of the many they had purchased. Icha trying to keep the eggs from cracking against one another in hers.

"What should we cook tonight? Maybe your 'kari ayam' and do up a small party?"

Emboldened

The 'pilot' was just a few months into her first stint flying commercially; her restricted license for light, fixed-winged aircraft. She was every bit a 'young buck' as her male counterparts, looking to escape the drudgery of her family's sheep farm. The Royal New Zealand Air Force had offered her opportunity to learn the art of ground support, to which she fittingly mouthed: "Thanks, but no thanks." Flying express shipment parcels between North Island and South Island and servicing the hundreds of thinly populated islets along the coast had proved a 'let down' to the dizzying allure she had imagined in her spirited youth. Adriana was an adrenaline 'junky' and had not been getting her 'fix'.

Bringing Adriana to the 'here and now': knees drawn tightly to her chest, skinned knees peeking from torn khaki shorts. Other than the metallic whiff carried by the lingering stench of burning petrol from the still-smoldering plane, she felt compelled to reassure herself: "Everything 'is just fine, hunky-dory." She berated everyone within shouting distance, for the fine mess they had made of things. She had been roughed up a bit, owing more to having returned the fight to her attackers. "Bugger," she swore to herself, thinking how she might have reacted differently when the gang set upon her as she was inspecting her aircraft before making the return journey to Timika. Her freight of Papuans had all stood by during the first comical attempts to set the aircraft ablaze, but quickly dispersed into the rancorous crowd cheering on the mayhem, carrying and dragging their possessions with them; some of the piglets squealing to 'high holy hell'.

"We are the military wing of the OPM," one of her captors shouted into her ear, holding her chin in his grip. "Remember, the West Papua National Liberation Army (TPNPB)."

Adriana mouthed, "I couldn't care less."

"We know that your flight had supplies intended for the Indonesian military. Do you understand how we Papuans have been trampled on for far too long? It ends now!" To which she twisted her head and bit down on the fleshy webbing between the thumb and index finger, drawing blood, and refusing to let go.

For the liberators of the Dawa Nduga, aptly named for the Nduga Regency they inhabited, this proved a 'chancy' opportunity to take their fight for Papuan succession to the international media, looking to pressure the Indonesian government into an East Timor-like surrender.[43] But filming of the hostage was not gone as planned; she was not proving a 'willing' participant.

---

43 *The Nduga Regency was created in 2008, carved from the highland Jayawijaya Regency.*

Riding in on a 'bird of paradise'

After conferring with Jakarta, it was decided that the least said, the better. After all, news of the actual rescue attempt had been kept 'tight-lipped', adhering to adage: 'loose tongues sink ships'. Support coordination had gone awry with Kumi-Krispe out of action, leaving only General Widodo, Colonel Agus, and Lieutenant Colonel Hassan, in the know, at least in Papua. None of the three placed any confidence in the police major 'acting' in his stead. As such, she was kept where she belonged: ignorant of all proceedings.

Initial reports brought some euphoria to the otherwise somber mood; TNI struggling to contain the 'wildfires' of frenzied rage burning out of control throughout the province. But success had not come without cost: the lives of Bravo team. The sobering news of their slaughter brought a solemness to what should have been cause for celebration.

The message from the 'three-star' Lieutenant Leneral was clear.

"Operational control, including decision-making, will remain with General Widodo. This mission is not over until it is over. BAIS concurs that current conditions as they are to make Wamena the logical holding area until arrangements can be made to evacuate the pair. All communications outside the 'chain-of-command' will be managed at our end. Furthermore, information in addition to that already been shared with the Americans through 'secure channels' will be forthcoming only when the targets have been repatriated to Jakarta. There is no urgency in moving the duo in haste or taking any unnecessary actions that could compromise their safety, or of those responsible for them.

Widodo reread the words printed on the screen in the tight space. "I agree!" While thinking, *as if I have any choice.*

Agus, reading over his shoulder, volunteered: "They are safe where they are for now, until we can secure 'lift'. I will take care of the arrangements. But it may involve some finessing to ensure nothing gets out."

"Ha, maybe you can put a saddle on a 'bird of paradise'; this 'lost-and-found' Commander can ride it like a cowboy. That would solve the problem." The usually circumspect Widodo, certainly in voicing his humor-tinged annoyance, had 'bigger fish to fry': like putting down an insurrection.

The function of a 'lacky' Second or First lieutenant in any Command is generally assumed to be to take on the dirty work, including those instances when the adage 'to kill the messenger' came to mind. Three days since his posting to Timika and assignment to the General's staff, the lieutenant poked his cleanly shaven skull through the tight space of the partially opened door. Agus was ready to pounce, until he read the urgency written on the officer's face, and the message handed to him. After a pause to allow the frightened junior officer a fast retreat, he shared with Widodo: "More than that, we have another hostage crisis in the making."

That TPNPB made a splash not so long ago in a remote mountainous village located in Nduga district, Nduga regency – the newly carved out (since 2022) Highland Papua province

– previously the Jayawijaya regency and province, marching a large group of mostly construction workers for a 'state'-owned company, just taken captive, to their execution-style deaths: by bullet.

Tale of 'Kuru'

It would be wrong to blame Djarum alone, the premier Indonesian producer of tobacco 'smokes', as we idled away our time. But the overpowering stench of clove-laced cigarette smoke left me gagging, desperate for fresh air. What I knew was 'not' to become that needling '*boulay*', letting my own wants and whims get the best of me. After all, these were my rescuers.

The heavy rains of late had forced all to seek shelter. My space had been invaded; small groups engaged in their own animated banter, each keeping to their own corner. Bakri and I leaned against the wall, imagining what would come next. At some point, our attention turned to food; a wonderful diversion to otherwise numbing reality.

The lieutenant was surely exhausted by my insistent questions about when transport could be arranged. I sounded 'even to myself' like some petulant child demanding a favorite snack. All the while, I knew he was as clueless as the rest of us. He would turn up the volume in his regularly scheduled check-ins, only to be rewarded by high-pitched static.

Over an open fire at the base of the knoll one very starry night, the rains having ceased and given way to desperately clear skies, the Lieutenant and his NCOs asked, "What is it you actually do? Why were you here in the first place?"

Looking over at Bakri, I answered in my best Bahasa: "I am not so sure anymore. We do, however, make a lot of waves: *membuat Masala* (making trouble)." I was first enthralled by an old Australian documentary from the 1950s filmed in a neighboring highland region on the PNG side of the border; and the story leading to the discovery of 'kuru', the first recognized human 'prion' disease; a precursor to the discovery of other 'prion' progressive neurodegenerative disorders like 'mad cow' disease. And more recently, reminded of kuru in a spellbinding documentary.[44] A colleague and Bakri's closest buddy at LITBANGKES, another Batak of course, an 'old school' zoologist by training and entomologist by passion, shared what felt like a 'first-hand', little-known account of how this condition first came to light. But that would place him in his 70s: impossible!

"Bakri, help me out here," I said as I took the plunge. "Let me tell you about kuru. I think you will better understand what it means to be a 'disease detective'. Kuru is fatal over time. Its discovery served as precursor in recognizing other prion related conditions. Mad cow disease for one. It is a degenerative disease that affects the central nervous system. Those affected lose control of their bodies, as if their movements have been disconnected from their brains; the some 'puppeteer' now pulling the strings."

Bakri interjected with the analogy of the '*wayang*': traditional Javanese puppet theater in which elaborately outfitted wooden characters with exaggerated pointed human features are cast in shadows to a riveted audience, entranced

---

44 *https://video.search.yahoo.com/search/video?fr=aaplw&ei=UTF-8&p=kuru+documentary#id=3&vid=744a21ad9c133f2cc5fd7fceb 477038f&action=view.*

by the staged drama; representing Hindu themes adapted to Buddhist and Muslim sensibilities, with more than a dash of Javanese folklore.

"Those infected by the lethal kuru 'prion', a type of protein that can trigger normal proteins in the brain to fold abnormally, exhibit tremors early on. Uncontrollable twitching, or jerking spasms, leave victims unable to stand or even sit unassisted. The disease, sometimes referred to as 'fatal insomnia' since sleep becomes impossible, is often accompanied by severe dementia. All in all, a horrific way to die." Trying not to make 'light' of this killer to my now-captive audience.

"But the less-told narrative, that really 'whet my appetite' is just how this rare and untreatable disease first gained the attention of the outside world, leading to the discovery and naming of this disorder.

"Anecdotal reports reached PNG health authorities back when Australia still reigned over the country. A strange occurrence was purported from the 'Okapa' district of the 'Eastern Highlands' province, the mountainous home to the 'Fore' tribe. Cases of severe burns over a period of months and sometimes years came to the attention of medical detectives who mounted an expedition to investigate this strange occurrence. Bodies were described as unwilfully flopping onto glowing coals of dying fires they huddled around for warmth against the cold mountain chill. And that is how 'kuru' was first encountered, as an outbreak episode involving burns.

"In the proceeding years, kuru, yet unnamed, would become known as the 'laughing death epidemic'; whereas victims all shared 'involuntary frozen facial smiles' from skin stretched, pulled back from their mouths. Like the 'Dani of old', the Fore tribe of PNG practiced cannibalism.

*The Dani as part of ritualism linked with warfare, the Fore
as a part of funeral feasting rites: eating the brains of the
'just' deceased relative; a practice born of love grief. It is
believed that this modern-day taboo led to the 'decades old'
spread of kuru; particularly among the women and children
who prepared and ate the prion-infected brain tissue."*[45]

A bit winded by my own exuberance, I wondered if what was
true for the Fore was not also for the Dani, and that kuru
was as likely epidemic in the Baliem Valley at one time, when
cannibalism was not spoken of in the past tense.

"But you were not scavenging for kuru when you got lost."
More a question, Master Sergeant Abraham asked. Staring
at the 'dancing flames', I wondered the same. Bakri, as always,
came to the rescue "'*Wabah babi*' brought us here." And he
continued with 'our' story.

The following morning, the lieutenant with the medic in
tow came and asked how my foot was mending. "All healed," I
said, walking without aid of the cane Bakri had made for me,
trying to keep from wincing; not altogether convincingly.

Later that day, the Lieutenant and Abraham conferred
with the two of us.

"It appears there has been some delay in arranging for
an airlift. We could wait, but there is also some urgency for
returning my men to Wamena, and as soon as possible, all of
us. I have proposed to my Command that we hike across the
valley, all together. Master Sergeant here will be responsible
for assisting you, even if we need to carry you. Are you okay
with that?"

"I am guessing we have no choice in this matter," responded
Bakri.

"What kind of distance are we talking about?" I asked.

45   *https://allthatsinteresting.com/kuru.*

"Hopefully, we will be sleeping in our own beds soon enough. Certainly not more than a fortnight," the Lieutenant responded.

"A fortnight," I exclaimed, "that is two weeks," not hiding the grimace on my face. "When will this all end?"

As we trudged back up the hill to what had been our home 'off and on', where I had been nursed back from the brink, not once, but twice, and fallen for the 'fire' red-haired Mola; for what I imagined would be our last night from under a surely 'star-studded' sky over overhead if not for the heavy cloud covering threatening once again to let loose on our parade. I found something to smile about playing at being facetious.

During the Spanish Anquisition, it was believed that 'flame'-colored hair was a sign of satanic practices: thieving fire from hell. I thought of Mola, and how I so misunderstood her. She was neither heroine nor devil. Maybe she had found her place, erstwhile just hiding from herself.

I was exhausted just thinking of our upcoming trek. But oh no, not Bakri. I even detected a little 'spring' in his step. He could not stop from scratching that 'itch' that came with each new adventure; our odyssey was by no means coming to an end.

'Other fish to fry'

The decision to 'go' with the recommendation of the operational Commander, his man on the ground, did not sit well with Widodo. He was only a Lieutenant, after all. But he had learned over his fledgling career to trust in the 'gut instincts' of soldiers. The 'three star' in Jakarta was agreeable; another 'action item' that could be postponed, at least until the 'force' could make its way to Wamena. By then, the crises at hand would have been dealt with, or at least contained. Wamena, while not in a 'sea of tranquility', was still calm. Widodo could only hope it stayed that way.

The Lieutenant General was 'pulling no punches':

> "Logistics are strained as TNI tries to 'turn the tide' of revolt. Word from Timika is that OPM has set its sights on the residential enclave where PT Freeport-McMoRan staff and their families reside. We are rushing reinforcements to insure everyone's safety. FCX has nevertheless started evacuating all 'non-essentials' temporarily to Bali. We are also looking to secure the access road to the coast; and of course, keep any disruption to mining operations to a minimum."

Communications with his CINCPAC counterpart in Hawaii had gone better than expected. The need for 'discretion' was appreciated: code for secrecy. "The Embassy will be notified when we have the Commander secured," he assured.

Never-ever-ending

I was rousted at 'oh-dark hours' by the medic slathering a 'tiger balm' mint-scented ointment gently on my foot before wrapping the gooey mess with a new gauze bandage. My foot was then fitted into a green netted army boot split up the middle and loosely held in place by laces: like an 'enchilada'; I could not help in thinking the analogy. I mumbled that, "I do not want anyone to give up their boots for me."

"I think these boots are from that Bravo team, the ones killed in the marsh," remarked Bakri looking on, while lacing his own. I took no comfort with that interesting tidbit, not wanting to walk in another man's shoes.

There was a commotion down the knoll, where the path began at the far end of the garden leading down to the river. Several Dani from the police contingent were talking loudly, shielding us from a group of women, including Lela. I heard a low-pitched wailing as they beat their fists to their chests. I limped over and pushed the men aside and grabbed hold of Lela's hands. "Please tell her she is my mother, and I will return to her." At that precise moment, I had no doubt that I would somehow keep to that promise.

There had been some discussion, as I understood it, on

what to do with the boy captured during the firefight on the canyon floor, just prior to our departure. Bakri and I soon learned as we began our descent, part of the caterpillar-like procession along the path that could not accommodate more than two across, that the boy was in our 'segment': hands tied around his back with a rope and another around his neck; the ends of which were fashioned into a rein from which the police corporal could steer his prisoner.

My improvised 'walking cast' allowed for precious mobility. But the wear on my good foot that I clearly favored left me seriously limping by the end of the day. The pace was purposely slow, and a tunnel carved out of the dense bush made the going less arduous than what might have been. I caught glimpses of soldiers fanned out along the steep slope above us; an added layer of camouflaged protection as we made our way downstream. I was not so surprised to see three of our contingent following in the same direction, but across the river. The Lieutenant was not taking any chances.

Our hike had eclipsed in only one day that point that Bakri and I managed in three, just a few short weeks ago. The only interruptions in making our way: a brief lunch; and an encounter with the much-feared 'fer-de-lance'.

While the medic was able to quickly administer treatment by injection, setting up an intravenous drip 'on the run' was more a challenge. The outcome was by no means assured: in the absence of a ventilator in case of breathing difficulties; and that the glass-vialed 'elixir of life', or antivenom, had not been kept refrigerated, not for some weeks now.

Skirting the now reed-clogged waterway near to the canyon where we made our 'last stand', our procession diverted to the ridged hills that offered a more exposed but easier going. And while not anticipating a 'run in' with OPM, neither had Bravo team.

My foot seemed to be healing nicely, maybe because of the blood flow forced with each step of the journey, supplying much-needed oxygenation. As dead mass sloughed off during cleansing, healthy new skin and tissue was beginning to take its place. The medic was fastidious about my twice daily embalming: morning and night.

A lean-to sheltered us from the on and off rains, more often just a steady half-hearted drizzle. Jamo from the Moluccas had another bad night, but his breathing at this early hour seemed less raspy, more rhythmic, steady. His calf, the fleshy part below the knee, was still woefully swollen; maybe engorged a more apt description. Blood had been seeping from the blistered limb, with skin so stretched as to tear apart. I distinctly heard the 'hiss' escaping his lips as if some demon had now taken possession, trying to discern something intelligible. "I think he is dreaming," I whispered to Bakri.

"Surely, that is a good sign." It was, I guessed, until it wasn't.

The morning brought no let-up to the foul weather. But our spirits were damped in a way the rain could not, with the passing of the young Malaccan soldier overnight, alone, while we slept. Making his death more personal, quite simply put, was because of the two of us. If we had not been here in the first place, he would still be alive, as would those from Bravo team.

As we again started out, I could not help feeling stuck in molasses: as if powering ahead, going through the motions, my arms and legs propelling me forward like a wound-up 'toy' soldier on parade. My mind kept replaying a scene as if in a National Geographic documentary: turtle hatchlings breaking free of their soft shells, racing instinctively to the water's edge on some pristine beach; only to be thrown back by the incoming waves, left 'high and dry' by the ebbing tide.

What passed for a week might have only been a few days. I did not lose count so much as stopped counting after our first night, 'on the run,' so to speak. I was operating as if by remote control. I found myself practicing my *Bahasa* Indonesian, uttering phrases lest I forgot how to communicate, as if I no longer trusted my memory. I thought of similarities between Spanish and Indonesian words, silently mouthing examples: "*Mesa* and *meja* for table, *camisa* and *kemeja* for shirt, respectively," reflecting on colonial linguistic influences of the Spanish Philippines: Spanish, from Mindanao in the south to Luzon in the north, carried to the Netherlands East Indies, now Indonesia, by trading seafarers. In return, Islam was transported to the Philippines indirectly, via the Muslim sultanate of Brunei. "A fair exchange, language for religion, given that the southern islands in the Philippine archipelago are today predominately Muslim." I grinned at my own humor; thinking, for sure, it would be lost on Bakri. "Maybe not!"

I was all too familiar with the 'saying' ascribed to my namesake: '*une armee marche a son estomac*'; quite literally meaning an army marches on its stomach. Napoleon was no dummy, and neither was the Lieutenant and his trusted band of NCOs. Bakri and I had forgotten how to taste food, or rather savor the flavors and textures, as opposed to just trying to fill our bellies to keep from wasting away. But meal after meal turned into a wonderful excursion into the delicacies of bushmeat. It was cooked and seasoned to perfection; I could not help oddly wondering, remarking, on how these 'prime cuts' would translate into a cookbook. Bakri could not resist in stating the obvious: "Have have lost your senses?"

Never looking back

"You should return to Jakarta," scolded Icha. The night sweats had left a rancidness that she had tried to rid from Gindo's room, vigorously flapping the mat in the direction of the window. This was the third time in so many days she had aired out the space, complete with a fresh change of bed sheets.

He was now spitting up phlegm dislodged from his lungs with his persistent hacking cough. Desi had exhausted her home remedies, notably steamy ginger-based concoctions inhaled under a wet towel, making for an aromatic head sauna; the sweet syrup provided by the clinic was likewise only marginally successful in stilling his cough, bouts of which could leave him gasping for breath. The 'reddish-purple' liquid left his mind foggy and cluttered, having to goad himself into walking a straight line; the 'blue' sapping him of all energy. "This will pass," was his stock reply.

Agus, too, half-heartedly urged him to leave Wamena. Gindo quipped that aside from the 'oxygen' treatment he was as good in Wamena as back in Jakarta. "I have a purpose here. I have nothing there. Besides, I am breathing in more soot and diesel back home than any gain from being chained to an oxygen tank."

To which Agus began offering reassurance; only to quickly chide himself into silence and nod his head in understanding: "I am always here for you. "Gindo was meticulous when it came to planning; the accountant in him ringing true. He convinced BNI to allow the 'dust to settle' in the province before transferring Pak Nono's yet unnamed replacement. He then spent the rest of the morning preparing for things to come.

Looking around the front room to make sure Icha and Desi were out of sight and earshot, he confided in Ali, "Make sure you give Icha this if anything should happen to me," over their weekly evening tea and gossip, slipping the envelop discreetly across the table. "I am counting on you!"

She cuddled her daughter, who was reaching for her shiny platinum-plated necklace, reflecting the light from the setting sun peeping through the curtained window.

Icha had an overwhelming sense of urgency in telling Desi what she meant to her. As if this bond could suddenly become frayed and torn apart. She had learned from her many 'life lessons' that all in this world was fragile, hanging on by a threat.

"You! Never have I had someone love me for my stubbornness. I know I am so bossy. You make me laugh when I take myself too seriously. Then reminding me that I am special. But you know all this. We are mother–daughter, sisters no less."

"I think I would rather be your sister." Desi laughed, wondering what had gotten into her friend. But she knew enough to keep the 'mood light', fearing as did Icha that whatever the 'white magic' offered by the local 'dukun', both shaman and traditional healer, all could evaporate into a puff of 'bad magic' – 'dukun santet': wrought upon them by some malicious force, up to no good. Icha professed no belief in the 'good' magic but was wary, as most Javanese, of the 'bad'.

"Let's bring some rice and cabbage to the '*dukun*'; a long time since we visited with him."

"A good idea," chimed Icha. "We can ask if there is something we can give to Pak Gindo."

Finding worthiness

Our march took us to a thin ledge on the side of a steep cliff. But I now felt immured from my own fears, such was my exhaustion. I did manage to break with my mojo when a soldier up ahead kicked loose some stone and earth and almost took a tumble, if not for the quick hands of the next in line.

We had long ago veered away from the river, our roadmap, in the 'mad dash' to Wamena. We had extricated ourselves, no longer beholden to that route which had taken us the long way around, having to negotiate the 'too' many twists and turns of the 'Lower Course': making its own run, to the sea. We had traded our riverine excursion for hill-climbing thrills, through steep-sided valleys and sometimes, near-impregnable jungle terrain. In fact, we had been heading for some days now in a direction that would take us as far from the river as possible, northward, at least for the time being.

Bakri and I realized after conferring with the Lieutenant and Abraham back in settlement that we had not been flying in a straight line from our pickup, at least to Wamena, when we came down with a thud. Bakri fervently believed that we had been sabotaged, by none other than our 'pilot'. Our location, Kataya, when pointed to on the map relative to the region we had conducted our investigation, confirmed as much. John had taken a southwesterly tact, rather than to the northwest; eventually intersecting the Baliem River, but much further downstream from where it passed by Wamena. Little wonder nobody could track us or approximate our location from the start.

We caught a glimpse of the terraced slopes: manicured, at least from a distance; withered stalks, long abandoned, when we got close-up. Bakri was sure we were approaching the beginnings of a settlement. I did not dare indulge in such a fantasy: expecting to stumble upon a bustling Wamena, just around the next bend.

The monotonous 'edge' to our trek, pushing through a numbing sea of twisted growth, a jumble of greens and browns, was interrupted by scenes of wonder: mottled spotted butterflies painted in colors that only nature could dream up; a doe giving birth to her fawn; and a beautiful green snake shyly poking its head from a clump of banana stalks. I was taking in all that was beautiful around me, as if capturing it with snapshot, 'for the first time in a long time.'

We kept pushing ahead: energized! "Have you done this before? I mean crossing the valley as now," I asked Abraham.

"Yes, and no!" He did not elaborate further. I thought to ask what that meant, only to 'hold my tongue.' My inquiry was indeed a bit foolish, meant more to assuage my own frustration.

"Better I do not show off my 'cranky' side, not when we are this close." Thinking only, *to just keep up.*

"You have nothing to feel ashamed of," Bakri spoke with a forcefulness that felt more an angry slap: the kind to bring someone to their senses. I had let my humiliation at being laid out on a stretcher wash over me. Tears avalanched down my face, cascading downward, suddenly and without warning. This cleansing was no less baptismal: a cathartic embrace.

"I was an ox, released from the heavy wooden yoke, pulling plowshare, breaking up the dry and crusted earth." So profound was this moment of realization that I was left gasping between sobs. Finally, and maybe for the first time in a long time, no longer blaming myself.

Last supper

My foot had divinely healed itself. But after limping for days, more out of habit than any physical discomfort, my knee supporting my favored leg felt the dagger of a sharp ache whenever standing.

This slinking 'caterpillar' at long last came across the Baliem River, although nowhere near the roaring waters racing through the valley downstream, from where we had begun this long trek.

We had not just chanced upon this small hilltop military outpost but took it by complete surprise. Three mud and thatched structures were ringed by a crude stockade: posts of tree limbs connected by a jumble of sticks, long and short, twisted and straight. The design of which was more to keep out wild boar and other four- and three-legged scavengers, not so much the two-legged human kind: most certainly not OPM.

Our troop rested for what was surely the last night of our 'long march', proving both marathon and sprint until now. The mood was relaxed, more so than at any time since leaving Kataya. There was laughter and good-humored prodding; it felt both homecoming and celebratory. Bundles of minnow were fried up in a batter of pounded taro root, making for a crunchy, lip-smacking, last meal. So tasty was the combination of curry-flavored rice and fish morsels that I begged for the recipe. We were just a short 'hop and a skip' from Wamena. At least that was what Bakri and I supposed.

The two soldiers manning the 'fort' told of the unrest now rumored to be sweeping through the town. Batteries for the radio long drained of 'juice' made sure that there was no other news. It also meant we could not announce our imminent arrival.

I had come to respect our Lieutenant, always keeping his calm, and not averse to my humor. As feats go, he had managed to get 'us' this far. Most telling was how he kept both discipline and morale, no matter the loss of Bravo team. His refusal to leave Jamo's side was not lost on his troop, including the two of us.

"I can walk tomorrow on my own," I made clear; steeling myself, so as to not give in and crumple across the finish line.

"We will walk together," Bakri echoed. The Lieutenant and Abraham nodded. "And the two of you need to hold your heads high: you saved our lives," Bakri added. The look on their faces was of a more somber reflection; neither seeing themselves as we did.

Sleep proved elusive when I needed it most. My thoughts were running as if on a treadmill, 'stills', as if from an old movie; only featuring Ramu and Bakri, and Mola and Lena. It seemed like we had avoided mention of Ramu over the last few weeks, Bakri and me, maybe trying to banish the memory of his loss. But tonight, I could not shake him loose.

Cheering crowds

The 'spirits' were playing us, like a fiddle: perpetrating a cruel hoax; or just watching over us. We began our final ascent of 'our' 'Everest', but with none of the fanfare that comes with conquering the mountain. The sky was still blackened when we rose, with only a hint of moon in the overcast skies. By nightfall, we were still walking. Me, barely!

Murmurs up ahead were followed by wooden planks underfoot: a bridge, opening onto a wider-still gravel road. The silence except for the crunch of stones underfoot and barking dogs felt strangely welcoming, as if signaling our passing from one world to the next. We passed darkened structures, and campfires encircled by drawn Papuan faces illuminated by the flames.

We strode into a large walled compound, still on the outskirts of town. But not before a loud and threatening exchange of words. I was too tired to pick up on the whatever was being shouted. But I knew things were not as they should when both police and soldiers from our group began to cock their weapons: kneeling and facing outward on both sides, to the right and to the left.

We finally made our way into a courtyard, where we laid

ourselves out for the night. A foul-mouthed police Major had come out of the headquarter building in a rage, barking at our Lieutenant. "I know nothing about this expedition," she said, nostrils flaring. "You need proper authorization, and I should have been informed beforehand."

The Lieutenant's instructions had been clear before leaving Kataya: "Do not introduce either our guests or the purpose of your mission to anyone until you have first notified Lieutenant Colonel Hassan or myself," Colonel Agus had commanded. And so it was.

A small group from the police contingent accompanying the Major stood with their 'mouths open', with expressions that screamed incredulous and embarrassed; having recognized many of their own from among this wary group of uniformed men seeking refuge. A senior NCO ignored his Major and walked to Abraham and offered a stiff salute, before embracing him. Then stepped back to face the Major who looked on with fury. "How dare you, I will have you brought up on chargers."

Giving way

"Stand down! The Indonesians will take care of this when the time is 'right.'" Colonel Dowdy had been making 'noise', obviously too much, through TNI channels since learning that Commander Jacques was now safety ensconced in Wamena. He was just off the phone with an irate Captain Lavender, barking like a rabid dog. Winny couldn't help chuckling at Rick's suggestion to send in the marines to extricate Jacques, as if he still needed rescuing.

The Ambassador had thought to object, if not for the directive coming directly from the PACOM Commander with concurrence from State. "Do not under any circumstances attempt to intercede or question Indonesian prerogative in managing this affair." Moreover, he understood Indonesia's heightened sensitivity to outside influences given recent events in this highly volatile province: likely to be construed as interference.

The Embassy needed full TNI cooperation to ensure US investments, in the billions, did not 'go south', in flames; never mind the security of the remaining Americans in Timika. "Ah yes, this is not the time to be riling public sentiment that was already sounding belligerent of perceived outside meddling," the DCM weighed in. "No less than an America if faced with a similar threat to their territorial integrity."

"This is not the time to push on this matter." All the while thinking he would not be begrudged in giving a gentle 'nudge'. After all, it is to be expected; being the Ambassador and all.

When worlds collide

She sat, anxiously, nervously folding one hand over the other, pressing down on her skirt, as if to smooth the wrinkles from the fabric. Icha was sure that this intrusion, this time, would disrupt the normalcy she so desperately spun for herself and her daughter.

The Jeep had delivered them to the army garrison, and to a waiting Lieutenant Colonel Hassan. Greeting the two, he ushered them into a concrete building that had 'COMMUNICATIONS' painted on the door. As directed, Gindo picked up the headset and listened.

"Yes, I know Dr. Bakri. We had the both of them to the house for Icha's scrumptious chicken-filled dumplings. I remember that Sunday luncheon quite well; just a few days before they departed."

He struggled to find the right word and could not think of another.

"But that was a 'long time back.'"

After an assortment of 'ums' and 'uhs', like a box of mixed filling chocolates:

"Bakri is a Batak, like me. I am duty-bound to help my brother in any way. And the American?"

"Of course. Yes, I understand. We will make them feel right at home."

If Icha were a dog, her floppy ears would have been rigidly standing up straight, taking in every word, syllable by syllable. Instead, she looked on intently as Gindo ended the conversation. No longer fidgeting.

Arriving back home, she waved to Desi, who was caring for her daughter that morning. Excitedly, she made clear that, apart from herself and Ali, nobody must know about their guests, swearing her to secrecy.

"The two doctors who visited many months ago have been found. After all this time, can you believe. And what's more, they will be staying here until a flight out of Wamena can be arranged."

Repeating again: *"Nobody must know!"* The extra bedroom was dressed up for the expected visitors. They had spent most of the afternoon preparing. It was decided that Desi would stay with Icha and the baby to help out.

"No fuss here," Ali said, laughing.

"Fat chance of that," came Gindo's whimsical retort. Freshly potted flowers and plants infused an airiness to the otherwise drabness of the place. The festiveness of the occasion was making all just a little giddy with anticipation.

No fanfare, just the sound of a car approaching, doors slamming, and footsteps – oh yes, and the neighbor's dog baying into the silent night – interrupted. Icha ran to the door and yanked it open before newly promoted, now 'Lieutenant', Rita could knock.

No luggage, only two small satchels of borrowed clothing. The weary travelers were the most unlikely of guests. The *boulay* from America especially, looking more a 'wild' man, his skinny face now hidden behind a knotted straggly beehive that passed for a beard. Neither Gindo nor Icha recognized him from the 'forever' ago when he joked and laughed and danced with the baby in his arms to traditional *'pop dungdut'*: the popular *'kampung'* music of the day.

Catch me when I fall
(from Ashlee Simpson's song)[46]

There is a dreamlike quality to my waking moments. I let this gentle state of mind wash over me and lull me back to sleep. The one lucid thought to enter my head is how my body itches: from head to toe.

My hip still aches, but less than the last time, as I try to remember, standing under the tepid spray from the showerhead. Bakri is waiting his turn just outside the stall. Neither of us realized how we forced every bit of adrenaline-fueled strength we possessed, in carrying us through the last few days, until now. And now we are left with literally nothing, barely able to keep from falling over, but with no energy even for that.

Icha shows no 'shame' or 'shyness' in taking scissors and razor to my face and head. As for me, I lost both to Lela, who found motherly pleasure in picking lice from my hair, no matter where on my body. Looking in the mirror, I cannot but think that the 'new' me, looking gaunt and stubbled, would be a good fit on a horror movie set.

---

46 *https://www.youtube.com/watch?v=HRtXuul0WUw.*

I recall a homemade banner, the kind that is tinselly gold, green, and red, and hung in celebration of something or someone. The exact wording of which escapes me, except for the 'Selamat Datang'. A 'brilliantly' white tablecloth laid over by a 'special' dinner setting, including 'real silver' forks and spoons, porcelain plates and bowls, sticks in mind. Funny though, I cannot remember what I ate, or if I ate. But I do remember being famished. A Lieutenant Rita accompanied by 'my Lieutenant' and a doctor and nurse team from Ruman Sakit Umum Daerah Wamena, the government regional hospital in Wamena, made their daily rounds to the house. This morning, the glucose and saline drips were removed, for good. Desi had become quite proficient at replacing the bottles over the past few days, offering us the necessary mobility of getting up and about, back on our feet.

The loud and boisterous doctor, going by the name of Amin, lived up to expectations: rotund, with a habit of bursting into rapturous laughter, at his own jokes, no less. I felt something akin to finding my soulmate, although acknowledging my humor was maybe on the drier side. His jovialness did lighten the mood of their visits, and provided Bakri and I with a glimpse of what was happening 'around town'.

> "I think they want to fatten you up, like a stuffed pig. There will be nothing to feast on if you do not take advantage of Icha's cooking. You would also be 'stupid' not to – her dishes will make you 'blush' with ecstasy. You are both smart enough to know that the intravenous feeds are little more than for show; so I can get rich charging the government for my services. Ha ha!"

A thought crossed my mind that I was indeed being prepared: 'fattened up' as Amin put it, like a 'lamb for the slaughter'

– or in my case, for a reception that would surely catch the attention of the media.

The imagery projected, more snapshots from black-and-white stills, of what the future held for the two of us was only fleeting. I had no desire to conjure up make-believe scenarios feeding fanciful notions of the mythical 'fame and fortune' that comes with discovery; or in our case, being: 'lost and found'.

As for me, I had the navy to contend with; figuring I would either be promoted straight to Admiral, skipping over Captain, or court-martialed 'for something or other'. It was not difficult in making fun of my own prognosis, thinking 'fat chance with the latter'.

"*Terima Kasih Icha, enak.*" Although Lieutenant Colonel Hassan more poked and prodded than tasted the freshly made fish-filled dumplings steamed in a vat of ginger water laid out on the table.

"Yummy!" I did not even bother translating into *Bahasa*. But I cleared my plate and was ready for my third helping: enough said. The pot of steamy rose-scented '*teh*' seemed to warm the room on this wet and chilly night.

"I wanted to personally thank you for your patience. But we thought it better to give you time and let you recover before throwing you to the wolves. That is a joke," he added, and as if on a roll, "for sure, you will be a 'star' of screen and stage, in the spotlight, like a bug under a microscope."

I was slow in translating his words in my head, maybe overwhelmed by soft dumplings that brought me to my knees, but getting the 'gist' of the message.

> "*There have been few flights in and out of Wamena since your return. A lot of commotion in Jayapura and Timika is making transport in the province challenging, to say the least. But I am here to share the good news. A*

357

*plane will be coming in the next few days to whisk the two
of you away. We have no exact day or time, but shortly.
When we knock next time, it will be to collect you. So
please be ready."*

The two lieutenants standing in the corner tried to conceal
their glances at the food on the table. Bakri waved them over.
"Please, come sit with us and eat." Napping suited me at this
time, proving restorative and shielding me from thinking
too much of what was, and what was to be. And so Bakri's
interruption of this, my new favorite pastime, felt like a
provocation.

"Jacques, I hear gun fire, not close, and nobody is home."

I immediately sat up, listening. "I hear it," I said, confirming
as much.

"I think we should hide. Something is not right." Bakri
expressing both our fears.

Yes, the closet. Bunched in, crouching, Bakri holding a
broomstick ready to battle any intruder. The scene worthy
of a 'comical' scary movie. "I am not sure this is a great
hiding place." Half serious, half joking. We could still hear
the distinctive 'popping' when there was a slamming of the
front door. Thinking, *not so funny now.* Our hideaway was
discovered soon enough by a wide-eyed Desi peering through
the widening crack of the door, machete in hand.

Icha sat at the table, chest heaving, trying to control her
breathing. Her face had taken on a ghostly pallor, made
more so against the black soot staining her forehead, cheeks,
nose, and chin. The gentle rhythm of inhaling and exhaling
coming from the bassinet lent at least some semblance of calm
to the otherwise chaotic scene. Desi was talking 'more than
a mile a minute'; Bakri nodding encouragingly, signaling his
understanding. Her 'spitfire' delivery left me unable to follow,

except for the odd word or two. I would rely on Bakri to make sense of it for me later.

"Look out here." Bakri pointed. Sure enough, the blackened edge of the skyline visible through the window was thick with dark smoke.

"You can smell it," I added.

Pulling no punches

The room full of senior officers created the desired sensory conditions, that of being tightly squeezed into a small space. Purposefully, the intel briefing was intended to bring home TNI's precarious hold on Papua, against concerted waves of OPM-inspired assaults.

"What they lack for in coordination, they more than make up for in numbers: like small wildfires that could eventually meet up and set the whole forest ablaze. Metaphorically speaking. If we let them.

"Simply, OPM has weaponized the power of 'rumor' to incite, create spontaneous uprisings among the indigenous peoples of Papua, regardless of whether they support 'the cause'. Simply put, this is about an independence movement for those of you who have not pulled up your shades and looked out your windows of late. This has allowed OPM to supersize itself without growing in real numbers; doing so by fanning rumors, real or imagined, inflaming already aggrieved local sentiment to that of open hostility. Our immediate concern is Wamena, which has been relatively quiet, until now."

The murmurs and background noises ceased in the airless confines of the cramped room. The 'Annapolis' pedigreed marine Colonel from Intel, plucked from navy's elite '*Denjaka*', or 'special forces', was party to the new 'Post-East Timor' doctrine coming out of BAIS TNI. He was not 'mincing his words'.

> "*First, a little history lesson for those of you unfamiliar with the brewing tensions now threatening to undo civil order:*"
>
> "'*Our*' *overreaction to the break-in at the army armory in Wamena. Yes, two of our soldiers were killed and weapons stolen. But the events that followed, displacement of thousands of the indigenous Dani, was a 'gift' to OPM. They seized upon and exploited pent-up anger and resentment and fed it. They only needed 'us' to provide the opportunity; the needle prick to burst the blister.*"
>
> "*Which brings us to our current crisis, as if we do not need another.*"

The Colonel was mindful his words were hitting home; evidenced by the shifting of chairs and audible change in stances that punctuated the quiet. His audience was uncomfortable with his directness, some more than others. Good!

> "*Earlier this morning, a mob incensed by the rumored kidnaping of a young Dani pelted the police compound holding the purported suspect, with stones I might add. Despite attempts to de-escalate the situation, including the safe return of the child to the family, mob anger was not assuaged.*"
>
> "*Rumors layered by more rumors fueled a full-scale riot. Nearby buildings were set alight. I am not condoning*"

or justifying what came next, but our security forces fired
on the crowd, leaving ten dead."

It was if the air, sweetly stale, had been sucked out of the
room. Everyone was holding their breath for what came next:

"Yes, we can all agree. We have a real mess on our
hands.

"The challenge now is that we are stretched, especially
so here in Timika, as you all are aware. The army garrison
and National Police in Wamena have mobilized all their
assets, fielding a security force of a few hundred. But of
course, this will not be enough.

"Before going off to do what you all do best, I would
only remind you: we need to learn from our mistakes. Not
repeat them. Enough of this exacting revenge. We cannot
be at war with ourselves.

"Please, let us not be the Dutch, or Japanese for that
matter. Let us not be colonizers!"[47,48]

---

47   Not by accident: particularly on the island of Java, where colonial
'indies-style' architecture with its distinctive gambrel roofing and
curved eaves is rooted in Dutch rule over the archipelago, lasting
over two centuries. The void left following the brutal Japanese
occupation during WW2 declaration emboldened the bloody
fight for independence, with Indonesian sovereignty recognized
by the Netherlands in 1949; https://searchworks.stanford.edu/
view/12986544#.
48   Dutch New Guinea (Western New Guinea) was handed over to
Indonesia under the terms of New York Agreement in 1963. At no
time was a plebiscite held by the Papuan people in support of this
action; https://books.google.co.th/books?id=cuVtQgAACAAJ&d-
q=isbn:033357690X&hl=en&sa=X&redir_esc=y.

Knock knock

Muttering, "So late," I pulled the borrowed, tight green military sweater over my head.

"No time," Bakri added, as we both hurried in silence, befitting the hour: sometime in the middle of the night.

I meant to wake up Icha, Desi, and Gindo, but they too had been roused by the pounding on the door. "Change of plans!" Lieutenant Rita spoke from the darkened corner beyond the reach of the single overhead light hanging over the table. Standing beside her was Abraham, or Master Sergeant, our savior, as I liked to think of him. "We are all going, but not to catch a flight." But not before Desi ran home to collect Ali.

The short ride took us past exhausted fires 'casting long shadows', silhouetted structures still smoldering. Small groups were spread along the road. Dani, I supposed. Some stoking campfires, others content with hanging out, 'whooping and hollering'. The driver was forced to weave in and out, around those taking to the middle of the darkened streets.

Except for the engine and shifting of gears, there was silence inside the cab. Outside, occasional shouts perforated the quiet, made all the more frightening by the threatening gestures and angry stares that followed. The cracks emanating from the small hole in the windshield served as notice to the violence that had erupted on this day; or maybe it was yesterday, since I had no clue as to the hour.

The early morning found us occupying a small room at police headquarters. Gindo had ventured into the compound where hundreds had taken refuge. "He is looking for some of the BNI staff," volunteered Icha.

Wandering into the open spaces, Bakri and I recognized no one, not surprisingly. They were all sizes, shapes, and colors, representing the whole of Indonesia: from east to the west, north to south. Papuans themselves, mostly Dani, making up most of our number, falling equally victim to the 'rage' taking place, not more than shouting distance from the surrounding walls.

As darkness approached, those having sought sanctuary had risen into the thousands. There was barely space to move, let alone organize any semblance of normalcy. Our 'makeshift community' made for sensory overload. The ripe smells of cooking, bodies, and newly cut passages flowing with sewage was an afront to my gastro-intestinal good working order; fortitude, it was all I could do to keep the sour bile rising in my throat and spilling out from my mouth. After commenting to Bakri about the stench, I let my irritation get the best of me: "And here I thought we had finally re-entered a world where 'order' prevailed. Fat chance of that," I mouthed. By his reaction, I inferred my 'pet peeves' were mine alone to bear. Not for the first time, especially alongside Bakri, it occurred to me that a little 'grace' would better suit me.

Icha and Desi were talking to an animated Dani woman with an infant. There was a battle going on, the back-and-forth cooing of babies, Icha with her own. "This is my friend Tami," Icha introduced.

Tami recounted how her daughter had not returned home from the market yesterday morning: 'Kat', her name.

"She would never leave her child, not ever. Something has happened to her. I visited the hospital, but they would not allow me past the entrance, and so I came here to look for her. But no one will talk to me."

"*I will go to the hospital, alone! You stay here with the baby.*"

"Absolutely not," Gindo almost yelling.

To which Icha countered with a steely stare: "And who will stop me?" Icha daring Gindo, with Tami's granddaughter suckling furiously at her breast.

"Please, Icha, you cannot go alone. We will speak with Abraham, the policeman who fetched us last night and ask for his help." All the while, I knew there was little he could do, even if I could find him.

Bakri and I had been deputized just as in movies, at least that is how I would describe the elevation of our status. Working under the army medic, 'the sheriff', the same who took part in our rescue, we became responsible for the 'impossible': environmental health. We set about the digging, or rather supervising those hammering the earth with pickaxes and shovels, two straight-line ditches about three meters deep in the field to the back of the compound, lining the bottoms with limestone. This would prevent too much seepage and allow for the burning of the 'shit' later. Separated by an improvised wall from old military tarps, men and women could now squat over the holes cut out from the boarding covering each trench in relative privacy. We even managed a handwashing station adjacent to our refuse waste disposal solution. Voilà!

'Merdeka' explained

"This is not organized, at least it wasn't at the start." He was speaking to the few staff who joined him, inspecting defensive positions around the town; trying to halt any movement on the roads, now littered with the dead and dying. Striking were the young corpses now blackened; they had been set alight. The anguished faces on many giving testimonies to the barbaric cruelty wrought on those getting caught up in the mayhem; some with their school satchels still laying by their side.

Not one to let his emotions ride his normally calm demeanor, at least on the exterior, he wanted to lash out, scream. And so he did. Only in silence, keeping it all to himself.

They all ducked at once at the sharp crackling sound, turning out to be nothing more than something popping in the still-smoldering barbed steel ruins as they passed yet another reminder of the rage let loose; this of a metals workshop. Recovering, his startled driver swerved out of the way, just barely missing the burned-out hulk of an abandoned '*bajaj*'.

Hassan's Command, a small but disciplined garrisoned force of military now joined by contingents of police, were left to protect what remained of the critical infrastructure around town. "A lot of good we are doing," speaking glumly, as plumes of smoke could be seen billowing skywards from the general direction of the Regency's administrative offices. The few soldiers he could spare in attempting to ward off an emboldened mob laying siege to the complex were not responding to the frantic calls on the walkie talkie.

His superior, a gruff 'old school' Colonel, the garrison Commander, had been borrowed prior to the Wamena uprising to assist in coordinating evacuations from Timika. Making matters worse, his police counterpart had been relieved of 'her' duties. *Maybe no great, that,* he thought to himself.

The racial tone of marked indifference when it came to the Dani, including those within her own ranks, had not done her in; ordering her police to fire directly into a menacing crowd, armed with only sticks and stones, had succeeded in doing just that.

Hassan had always thought of the police as the front line in maintaining order: 'the street arbitrators of justice' as he liked to think of them. But this time and in this place, they had acted as 'perpetrators', leading to the present calamity.

Not generally shy of expressing his thoughts to those closest around him, he did now. "What happens here over the next few days could very well 'spell the fate' of Papua."

Master Sergeant Abraham and Corporal Isaac, whom he requested by name and were now assigned to his 'team', provided liaison and connectivity with police assets. More importantly, they both offered a unique Dani perspective of the crisis at hand: critically lacking among his troops. It was Corporal Isaac's words from the previous evening that resonated now with the Lieutenant Colonel:

"They are bent on destroying all reminders of Indonesian rule, maybe in retribution (settling old scores), or just 'running amok'; but a swipe nonetheless at the

Indonesian notion of Merdeka, the 'spirit of independence and freedom', held dear to those of us who serve 'our' Republic. But the problem is that many Papuans do not feel those principles are fairly applied to them.

"Most of the Dani, my people, are content to live as they have lived, since long before my great-grandfather's time. They are okay, as long as we and our traditions are respected, our concerns taken seriously."

Little wonder Colonel Kumi-Krispe placed so much trust in this man, thought Hassan. Equally compelling was the Lieutenant Colonel's 'gut sense' that both men would 'step in front of a bullet' for him.

Back to the here and now. Lieutenant Colonel Hassan was left 'holding the bag', responsible for fixing 'this fine mess': recalling an old 'Laurel and Hardy' film going by a similar name: *Another Fine Mess*.[49] He often thought back to a more innocent time, gathering with his family as a young boy, enthralled by the movies projected onto the outdoor screen in his village. Such memories had a way of invading his thoughts at precisely these times of uncertainty, however fleeting. Tonight, as then, swarms of fireflies illuminated the night, attracted to the light of campfires and still-smoldering remains of a battered but defiant Wamena.

The last order from Timika was to now concentrate his resources in securing the airstrip. Fretting to anyone who was in earshot when he took the message. "Not for landings, at least not yet, but for food drops." A reminder that there was a hungry town still to feed.

---

49   *https://en.wikipedia.org/wiki/Another_Fine_Mess.*

Coming to grips

The siege mentality festering inside the compound was by no means unwarranted, the threat outside the walls no figment of the imagination. But nobody was looking to 'storm the castle' or 'cross the moat'. Many had witnessed horrible scenes that defied all intelligible reasoning; personal loss was not only of meager possessions, but of family and friends. "They are entitled," Bakri spoke to no one in particular.

Food was finally making its way to hungry mouths. But there was no 'rush' on the rice mush being prepared in the clearing behind the headquarters. A prevailing stoicism was nevertheless morphing into vocal demands. Gindo weighing in, "There is no thought of going back to what was, at least for the time being."

Both turned in the direction of the loud commotion, the source of which was hidden in the growing crowd of onlookers. The threat posed by crazed mobs on the outside was petering out, converse to that on the inside.

Both pushed their way forward until coming across a ferocious Icha standing defiantly, facing two women hurling obscenities and rocks; behind her crouched a bloodied Tami. Two soldiers pushed forward, one firing their automatic weapon into the air, instantly dispersing the crowd that had gathered.

"Take them to the room," Bakri commanded of Gindo. Then faced the two who clearly had perpetrated this hate upon Icha and Tami.

> "*Why would you turn on one another? We are all here just trying to survive. You should feel shame. You are worse than those outside our fortress trying to tear down the town.*
>
> "*Is it because Tami is Dani? Or maybe because Icha is giving life-saving milk, her milk, to a Dani infant? Is this what 'the Prophet Muhammad' would expect from you? The Dani here are more victim than yourselves. You make trouble again, and I swear on 'my bible', to make 'double the trouble' for you.*"

He felt his heart racing at a speed that would surely cause it to rip from his chest, his body shaking uncontrollably. Bakri did not see himself as a heroic figure, but there was no denying it: arriving on the scene just in time to hear his sharp rebuke, watching from the sidelines. I quipped to myself that, "Bakri had long lost his bible," thinking back on our rafting disaster. And here he was, a Christian, extolling the 'Message' and 'Messenger', in the name of 'Allah', creator of the universe.

Feathered 'best' friend

The corridor was narrow, leading to the curtained-off section. 'Grunting and honking' noises and the sound of 'flapping': I could not help but investigate. Doctor Amin was squatting with a 'Papuan hornbill' on his arm, or 'Kokomo', the local name I was familiar with, gently stroking the feathers of one large, riled-up bird. Looking up, greeting me with his 'laughing smile,' 'tired' as it was.

Contributor: Stijn De Win; who manages to capture the intimate beauty of the Papuan hornbill in the wild; so graciously sharing this triumph with the author.[50]

---

50   *https://www.birding2asia.com/tours/reports/West Papua2018. html.*

"Ah ha, my favorite American."
Trying to match his attempt at wittiness:

"That is only because you have never met another."
"This is my 'big boy'. You must speak gently with 'Arang'. For your English ears, that means charcoal. He is very sensitive and feeling a bit out of sorts at the moment. I am only taking a breather, working from the small clinic we have organized upstairs.

"Do you have any fresh fruit? His mood would improve considerably if he had some figs to munch on. I have some Dani women collecting insects for the time being."

My expression, open-mouthed, prompted Amin to add:
"A gift, from a grateful patient, from my private clinic." Trying to find the right word: "And so, so 'handsome.'"
"Yes, usually found in the lowlands. But like everything else, trading in baby chicks for something or other with the lowland coastal region is not uncommon."
Quickly adding, "Did you know they mate for life, with a life expectancy as much as thirty years?"
I could not help but notice as Amin's 'eyes lit up' when talking about his 'feathered friend', a reveal of his deep affection for the bird.
Later, I introduced Icha and Desi to 'Arang', more as a diversion from the burdens of life here in the camp. They were immediately smitten, irresistibly taken in by his obvious 'charms'.

All good things must end

Ali had just returned from an inspection of the town, now that the 'dust had settled'. There were more 'boots on the ground', soldiers, than inhabitants. "Our neat little neighborhood is still a neat little neighborhood. Nothing has been touched. I cannot say the same for the Meteorological Station. But we will build again."

"You need to join us, please! You are sick! Those 'fits of coughing' that leave you trembling will end with you gasping for air as your lungs fill with fluid. You know that!" Bakri could not have been more emphatic.

Only Gindo was in no mood, dismissing such pleas: "You need to be reasonable. There is no care for you here. There is nothing for you here."

"The cattle are being let out of the pen," observed a somber Amin. Exhaustion had drained his 'good-natured' energies. At least Arang seemed to be enjoying the moment.

"Will you have time to join us for a last meal, before your flight, that is? Desi and I have so much to do now that we can return home." Bakri and I insisted we would walk to the airstrip, promising Lieutenant Rita to be there no later than noon. I could not help myself. Raising up my right hand, intoning a 'Scout's honor'.

"There are no reservations, but you are prioritized on the first flight out." Before separating from our gang, I asked Icha why she would stay here. The riots had been quelled, but would anything change, be made right?

"Here, I am with family! Desi is as much my mother as my sister. Even more so than the family I left behind not so long ago. We have nowhere else to go, my daughter and I. Here, I can be more than a 'pembantu', or be myself, just a 'pembantu'. But my daughter will not be treated so, not here."

Her honesty struck me, as if zapped by a stun gun. I could feel the electric current bringing a tingling shiver to my spine.

"You are so, so special, so much more than a 'pembantu'. Do not let anyone ever again make you feel less so." Feeling a little bit, the preacher in all of us, I could not help but add:

"Rise up and inspire us to do great things. By your example." Our embrace was the real thing. Neither of us felt shy or willing to let go as the others looked on. I could feel the wet warmth of her tears on my now sodden, borrowed khaki shirt. Hers mixed with mine. Not sure exactly what was happening, except that time had stopped for that moment.

Digesting it all

Bakri and I wandered the now empty, no longer 'mean streets' of the town, finally joining the hundreds of others waiting on the incoming C-130 transport planes that would ferry us to a better place. Between us, the only thing other than our dental fillings that we were taking back with us from whence we first arrived was Bakri's talisman, and hence mine: his binoculars, hanging by a slip knot from the leather strap around his neck.

None in the anxious crowd could fathom the 'baggage' we would carry into the future. The weightiness of it all would settle in; of that we were all sure.

"Amin, we missed you," Bakri said, giving his best smirk. "Are you joining us?"

"How could I not resist the charms of your company for a bit longer? Yes, I am taking a break, off to visit my family."

"And where is Arang," I demanded. "Roasted, being forked into someone's mouth as we speak?"

"Hehe, my 'big boy' is at this moment enjoying the charms of Icha. Which of us should be the more jealous?" Amin had spoken it, but I was thinking it.

Lest I forget about our 'w'abah babi' outbreak, which set

in motion our 'adventure like no other'; the catalyst of it all. I have come to fathom the fragility of the Dani, and for that matter, indigenous peoples everywhere, beyond the reach of a civilization bent on extending its tenacles into every nook and cranny. We would come to estimate 17,000 Dani deaths over a period of four months, attributed not to some novel pathogen, but the probable culprit, 'seasonal influenza'. That figure would account for almost seven percent of the Dani population inhabiting the Baliem Valley.

I could not help to think about the scourge of syphilis, and how, brought by the early Europeans in their exploration of the Americas, it decimated whole indigenous Indian populations, some to extinction. Such thinking begged even broader consideration of the events leading up to the present, each serving as a falling domino, tipping over the next: 1) hostage-taking; 2) massive troop deployments from Java and Sumatra in response; and 3) contact with the Dani living in the remote jungle highlands. But only now, in hindsight, against the backdrop of a 'beaten and bowed' Wamena, could I see our outbreak in the context of this 'domino effect'.

It was not lost on those who bore witness in the aftermath of this outwardly senseless rampage that left the town 'bloodied and bruised' that this was a swipe at the very notion of how Indonesia views itself: principled, espoused in all that is 'Merdeka'.

Contributor: Tjetjep Rustandi; happy 70th anniversary, Indonesia! – Image ID: GH3931 (Alamy).

Or maybe I had it all wrong. I was oh so tired!

A fitting end

The glare of the sun bounced off the gray metallic coating of the transport plane sporting the Indonesian 'red and white' on its tail. He had only just been messaged that Jacques would be arriving on a C-130 out of Wamena, scrambling over to the airfield.

As its belly opened up, the bedraggled passengers peeked tentatively from the ramp, leading from the 'mouth of the beast' onto the tarmac. Norman scoured the crowd as they now poured out, trying to 'white out' all of whom were not in his 'sights'.

Instead of manacles, as Jacques' wild imagination had played out this moment, Norman pulled a cold beer from a Styrofoam container that smelled of fish. But instead of handing it over, he shook the Bintang up and down, pried the cap, and let the explosion of foam spray the two: Jacques and Bakri, inseparable, holding hands.

"There is no rush. A special plane is coming for the special boys. But that will be for another day. But on this day, you are mine to do as I please. Welcome back to planet earth, at least as you remember it; probably no saner than the one you just came from."

'Not' an epilogue

The outbreak, from which this story was hatched:

"Impact of epidemic influenza A-like acute respiratory illness in a remote jungle highland population in Irian Jaya, Indonesia."

A suspected epidemic of unknown etiology was investigated in April/May 1996 in the remote jungle highlands of easternmost Indonesia. Trend analysis demonstrates the area-wide occurrence of a major respiratory infection outbreak in November 1995 through February 1996. The monthly mean rate of respiratory infection episodes for the peak outbreak months (2,477 episodes/100,000 persons) was significantly higher (P < .0001) than for the 34 months leading up to the outbreak (109 episodes/100,000 persons). Notable were the high attack rates, particularly among adults: 202 episodes/1,000 persons aged 20-50 years in one community. Excess morbidity attributed to the outbreak was an estimated 4,338 episodes. The overall case-fatality rate was 15.1% of outbreak cases. Laboratory evidence confirmed the circulation of influenza

A/Taiwan/1/86-like viruses in the study population, and high hemagglutination inhibition titer responses were indicative of recent infections. Historical documents from neighboring Papua New Guinea highlight the role of influenza A virus in repeated area outbreaks.[51]

'Post-outbreak' response training:

As a WHO-SEARO Collaborating Center for Emerging and Re-emerging Diseases, NAMRU-2 – going by the alias of NMRC-Indonesia, conduct 10-day outbreak workshops throughout Indonesia and the region. Training as captured in photo was carried in Wamena, by the Ministry of Health, following the investigation that led to this novel; Asia Pacific Defense Forum, Volume 24, 1999.[52]

---

51 *https://www.semanticscholar.org/paper/Impact-of-epidemic-influenza-A-like-acute-illness-a-Corwin-Simanjuntak/4031f2d1ca 51454e2309cc7951646b7daae8aa7d .*

52 *https://books.google.la/ books?id=LNO5AAAAIAAJ&printsec=frontcover&source=gbs_ ge_summary_r&cad=0#v=onepage&q&f=false .*

Appendices

Institutions

Tentara Nasional Indonesia (Indonesian National Armed Forces), otherwise referred to as TNI.

Komando Daerah Militer (Regional Military Command); Indonesian Army Special Forces (Kopassus).

National Institute of Health Research Indonesia (LITBANGKES).

National Center for Disease Prevention and Control Indonesia (P2M).

International Committee of the Red Cross (ICRC).

Missionary Aviation Fellowship (MAF).

Free West Papua Movement (OPM).

US Naval Medical Research Center (NMRC) – Indonesia; the fictional synonym for US Naval Medical Research Unit No. 2 (NAMRU-2), headquartered in Jakarta, Indonesia.

Merpati, the Indonesian airline serving Papua, with stopovers on the Island of Biak and Makassar (capital of Sulawesi).

BAIS TNI, short for Baden Intelijen Strategis Tentara Nasional Indonesia (Indonesian National Armed Forces Strategic Intelligence Agency).

PT Freeport-McMoRan Indonesia (FCX), an American-based company along with their Indonesian partners, operating the largest copper mine in the world, out of Timika, Papua.

Gatot Soebroto Rumah Sakit, the premier tertiary referral hospital of the Indonesian Armed Forces.

West Papua National Liberation Army (TPNPB), the military arm of OPM.

State, referring to the US State Department.

Annapolis, short for United States Naval Academy, located in Annapolis, MD.

Denjaka, the Indonesian Navy's elite special operations force.

Characters

Commander Jacques Bonaparte, navy investigator – principal narrator and lead character.

Dr. Bakri Ginting, researcher at LITBANGKES; friend and companion to Commander Jacques.

Laksi, Luk, and Jar, Papuan porters on highland jungle trek between Ninia and Soba.

Ramu, guide, friend, and savior, 'speaking volumes', in whispers with few words.

Dr. Narsiem, researcher and clinician at NMRC-Indonesia; friend and guru to Commander Jacques.

Commander Norman Bates, Navy entomologist.

Dr. Soudoso, Head, Department of Surveillance, P2M.

Beti, Administrative Assistant, Emerging Disease Program, NMRC-Indonesia.

Dari, senior investigator in Emerging Disease Program at NMRC-Indonesia.

Dr. Eka Dewi, Minister of Health, Republic of Indonesia; friend to Commander Jacques.Colonel Winslow (Winny)

Dowdy, Defense Attaché (DATT), US Embassy Jakarta.

Captain Rick Lavender, Commanding Officer, NMRC-Indonesia.

Jesper, shop keeper from Sentani.

Gindo, former Bank Director in Wamena.

Nono Maraud, Acting Bank Director in Wamena.

Icha, young Javanese widow working as a '*pembantu*' – housekeeper, in the residence of the BNI Wamena bank manager; central character and 'most' unlikely hero.

Brigadier General Widodo Soeprapto, Koopssus, Commander, Mapenduma Hostage Crisis.

Colonel Agus, General Widodo's confidant and aide-de-camp to General Staff leadership.

General Salim, Deputy Director, Office of Strategic Policy, a think tank attached to the General Staff.

Commander Marvel, senior officer conducting 'informal' investigative review.

John, helicopter pilot with MAF in Wamena, '*who got us into this fine mess*'.

Captain 'Wild' Bill Smarts, acting Commanding Officer of NMRC-Asia; nemesis and temporary replacement for Captain Rick Lavender.

Lieutenant Colonel Hassan, Deputy Commander of the Wamena garrison.

First Lieutenant Rita, junior officer assigned to Lieutenant Colonel Hassan's staff.

Desi, Icha's neighbor and best friend, and *pembantu* extraordinaire.

Ali Suliman, Director of the Jayawijaya Regency Meteorological Station; nicknamed '*petugas cuaca saya*': 'my weatherman'.

Colonel Simanjuntak, TNI Airforce Liaison Officer, Provincial Military Command, Sentani, West Papua.

Mola – meaning those warm colors in the Dani language, to include 'red' – the name given to the red-haired Aussie, Jan, who settled in Kataya village with her Dani husband.

Tami and Kat, mother and daughter, friends and guides in Icha's search for Nono.

Lieutenant Colonel – promoted to full-bird colonel – Kumi-Krispe Kuri, Grand Police Commissioner Adjutant, Kepolisian Negara Republik, Jayawijaya, West Papua.

Lela, a Dani woman from the Kataya settlement.

Non-Commissioned Officer (NCO) Master Sergeant Abraham Kambuaya, Team Leader, Special Reactionary Force, Jayawijaya Province.

Brigadier General Radolfo Putri, a senior intelligence officer in TNI (Chief, Papua's Intelligence Agency).

Corporal Isaac, a Dani, assigned to Office of the Grand Police Deputy Commissioner, serving as de facto bodyguard to Lieutenant Colonel Kumi-Krispe Kuri.

Adriana, 'pilot'; hostage taken by TPNPB in Nduga.

Jamo, Moluccan islander, soldier; death by 'fer-de-lance'.

Doctor Amin, a clinician at Wamena General Hospital; bringing his style of humor to his bedside manner – a unique attribute in Indonesia.

Arang, a big and beautiful Papua hornbill, and 'light of Doctor Amin's life'.

Dreamt characters from the 'big screen' and print

Norman Bates (played by Anthony Perkins, a fictional character from Alfred Hitchcock's 1960 horror movie classic, *Psycho*, as the owner/manager of a motel, flittering between multiple personalities, including the persona of his mother as a deranged killer of unsuspecting guests).

The African Queen – a classic 1951 movie starring Humphrey Bogart and Katharine Hepburn, filmed on location in the Belgium Congo, chronicling their river adventure on an old steamer, as two mismatched opposites finding love, salvation, and purpose, with one another.

Dick Tracey – a comic-strip character launched in 1931 and made later into a movie/series, playing a 'hard-boiled, strait-laced' sleuth detective, combating the criminal elements of society to make the streets safe for law-abiding citizens.

Tarzan – a fictional character, raised by apes since surviving a plane crash as an infant that killed his parents. A larger-than-life force of good against the likes of trophy hunting and tribal and cultural subjugation. One of the first Western action heroes to take up the conservation of the animals inhabiting the jungles and savannahs of Africa, and for humanizing the indigenous peoples of the continent. First introduced as a silent film in 1918, and then made famous in 1932 by Johnny Weissmuller, the Olympic Gold Medalist swimmer, as Tarzan.

Dorothy Gale – Judy Garland in the 1939 classic *The Wizard of Oz*, as a young and innocent farm girl from Kansas. She finds herself in a faraway magical land after losing consciousness during a tornado, encountering an ensemble of characters, not of this world, but also of this world. Dorothy's quest as she searches for a way back home to Kansas is not unlike that of Commander Jacques Bonaparte.

Words/expressions

Kopi/teh – coffee/tea.

Bahasa – a Malay dialect that serves as the Indonesian language.

Boulay – Indonesian word for foreigner.

Pembantu – domestic housekeeper.

Jahat – evil.

Addressing elders as *Pak* for males and *Ibu* for females, before their names, as a sign of respect.

'*Wabah babi*' – literal translation referring to an outbreak of 'swine flu'; and the name bequeathed the local press to a purported event that served as the basis for this novel.

Ibuku/ibu – literary, my mother. But also used as a sign of respect/affection in addressing a woman.

Kari ayam – chicken curry.

Pernahkah Anda melihat pria ini – have you seen this man.

Gila – crazy.

Warung – a small shop or restaurant.

'Zero Dark Thirty' (military terms that refers to the small hours of the night, generally assigned to when a soldier or sailor stands duty).

Ikipalin – Dani word for tradition of 'finger amputation'.

Mungkin – maybe.

Geschenk van god – Dutch for 'gift from god'.

Terima kasih – thank you.

Koteka – penis sheath, traditionally worn by the men in the central highlands of west (and east) Papua, including the Baliem Valley.

Pujilah Allah – Praised be Allah.

Gosip – *Bahasa* for gossip.

Selamat pagi – good morning.

Dungdut – popular Indonesian pop music played in the *Kampung*.

Kampung – referring to the villages in the countryside.

Honai – circular stick and thatched hut throughout West Papua.

Selamat datang – meant to convey welcome.

Enak – delicious.

Pulling no punches – being direct, not trying to soften the impact of his words/message.

Mincing of his words – being 'brutally honest'; sometimes referred to as delivering an uncomfortable truth.

Merdeka – a symbolic word of special significance to all Indonesians, expressive of 'Independence' and 'Freedom'; often uttered in the same breath as 'Republic'.

Bajaj – the Indonesian three-wheeled petrol-powered passenger carrier; the choice mode of local transportation throughout the archipelago nation.

Amok – from the Indonesian/Malay word '*amuk*', referring to the frenzied tendency to violence of crazed individual or mob; often included in the string: 'to run amok'.

Places

Jakarta, capital and largest city Indonesia, located on the southwest coast of the island of Java.

Irian Jaya, renamed Papua on January 1, 2000, to reflect the distinct ethnic and cultural identity of the Papuan peoples. The largest and most eastern island in the Indonesian archipelago bordering Papua New Guinea (PNG) to the east, the region along with Aceh in northern Sumatra has been conferred with special autonomy powers.

Jayapura, provincial capital of, then, Irian Jaya – now going by the name of West Papua.

Sentani (lake and surrounding communities just outside of Jayapura).

Wamena, 'more' small town then actual 'seat' of regional government for the Jayawijaya Regency; and jumping-off point for hostage negotiators and outbreak investigators.

Ninia and Soba, Dani communities visited during the outbreak investigation, remote villages lying to the southwest of Wamena.

Ugem (a small Dani village about half a day's journey from Wamena; a destination on the trek taken by adventure-seeking tourists looking to authenticate their experience, immersed into the local culture).

Baliem Valley (also known as the Grand Valley, comprising a highland region in West Papua, and home to the Dani tribe).

Kurima (a large Dani village near Wamena, where the road ends, and the hike to Ugem begins).

Padang (a city in Sumatra, but more famous as a 'spicy' serving of different Indonesian dishes from the same, served up in small bowls or plates; *warungs* throughout the archipelago offering up this delicious fare).

Pasar Nayak (the open/wet market in Wamena).

Nduga district, Nduga Regency (home of the Nduga Dawa people, and active TPNPB-OPM insurgency movement).

Links (to real events)

The 'wabah babi' Outbreak

https://pubmed.ncbi.nlm.nih.gov/9564469/

Mapenduma Hostage-Taking Crisis

http://www.ipsnews.net/1996/01/indonesia-irian-jaya-hostage-crisis-continues/.

Negotiations (ICRC)

https://www.icrc.org/en/doc/resources/documents/
misc/57jpz2.htm.

Rescue

https://www.youtube.com/watch?v=ua1LPwiGvHg.
https://www.independent.co.uk/news/hostage-watched-as-
two-friends-were-killed-1347695.html.
https://en.wikipedia.org/wiki/Mapenduma_hostage_crisis.
https://papuaisindonesia.wordpress.com/2017/11/22/
breaking-news-west-papuan-hostages-rescued-by-
security-forces/.

Tower Massacre

https://www.republicworld.com/world-news/rest-of-the-
world-news/attackers-kill-8-technicians-in-indonesias-
papua-province-articleshow.html.

Bridge Massacre

https://www.bangkokpost.com/world/1587510/indonesian-
police-say-32-dead-1-missing-in-papua-attacks.

Riots and Refuge

https://en.antaranews.com/news/133428/thousands-seek-
refuge-at-jayawijaya-police-headquarter-after-riots.
https://www.abc.net.au/news/2019-08-30/papua-
protesters-torch-buildings-cars-as-unrest-
continues/11464212.
https://www.theguardian.com/world/2019/sep/28/i-feel-
like-im-dying-west-papua-witnesses-unrest-indonesia-
police.
https://news.abs-cbn.com/overseas/09/27/19/thousands-
scramble-to-flee-unrest-in-indonesias-papua.

https://en.antaranews.com/news/133626/24-paramedics-
deployed-to-wamena-hospital-in-the-wake-of-deadly-
riot.

Ambush and Assassination
https://www.nytimes.com/2021/04/27/world/asia/
indonesia-general-papua.html.
https://thediplomat.com/2021/05/in-papua-fighting-
indonesian-forces-claim-rebel-Commander-killed/.

Nduga Hostage-Taking
https://www.bangkokpost.com/world/2501879/rebels-
take-new-zealand-'pilot'-hostage-in-indonesias-papua.
https://www.theaustralian.com.au/subscribe/
news/1/?sourceCode=TAWEB_
WRE170_a&dest=https%3A%2F%2Fwww.
theaustralian.com.au%2Fworld%2Fpapua-rebels-are-
marching-kiwi-'pilot'-to-jungle-base%2Fnews-story%2F
50bf061ea4dcb464830a9a05facdef33&memtype=ano
nymous&mode=premium&v21=dynamic-groupa-test-
noscore&V21spcbehaviour=append.

Nduga Massacre
https://thediplomat.com/2018/12/massacre-in-nduga-
indonesias-papuan-insurgency/.

Wamena Incident
https://en.wikipedia.org/wiki/2003_Wamena_incident.
https://www.usnews.com/news/world/
articles/2023-02-23/indonesia-tightens-security-in-
papua-after-nine-killed-in-riot.

The author, this book

This is a work of fiction, above all else. But the story liberally borrows from real events in adding to the context and authenticity of settings and circumstances described, as related to West Papua, Indonesian. Notably, the experiences of the author investigating an outbreak in the midst of a hostage-taking crisis served as the impetus for the novel.

After spending thirteen years as a US navy infectious disease epidemiologist based in Jakarta, Indonesia, chasing down disease outbreak threats, the author taps into his own experiences investigating 'wabah babi' – Pig disease, setting the stage for this, his first work, titled '*Lost and Found' on Planet Dani*: a quest born disease, hostage-taking, and insurrection. The author 'casts' himself as the central character, attempting to use humor and guile as things go from bad to worse. But it is his demure Batak companion that 'steals the show': small in stature, but a giant in 'heart and spirit'.

The 'principal' loves to evoke movie scenes from the old 'classics' as he tries to balance his own sanity with the surreal.

Although never intended, Jacques becomes almost a side-show to other characters that are brought to life and evolve as the story progresses. A young Javanese housemaid becomes heroine amidst a gaggle of supporting cast.

This is a story that cannot be told without delving into the ethnography of the Dani people from the Baliem Valley, where this adventure takes place.

The reader is encouraged to 'dig deeper' in appreciating the volatility of this island province, then as now, ruled by a distant 'authority': trading in Amsterdam for Jakarta.

Lastly, the author looks to avoid falling into the proverbial geopolitical 'rabbit hole' by rendering judgment or opinion; there is enough of that in the literature should the reader choose to explore further.